ILLUSTRATED LIBRARY OF NATURE

AN ENCYCLOPEDIA OF NATURAL HISTORY ENCOMPASSING
ALL ASPECTS OF NATURE AND WILDLIFE
PREVIOUSLY PUBLISHED AS
LIFE NATURE LIBRARY

VOLUME

1

PRIMATES

1984 EDITION

H. S. STUTTMAN INC. PUBLISHERS • WESTPORT, CONNECTICUT 06889

© 1980 Time-Life Books Inc. All rights reserved.
No part of this book may be reproduced in any form or by any electronic or mechanical means, including information storage and retrieval devices or systems without prior written permission from the publisher, except that brief passages may be quoted for reviews.

3P(763)50-131

Contents

1 What Is a Primate? 9

2 The Monkeys: Success in the Trees 35

3 The Apes: Pioneers on Two Legs 61

4 The Rewards of Childhood 85

5 Life in the Group 104

6 The Group and the World Outside 129

7 Clues to Human Behavior 151

8 From Ape toward Man 177

Bibliography 193
Credits 194
Index 195

About the Author

This volume in the LIFE Nature Library has two authors—Irven DeVore and Sarel Eimerl. For *The Primates*, it could hardly be otherwise. The whole field of primate behavior is a new and vastly exciting one—and it is developing so rapidly that the men and women most closely concerned with it barely have time to publish their own findings let alone put together the accumulated knowledge of the last decades. DeVore, now at Harvard, spent many months observing primates in the wild; his further commitments made it impossible for him to write the book himself. He agreed, however, to supply the information for this book, provided the text was written by someone else. This task was undertaken by Sarel Eimerl, a graduate of Oxford living in the U.S., whose wide-ranging writings include a novel, a work of nonfiction, the editing of much scientific material and magazine articles on a variety of subjects. To prepare for this assignment, he spent three months in California talking with such other eminent figures in the field of primate behavior as Sherwood L. Washburn and Phyllis Jay.

LIVING REMINDER of the primates' humble start, Madagascar's ringtailed lemur also looks rather like today's monkeys. It shares many basic traits with others of its primitive suborder, the prosimians.

1

What Is a Primate?

It might, at first glance, appear surprising that the study of monkeys and apes should be considered as a subject worthy of a name all its own—primatology. Here is a science that has within the short span of a few decades suddenly emerged as not only one of the most fascinating of all sciences but also as one of the most important—a discipline which has drawn to itself not only zoologists and biologists but also psychologists, physiologists, biochemists and what is perhaps most interesting of all, anthropologists in increasing numbers.

Why, we ask, should any anthropologist devote his career to it? Anthropology is, after all, the study of man; and anthropologists, pursuing man's own origins, would seem to have enough work on their hands without taking on the lower members of his order. The answer is that zoologists for many years have classified man with the primates because of their close anatomical similarity. Recent developments in the field of biochemistry support this classification by showing that similarities of cells and blood also exist between man and all the other primates, depending on how closely related they are.

Now, thanks to a tremendous recent upsurge in studies of monkeys and apes in their natural environment, it is becoming clear that in their social behavior,

WHAT IS A PRIMATE?

A SHOW OF HANDS

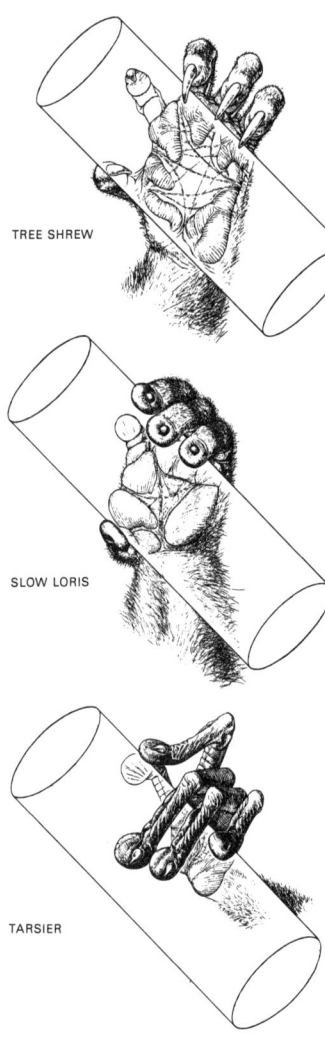

TREE SHREW

SLOW LORIS

TARSIER

As seen in the drawing on these two pages, all the primates have hands with movable fingers. But these often differ vastly in structure and variety of use. They all evolved from hands like those of the tree shrew, which are little more than elongated paws capable only of performing such functions as holding onto a branch by digging in with claws. The hands of the slow loris have a highly specialized pincer-like grip. The tarsier, a jumper, has hands with disks on the finger tips that help it hold on after leaping.

too, they stand much closer to man than anyone had suspected. Many live in highly organized groups in which familiar routines and sharing of knowledge permit a relatively stable social organization. A few groups are ruled by a single, all-powerful leader. Others, like the chimpanzees, live in more loosely organized groups. Whatever the size or structure of the group, some members will be good friends, others dedicated enemies; some will be collaborators, others rivals; some will be popular, others despised. Infant apes and monkeys, as they grow up, must learn a code of behavior, much as a human child has to do; and all the members of a group are linked together by an elaborate system of communication that embraces both sounds and gestures and goes far beyond what is necessary for mere brute survival. The comparison with human behavior, of course, must not be pushed too far. Yet in their daily routine and, in many respects, their relationship with their fellows, there are surprising resemblances between man and the nonhuman primates.

A CONSIDERABLE part of this book will be devoted to an account of what has been learned about the social life of monkeys and apes. Possibly the reader will come to share some of the scientists' sense of fascination as they observed nonhuman animals in their natural environment behaving on occasion so much like humans that they might almost have been men and women in disguise. But before one can see the relationship between man and the primates in proper perspective, it is first necessary to gain an understanding of what kind of animals primates are.

At once a problem of definition arises, because the order primates embraces some 200 living species. They range from creatures as primitive—and as similar—to the primates of 50 million years ago, as the lemur at one end of the spectrum to highly complex man, an evolutionary newcomer, at the other. And since the order contains a large number of extinct fossil forms as well as their highly diversified descendants, any attempt to define the entire order on the basis of their few common characteristics ignores many of the subsequent adaptations of later forms.

At best it can be noted that all primates, living and extinct, share a characteristic structure of the ear and molar teeth adapted for eating some vegetable material. In addition, most primates show a variety of other complex and often far-reaching adaptations that seem to be related to the typical primate ability of grasping with their hands. These appear in the structure of primate brains and the possession of fingernails and toenails and opposable digits; in the way primates use their senses of smell and sight and touch; in the way they give birth to and rear their young. The various species do not possess all the same features, but all show at least trends toward development of them —and these trends are characteristics of the entire order. And there is one quality that is shared by all the living primates except the controversial tree shrews: the ability to climb by grasping.

The ultimate origin of the grasping abilities of primates is an interesting and unsettled evolutionary problem. For many years students of primate evolution felt that the unique grasping abilities of primates, together with other features of their eyes and skull shape were the result of the arboreal nature of the earliest primate ancestors. In the 1970s, however, Dr. Matt Cartmill pointed out that other arboreal mammals such as squirrels, opossums and a variety of Australian marsupials do not show these same adaptations for life in the trees. He suggested that some other type of behavior must have started the early primates on the path toward a life of climbing by grasping.

Cartmill suggested that the earliest primates were adapted for grasping insects and other invertebrates on the forest floor and argued that such a grasping predator taking to the trees would already be committed to a primate-like way of hand use. Such a grasping adaptation would lead to more and more adaptations for arboreal locomotion in subsequent lineages of grasping, visually oriented primates. Grasp was the key because grasp meant security. It enabled primates to climb more safely along delicate branches and so expand their range of food. It reduced the risk of falling, and because of the superior purchase it provided, grasp permitted them to grow much larger than they might otherwise have done had their weight been supported by less versatile claws instead.

The evolution of primates has been going on for over 60 million years: It began with a group of small creatures strikingly different from today's monkeys. Some of the earliest primates were furtive, inconspicuous little insectivores that may have resembled the present-day tree shrews of Asia or other forest-floor scavengers. Others were more herbivorous, groundhog-like animals with thick limbs, bushy tails and claws. Because of certain features of the skull and teeth these animals are usually included in the order primates by paleontologists. At the same time, there are many aspects of the anatomy and reconstructed behavior of these early creatures that clearly indicate they were very different from the prosimians that began to evolve from them an estimated 55 million years ago.

German naturalists have described the prosimians as *Halbaffen*, half-monkeys. The title is inspired. Prosimians are exactly that: a transitional stage between the insectivores and monkeys. For millions of years, prosimians were the only primates. They spread across North America, Europe, Asia and Africa, diversifying as they migrated into a vast variety of forms. The fossil remains of more than 60 now-extinct genera have been unearthed in various parts of the world, and there certainly must have been others whose traces are still waiting to be discovered.

EVENTUALLY they lost their mastery of the trees to the monkeys. Today there are no prosimians left in the Americas or in Europe, while the few that still survive on the mainland of Africa and Asia do so only because most are nocturnal animals and thus do not compete with the diurnal monkeys. One group of prosimians, however, made its way to Madagascar and a few smaller islands in the Indian Ocean—probably by drifting on natural rafts across intervening stretches of water. There they found themselves free of competition from monkeys and predation by large carnivores, and they evolved into several very distinct families. Today some 20 species still exist, scattered through the island's forests. Fortunately, some closely resemble the early prosimians of 50 or more million years ago. So, by studying both the fossils and the living forms, one can obtain a fairly accurate impression of man's earliest fully arboreal ancestors.

All the Madagascar prosimians come under the general heading of lemurs. Whether one judges them by their behavior or their anatomy, they embrace a very wide variety of forms. Some move around by day, others in the evening, yet others only at night. There are very small types, the size of mice, which live mainly on insects. There are also larger species, the size of a large dog, which eat leaves and buds and fruit. Some are solitary, others highly social.

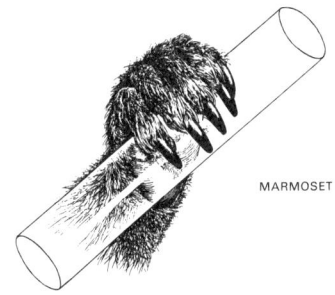

MARMOSET

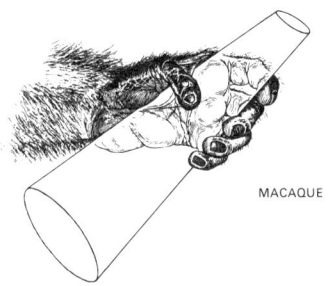

MACAQUE

CHIMPANZEE

Of the monkeys, the marmoset has the most primitive hands. Its grasp is awkward since its fingers all move in the same plane and must press an object against the heel of the hand. By contrast, the hands of the macaque and the chimpanzee are far more dexterous. Both are able to move their thumbs so that they can pick things up between thumb and finger. The chimp's thumb is shorter than the macaque's and thus inherently less efficient. But its brain is so much larger that it can do more with what it has.

WHAT IS A PRIMATE?

Some lemurs are quadrupeds, while many species are quite adept at leaping as a form of locomotion. Members of one family, the Indriidae, move in a unique style, holding their bodies vertically upright, even when they jump from one tree trunk to another.

Despite such variations, the lemurs have many things in common and share many characteristics with other primates—even with other mammals. The mouse lemur, for example, has a long, projecting snout with a moist muzzle, like a dog's, and tactile whiskers on each side. Its ears resemble a cat's. Its eyes are large and set quite close together in the front of the face. But unlike a cat's or a dog's, the fingers and toes are elongated and capable of spreading apart; instead of digging its claws into the branch to get a hold, the mouse lemur wraps its digits around it.

To watch a prosimian is, in a sense, to be transported back to the world of 50 million years ago. For it requires only a little imagination to perceive in these furry, bushy-tailed, transitional little animals the early forms of adaptation to arboreal life. Consider, to begin with, their eyes and their snouts, the vehicles of sight and smell. To a considerable degree, these two senses are complementary. Both are methods of obtaining information, and the more use an animal makes of one, the less it will depend on the other. The balance is dictated by the way it exploits its environment. To an animal that lives on the ground and is active at night, smell can be extremely useful: It can identify objects not by looking at them but by sniffing them. To one that lives away from the ground and is active by day, the value of the sense of smell is lessened and that of vision is increased: This is seen particularly well in birds, whose sense of smell is as poor as their vision is keen. Even in the trees, the sense of smell is far less valuable than it is on the ground, and vision is far more; for the latter helps its possessor to avoid possibly fatal falls and also to identify food amid the rich and colorful foliage.

Just as natural selection in the arboreal environment has favored better grasping in primates, so it also favored vision and acted against smell. In a tentative form, the transition from reliance on smell to reliance on vision is apparent in a prosimian. Its snout is less prominent than an insectivore's. A slightly smaller portion of its brain is devoted to smell and a slightly larger portion to sight. This shift is reflected in the position of its eyes. Most primitive mammals have eyes set at the sides of their heads so that they can see over a full half circle without turning their heads. But this advantage is offset by an accompanying drawback. As their visual fields do not overlap, they cannot see very accurately in depth. To such an animal, the ability to judge distance precisely may not be critical to his survival; to a grasping primate, it certainly is. In time, therefore, prosimians' eyes moved closer to the fronts of their faces, their fields overlapping in a number of species to give them much better vision in depth.

In any discussion of primate evolution, one inevitably returns before very long to considering how primates move—in other words, to how they escape from their enemies and reach their food. Locomotion is closely related to grasp, and it was in their ability to grasp that prosimians moved furthest away from their insectivore ancestors. They acquired highly movable digits, most of them equipped with pads on the inside and nails instead of claws on the outside on all but the second digit of the foot. But while they all secure their holds by grasping, the prosimians' actual modes of progress vary. Many walk, or run,

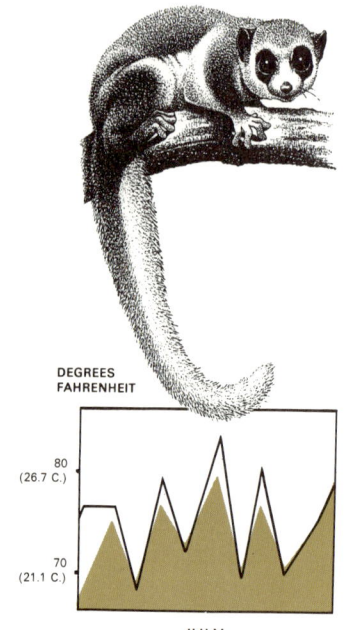

FLUCTUATING BODY TEMPERATURE

Some prosimians, like the dwarf lemur above, have periods of lethargy that cause their rudimentary temperature regulating mechanisms to become relatively inactive. When this happens, body temperature is greatly affected by the environment and, as the graph shows, it rises and falls (black line) to conform almost exactly to changes in the surrounding air (colored areas). This lethargy occurs during the cool, dry season in Madagascar and may last for a month or so. While it remains inactive, the lemur lives on fat that it has stored at the base of its long tail.

on all fours. Others also use this form of movement, but are especially adept at hopping about on branches and performing virtuoso leaps through the air. The little African bush baby, for example, moves in long hops, using its back feet like a kangaroo. These creatures are amazingly fast, agile and accurate. A captive bush baby once jumped 20 feet (6 m) downward to land securely on a door top, two inches (5 cm) wide, and on another occasion, leaped from the floor to its owner's shoulder, holding a half-eaten mouse in its hands.

Other mainland prosimians, the lorises of Asia and the pottos of Africa, are as slow in movement as the bush babies are rapid. Their method of progress is beautifully suggested by the native word for the potto, the "softly-softly." They proceed with enormous deliberation along the branches, sometimes on top and sometimes underneath, progressing in undulating slow motion as they advance alternate hands and feet. In feeding, lorises will often hang by their feet with a grip so strong that they can pull themselves back up on a branch without using their arms.

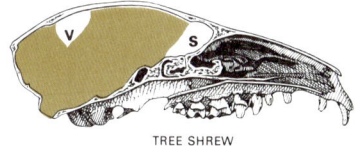
TREE SHREW

There is another animal, the rat-sized, nocturnal tarsier, which occupies a unique position in the history of primate evolution. The living tarsier is probably the most specialized jumper of all the prosimians. Its legs are long and its arms are short. Its eyes are enormous; it relies much more on sight than the other prosimians do and much less on smell, and consequently the area of its brain devoted to vision is relatively large. Its snout is short and its nose is as dry as a monkey's. Clearly, the tarsier is not a typical prosimian. On the other hand, it certainly cannot be called a monkey. Where, then, does this creature belong?

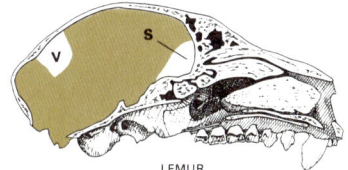
LEMUR

The position of the tarsier in the primate family tree is unresolved. Some experts believe that tarsiers are a side branch of the earliest primates. The majority of primatologists, however, see the tiny tarsier as a remnant of the type of prosimian that gave rise to the so-called higher primates—the monkeys and apes. Unfortunately, the many genera of fossil tarsoids that once lived in North America, Asia and Europe are little help in this debate because they rarely show features that could be considered intermediate between living tarsiers and monkeys and apes. It is primarily in the anatomical details of the blood supply to the brain, in the structure of the placenta and in the shape of the nose—which cannot be recorded in fossil remains—that we see hints of monkey-like features in the tarsier.

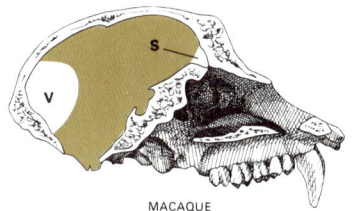
MACAQUE

BRAINS FOR SMELLING AND FOR SEEING

One important difference between the tree shrews, the more advanced lemurs and still more advanced monkeys and other higher primates is that the former depend primarily on smell and the others increasingly on sight. These characteristics are reflected in the brains of the animals, as these diagrams show—with the centers of vision marked with a "V" and the centers of smell marked with an "S". In the tree shrew and the lemur, the smelling center is relatively large. In the macaque it is smaller. Vision centers are just the opposite, being largest in the macaque.

The earliest appearance of the higher primates—monkeys and apes—goes back over 30 million years and is marked primarily by a continued shift in the relative importance of the various senses. Although prosimians were already developing stereoscopic vision with accompanying changes in the brain, they still retained many features of the primitive mammals. But in monkeys and apes the processes already begun with their prosimian relatives acquired quite a new emphasis.

As we see today, a larger part of their brain is devoted to receiving and interpreting visual stimuli. They have also lost much of their sense of smell. Their snouts are small, they no longer have the prosimian's moist muzzle, and the area of the brain devoted to smell is radically decreased. Their sense of touch is transferred from the end of the nose with its tactile hairs to the hand. This does not mean the sense of smell has lost its importance altogether. Far from it. Many monkeys use a scent-and-smell system to keep track of each other, and in some species a sense of smell plays a vital role in sexual

HOW THE TARSIER GOT ITS NAME

The tarsier is named for two greatly elongated tarsal bones in its foot, shown in color in the drawing below, along with the same bones in the human foot for comparison. The short length of bone behind the ankle, compared with the length of the bone stretching to the toes, gives the tarsier better leverage for leaping. About the size of a chipmunk, it can cover four to six feet (1.2 to 1.8 m) in a single jump.

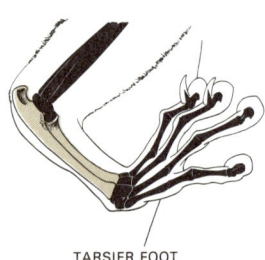

TARSIER FOOT

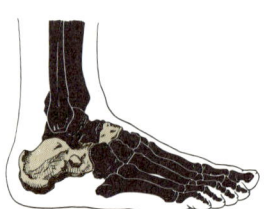

HUMAN FOOT

WHAT IS A PRIMATE?

behavior. Nonetheless, the dependence on vision is clearly reflected in the structure of their skulls, with greatly increased volume in the part that holds the brain, and with the bony orbits that hold the eyes directed forward and walled in on the sides and back for protection.

The great advantage of stereoscopic vision is that it enables its possessor to see clearly in three dimensions. This kind of acute perception permits man to manipulate delicate tools. It helped monkeys to see very clearly the branches they were about to grasp and also, buttressed by their color vision, to identify any suitable food within reach. Relying as they did on vision, it was natural for monkeys to examine strange objects not only by leaning over to sniff at them but also by reaching out and holding them up in front of their eyes, which permitted a much more accurate appraisal.

To reach out and seize an object a short distance away may not appear a particularly demanding feat. We take it for granted because we are continually performing vastly more exacting tasks, such as threading needles or parking automobiles. But consider the problems it presented to prosimians. They had command only of what is called whole-hand control—i.e., while they could move their digits, they could only move them all at once, not individually. When they reached out to grasp a branch, all five of their fingers closed over it at once. When they reached out to pick up something, their fingers worked simultaneously in the same way.

Clearly, this way of grasping has its disadvantages—and the monkeys, as they evolved, improved upon it. In feeding, grooming and their other specialized activities, selection increasingly favored refinements of control over the digits, to the point where at last monkeys were able to seize even very small objects with precision between their thumb and forefinger. This required a highly complicated set of interactions between the hand and the eyes and therefore a highly efficient controlling nervous system. And as monkeys kept improving their ability to grasp, their brains and nervous systems became increasingly elaborate.

Much of the increase in the size of the monkeys' brains was devoted to areas controlling their hands and their feet, their fingers and their toes. Most of the remainder served to make their vision more acute and their memories more capacious. Monkeys, in consequence, became able to observe more intently, to discriminate more acutely between objects, to store up a vast and significant reservoir of visual images and to summon up, for comparison, a larger number of meaningful memories that could help them to handle the various situations they confronted. In brief, the monkeys' larger brains enabled them to learn more and survive successfully in their environment.

Possessed of all these advantages, monkeys and apes were able to displace the prosimians, and they expanded rapidly throughout the forests. By about 30 million years ago, one group was established in South America, while another had developed in Africa. Many species were later to acquire new characteristics and specializations, but the monkeys' fundamental structure was set. And so, it might surprise the reader to learn, was the sensory system of the entire post-prosimian primate order, up to and including man. The human brain is perhaps a dozen times as large and vastly more complicated than that of any monkey, but most of this additional brain is devoted to memory, association and speech: that is, to abstractions. So far as his method of perceiving the world around him is concerned, man has advanced hardly at all beyond the stage reached by monkeys and apes some 25 million years ago. He may not react like a monkey, but essentially he smells and tastes, hears, touches and sees very much as a monkey does.

Anatomically, however, men and monkeys are very different animals. Monkeys, being quadrupeds, retain many of the characteristics of primitive four-legged mammals. Their trunk is long, narrow and deep, and their limbs are hung from it in a very special way which restricts their movements largely to using their arms and legs in a backward and forward plane, as in walking or running. The general proportions of a monkey's trunk are much like those of a dog—and like a dog, a monkey tends to keep its arms and legs parallel. Even when stretching, it will reach out forward, as a dog does when it awakens from sleep, rises, yawns and stretches out its legs. And in the trees, monkeys for the most part move the way a four-legged animal moves, walking or running along the top of a branch.

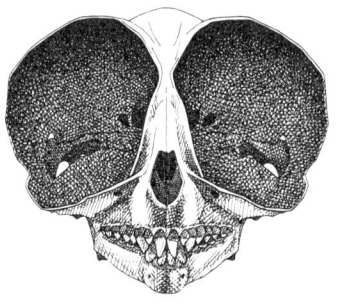

A SKULL FOR LARGE EYES

The most striking features of the tarsier's skull are its immense eye sockets, necessary to house its large, night-adapted eyes. If a man's eyes were proportionately as large, they would be the size of small grapefruit. Another characteristic of its head—as well as that of most other prosimians and all higher primates—is eyes that look directly forward, allowing stereoscopic vision. All-but-solid walls of bone at the back of the eye sockets protect the eyeballs. In monkeys, apes and man these walls are completely closed; other prosimians have less complete closure.

W‌ITH apes, it is quite different—as it is with man. The fossil record indicates that the earliest higher primates were more like apes than monkeys. We do not know when or where the earliest Old World monkeys began to appear from this apelike stock. We do know, however, that there were ape ancestors 30–35 million years ago and that by 15–20 million years ago they had spread across much of Africa, Europe and Asia.

There are today four main genera of apes, divided into two families. One family includes the African gorilla and chimpanzee and their Asiatic relative, the orangutan; the other family is that of the Asiatic gibbon. All are quite different anatomically from any monkey. The most obvious distinction is that they are built for a different mode of travel, with short, wide, shallow trunks and long, free-swinging arms that rotate at the shoulders. These adaptations allowed early apes to reach out in all directions in the trees, swinging their bodies under the branches, arm over arm, in a form of locomotion called brachiation.

Apes move in ways quite different from the Old World monkeys. Each of the living apes has different habits of locomotion from the others. The gibbon is the only true brachiator—in other words, the only one that habitually travels by swinging under branches. While the other living apes share essentially the same kind of trunk and arms as the gibbon, the adults are generally too heavy for this form of travel. Orangutans have been seen to swing from branches that are strong enough to support them. Usually, however, they use their hands and feet interchangeably. The African apes—the chimpanzee and the gorilla—usually walk quadrupedally on the ground. But unlike most quadrupeds, they walk on the knuckles of their hands, rather than on the palms or fingertips. A chimp may occasionally brachiate, especially a young one; but the gorilla, the least arboreal of the apes, does so only on the rarest occasion. More commonly all of the apes use their long arms for climbing among the large boughs rather than swinging underneath them. Only man is an efficient biped, and the structure of his pelvis and legs, which makes possible his characteristically erect posture and bipedal locomotion, is very different from that of the apes.

Exactly how or why apes came by their long arms is debatable—but the most satisfactory explanation is that selection favored climbing with all fours as a means of obtaining food. Most branches in the forest canopy are too delicate to bear even the weight of an average-sized monkey moving along them on all fours, let alone that of a big ape—but if the weight can be divided by hanging from several branches with two feet and one hand, then a lot of hitherto unreachable food becomes available. This is the way some apes do feed, in perfect comfort.

A major change in locomotion usually involves changes in more than just a few parts of the body. The practice of climbing with hands and feet in the apes prompted a series of further changes which significantly altered the primate anatomy and paved the way for development in two separate directions—on the one hand providing the potential for tool-using man and on the other the specialized adaptations of the modern anthropoid apes.

In order to reach and climb more effectively with their arms, the apes acquired a whole new complex of characteristics—in their shoulders, their elbows and their wrists—that combined to make their arm movements much more flexible. Apes can swing their arms out in a wide circle from their shoulders—forward, sideways, backward and up. With their more flexible elbows they can straighten out their arms, and their wrists are much more mobile than a monkey's—more so, in fact, than a man's. An ape can hang from a branch by one hand and rotate its body completely around, thanks to the flexibility of its arm and wrist joints.

Nor did the changes which sprouted from their arm-swinging stop at the apes' arms and shoulders. Ultimately they affected the whole of their upper bodies, giving them their characteristic short, relatively inflexible spine, the wide, shallow trunk with its resultantly different arrangement of the viscera, and a pelvis splayed out to provide additional room for the attachment of muscles. All of these changes helped to produce animals which, from the waist up, physically resemble man. From the pelvis to the skull, an ape looks and moves very much like a man, as one can see by observing an ape from behind while it is eating. Sitting there, reaching for food and carrying it to its mouth, it looks almost exactly like a man helping himself to various dishes at the dinner table.

For a variety of reasons, certainly including ignorance and possibly conceit, man has always had a tendency to consider his own qualities as being unique. In the course of so doing, people have tended to lump apes together with monkeys as animals that resemble each other, both physically and mentally, much more closely than either resembles man. So far as their intelligence is concerned, this assumption may or may not be accurate. The relative intelligence of any two species is a difficult thing to determine, but as any close observer of apes and monkeys knows, man stands physically much closer to an ape than an ape does to a monkey.

Nonetheless, it is important to remember that men and apes are very different, and man is no more the descendant of a modern ape than one grandchild of a common grandparent is the descendant of another grandchild. Still, just as a grandchild is linked to its grandfather by an intermediate parent, so man must somehow be linked to an apelike ancestor. We shall be discussing this point in more detail in a later chapter. For the moment, it is enough to say that man, as he has currently evolved, is the beneficiary of millions of years of evolutionary change spurred by the exacting demands of arboreal life and subsequently by the need to adapt to life on the ground. Although he long ago went his own separate evolutionary way, he has good reason to see in the anthropoid apes of today a vision of what his own ancestors may once have been.

THE GEOLOGIC TIME SCALE

For many years experts have argued about the dates to be assigned to the eras, periods and epochs of the geologic time scale. The scale generally accepted for many years has been based on one devised by J. Laurence Kulp of Columbia University. More recently a scale compiled for the Elsevier Scientific Publishing Company has gained wide acceptance. The scale used in this book is an updated Kulp scale: Its relationship to the Elsevier scale is shown in the table below.

	DATE (MILLIONS OF YEARS AGO)	
	Kulp Scale	Elsevier Scale
Paleozoic Era		
Cambrian Period	600	570
Ordovician Period	500	500
Silurian Period	440	435
Devonian Period	400	395
Carboniferous Period		
Mississippian Epoch	350	345
Pennsylvanian Epoch	325	310
Permian Period	270	280
Mesozoic Era		
Triassic Period	225	230
Jurassic Period	180	195
Cretaceous Period	135	141
Cenozoic Era		
Tertiary Period		
Paleocene Epoch	70	65
Eocene Epoch	60	55
Oligocene Epoch	40	35
Miocene Epoch	25	22.5
Pliocene Epoch	10	5
Quaternary Period		
Pleistocene Epoch	2	1.8

THE GALAGO, OR BUSH BABY, IN VARIETY AND ABUNDANCE IS ONE OF THE MOST SUCCESSFUL PRIMITIVE PRIMATES OUTSIDE OF MADAGASCAR

Primate Beginnings

Primate, meaning first, is the name Linnaeus chose for the animal order containing prosimians, monkeys, apes and man. From a little shrewlike progenitor in the Paleocene or an earlier epoch, these creatures came to dominate the animal kingdom. How the primates evolved—starting with the prosimians and ascending toward man— is a story now being revealed in ever new and fascinating detail.

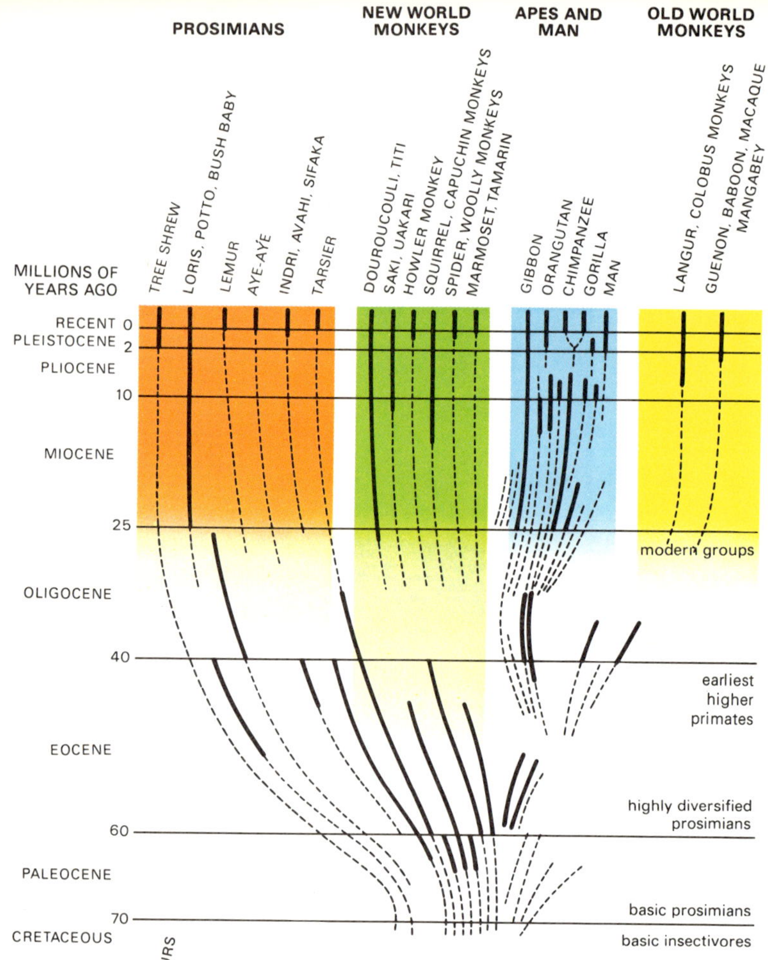

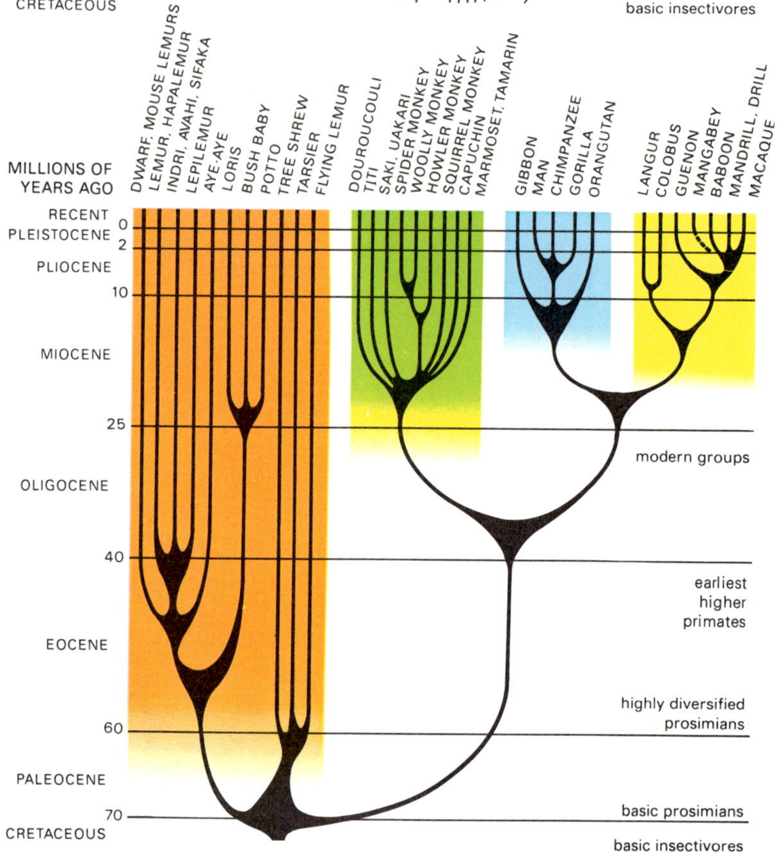

Primate Genealogy

Two distinctly different methods are currently being employed to determine primate evolution. The pictorial chart above and the genealogical chart at top left are based upon fossil finds. (The dating of the fossils is

shown by solid lines in the latter chart; the dotted lines are guesswork.) The chart at bottom left traces the divergence of primates through biochemical methods as employed by Dr. Vincent Sarich at the University of California.

The biochemical studies—which show relationships among man and animals by comparing substances found in their molecules—occasionally vary from the fossil evidence. The tree shrew, for example, is often excluded from the primate order on the basis of fossils. Dr. Sarich's biochemical studies, however, reveal it to be as much a primate as tarsiers.

The molecular study further finds that New and Old World monkeys diverged at the same time—some 30 million years ago—from a common ancestor. Such a view contradicts the traditional belief that New World monkeys broke away from the basic primate line earlier than Old World monkeys.

THE PEN-TAILED TREE SHREW from Borneo and nearby islands differs from most other tree shrews in being nocturnal. As a consequence, its eyes and ears are larger than its cousins'.

THE COMMON TREE SHREW with its long bushy tail looks so much like the squirrels in Malaysia that local natives make no distinction between the two, calling both of them *tupai*.

TOOTH TO TOOTH, lesser tree shrews battle in a cage. Though little observed in the wild, such belligerence leads naturalists to believe that the contesting of territorial rights plays an im-

The Puzzling Tree Shrew

Scientists are confronted with a difficult problem when they attempt to classify tree shrews. Their general appearance, coupled with their appetite for insects, inclines some scientists to group them with the insectivores—the order that includes the shrews and moles. Yet considering such traits as the bony rings surrounding their eyes and other characteristics of

portant part in their everyday lives. If these males were left in the same cage, one would certainly end by killing the other. (However, the scar on the nose of the shrew on the right is a cage mark.) Tree shrews seem wildly irate, gluttonous and libidinous—excesses that led anthropologist Carleton Coon to describe them as caricaturing "uninhibited human behavior."

their skulls, these little Southeast Asian mammals are placed at the bottom of the primate ladder by other experts. Still, they are a far cry from the lemurs, which are undisputed as early prosimians. With eyes set on the sides of their heads, they are poorly equipped to see in depth. Their muzzles are long, their noses moist, and they have no fully opposable digit. Tree shrews may be said, then, to straddle the fence between insectivore and primate. Herein lies their special interest, since evidence points to their resembling that small insectivorous mammal that took to the trees some 70 million years ago in the Paleocene or the earlier Cretaceous epoch and, by so doing, founded the primate order.

STARING STRAIGHT BACKWARD over its long, brush-tipped tail, a tarsier shows the mobility of its head, able to swivel 180° right or left. Below it, a companion clutches a lizard.

The Tarsier: One of a Kind

The tarsiers, once widely distributed over most of the Northern Hemisphere, have dwindled to but a single living genus that is now restricted to a few Southeast Asian islands. Still, this survivor holds a number of primate records. For its size, roughly that of a rat, its eyes are the largest in the order, and it also has proportionately the longest legs and largest ears. Large eyes and ears are adaptations for nocturnal life, while its long legs are used for jumping about in trees, a startling, but long-used, form of locomotion that seems more like that of an arboreal frog than of any primate.

DISPLAYING DROWSY CONTENTMENT, A TARSIER CLEANS A GROOMING CLAW

A MOUSE LEMUR, ACTUALLY CLOSER IN SIZE TO A RAT, STRETCHES OUT TO SNIFF A CARNATION. PRIMARILY AN INSECT EATER, THIS LITTLE LEMUR IS

Lemurs Come in Many Forms

For the lemurs Linnaeus chose the Latin word *lemures*, meaning "ghosts." And noisy ghosts they are for the most part, too, moving in a now-you-see-them-now-you-don't manner through the forests. But among the nine genera, all of them living on the tropic island of Madagascar, there is a wide variation in form, size and habits. The two above, the five-inch (13-cm) mouse lemur and the four-foot-tall (1.2-m) indri, serve to illustrate the extremes. The mouse lemur, though arboreal and able to grasp branches with both its hands and feet, like any non-human primate, is as much a quadruped as is its rodent namesake. It lives in nests where, during the day, it curls up in its long bushy tail. There, too, the female raises its young in litters of two and three.

The indri, on the other hand, behaves like a more

24

ALSO FOND OF SWEETS, PARTICULARLY FRUITS, HONEY AND NECTAR

BIGGEST PROSIMIAN IS THE INDRI, FOUR FEET (1.2 M) TALL

advanced primate. Like a monkey, it sits in an erect posture, though its spectacular leaps through the trees on powerful hind legs resemble more the locomotion of a tree-living kangaroo. On the ground it hops along on its hind feet, holding its torso upright like a gibbon. The female bears only one young at a time, which she carries along with her, clinging to her belly, wherever she goes. Socially, the mouse lemur is solitary and belligerent, staking out for itself a specific territory and defending it ferociously against all other mouse lemurs; the less solitary indri lives in small family groups. Finally, the nocturnal mouse lemur eats some fruits but mainly insects, whereas the indri, one of the diurnal lemurs, feeds during the day on leaves, fruits and buds. A further variation of the lemurs' many forms is shown on the next two pages.

25

THE SIFAKAS, related to the indri on the previous page, share its agility in the trees and bouncy gait on the ground, but in place of the indri's stumpy tail they have long furry ones.

IN MID-STRIDE a sifaka shows why it is bipedal on the ground: Its legs are long and its arms are short. It would be even more awkward for it to walk on all fours than it would be for a man.

CARRYING HER BABY like a money belt around her waist, a sifaka mother bounds off the ground with a powerful kick. A stunning cowl of white fur frames her naked black face and ears.

IN FLYING DIVES of 30 feet (9 m) and more, sifakas show their common mode of travel. Here *(top picture)* a sifaka is caught at takeoff, its strong legs fully extended, its arms over its head like a diver's. In the bottom picture, leaping back again, it is captured in mid-flight as it twists around for the landing, swinging its feet forward to take the shock of impact.

A SAD FACE AND LUDICROUS CARE WHEN CLIMBING LED COLONISTS TO NAME THIS ANIMAL LOERES—A DUTCH VERSION OF DISNEY'S DOPEY

The Lorises: Wide-eyed Sluggards

Besides the primitive tarsiers, the only sizable group of prosimians to survive outside of Madagascar and a few other islands in the western Indian Ocean are the lorisoids. These include the rapid-jumping little African galagos and the larger, slow-moving lorises themselves: the slender loris of Sri Lanka and India, the slow loris of Southeast Asia *(above)* and in Africa, the potto and the rare angwantibo. Moving slowly like South American sloths, lorises have claimed an empty niche alongside their more active and intelligent cousins, the monkeys and the apes. Sluggish in movement, solitary and nocturnal, the

28

SMALLER THAN THE SLOW LORIS (LEFT), THE SLENDER LORIS (ABOVE) HAS THE SAME STARING EYES ADAPTED FOR HUNTING AT NIGHT

animals feed largely on insects, birds and birds' eggs. In keeping with its torpor, a loris' metabolic rate is so low that even in the tropics it would die of cold if shorn of its thick coat. But slow as it generally is, a loris will move rapidly enough when necessary —when it is seizing prey, for instance. Unlike the sloth, which always progresses upside down, hanging from hooklike claws, a loris is as much at home on top of a tree branch as it is underneath one. It has an unusually long backbone with more vertebrae than any other primate, giving it the extra measure of flexibility it needs for moving around in the trees.

THE POTTO of West Africa, besides having the long and supple spine common to lorisoids, has an added feature: Several vertebrae at the base of its neck protrude above the surface amid numerous long hairs. Although no one is quite sure, it is supposed that these vertebrae afford some protection for the vital spinal cord when the potto curls itself up into a ball to sleep.

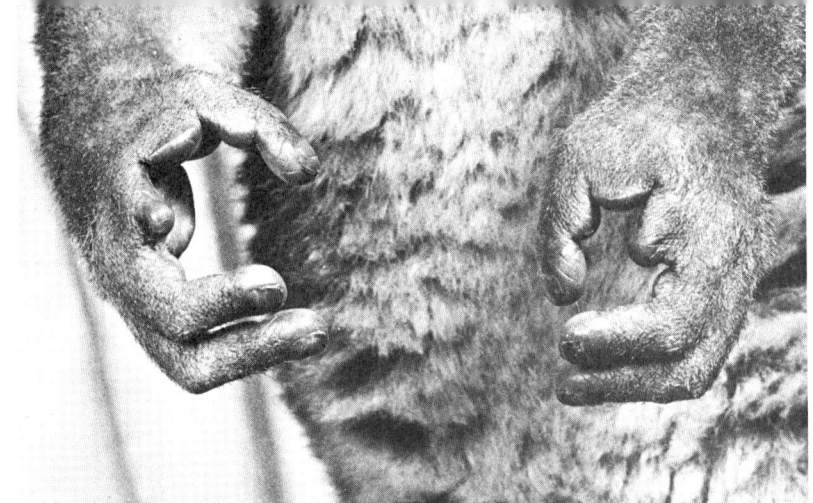

A POTTO'S HANDS have the most perfect opposition of any primate's. Where the index finger normally would be, there is only a vestigial stump, a modification that widens and strengthens the potto's grip.

A POTTO'S FOOT shows the single claw on the second toe, characteristic of its group. Called the grooming claw, it is used to clean and comb the hair. Other digits have the flat nails common to primates.

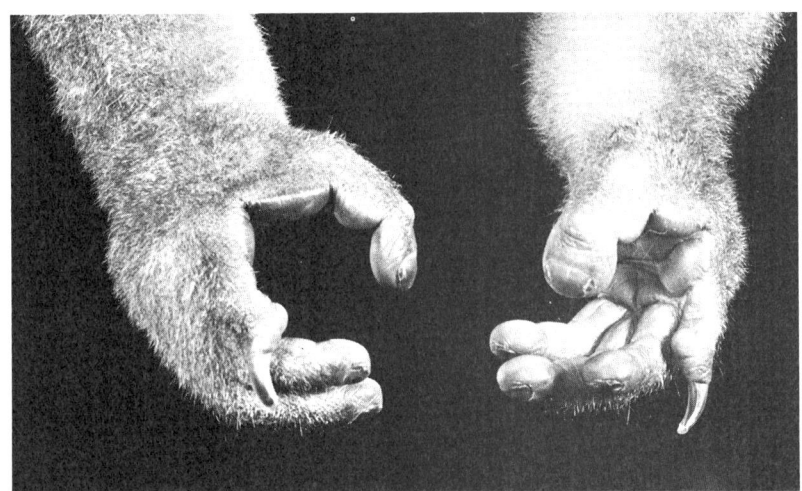

A BABY POTTO suckling from an eyedropper clings tightly to its artificial mother: a crumpled piece of tissue paper. Pottos bear one young at a time, and from the day of birth the infant tenaciously clutches the hair of its mother's front. In that position it travels for the first few weeks of its life. This three-day-old female, born in captivity, was deserted by its mother.

COCKING AN EAR FOR BEETLE GRUBS, AN AYE-AYE TAPS AND PROBES A BRANCH WITH ITS SPECIALLY ADAPTED, LONG MIDDLE FINGER

The Oddball Aye-Aye

One of the most puzzling of primates is the aye-aye of Madagascar, so aberrant that taxonomists have assigned it a family all its own. Almost as large as its cat-sized body is its long bushy tail. Its teeth, made for gnawing, resemble a rodent's: They grow as they wear, taking a fine chisel edge. Its eyes, however, like those of many lemurs, are adapted to night vision and fitted with nictitating membranes which wipe them clean. Its nose is short, its ears are large, naked and protruding. Like all primates with the exception of man, aye-ayes grip branches with both feet and hands, but only their big toes are fitted with flat primate nails—the other digits all have claws. Like mouse lemurs, aye-ayes sleep through the day in nests, wrapped snugly in their ample tails. At night they use their specially adapted middle finger—incredibly thin and looking like a bent piece of black wire—much as a woodpecker uses its bill, tapping and probing for grubs under bark which they then rend with their strong teeth. In this nocturnal game of hide and seek their acute senses of hearing and smell are vital aids.

ITS PECULIAR CLAWS AND WIRY MIDDLE FINGER SHOW IN A CLOSEUP OF AN AYE-AYE'S CRAGGY HAND

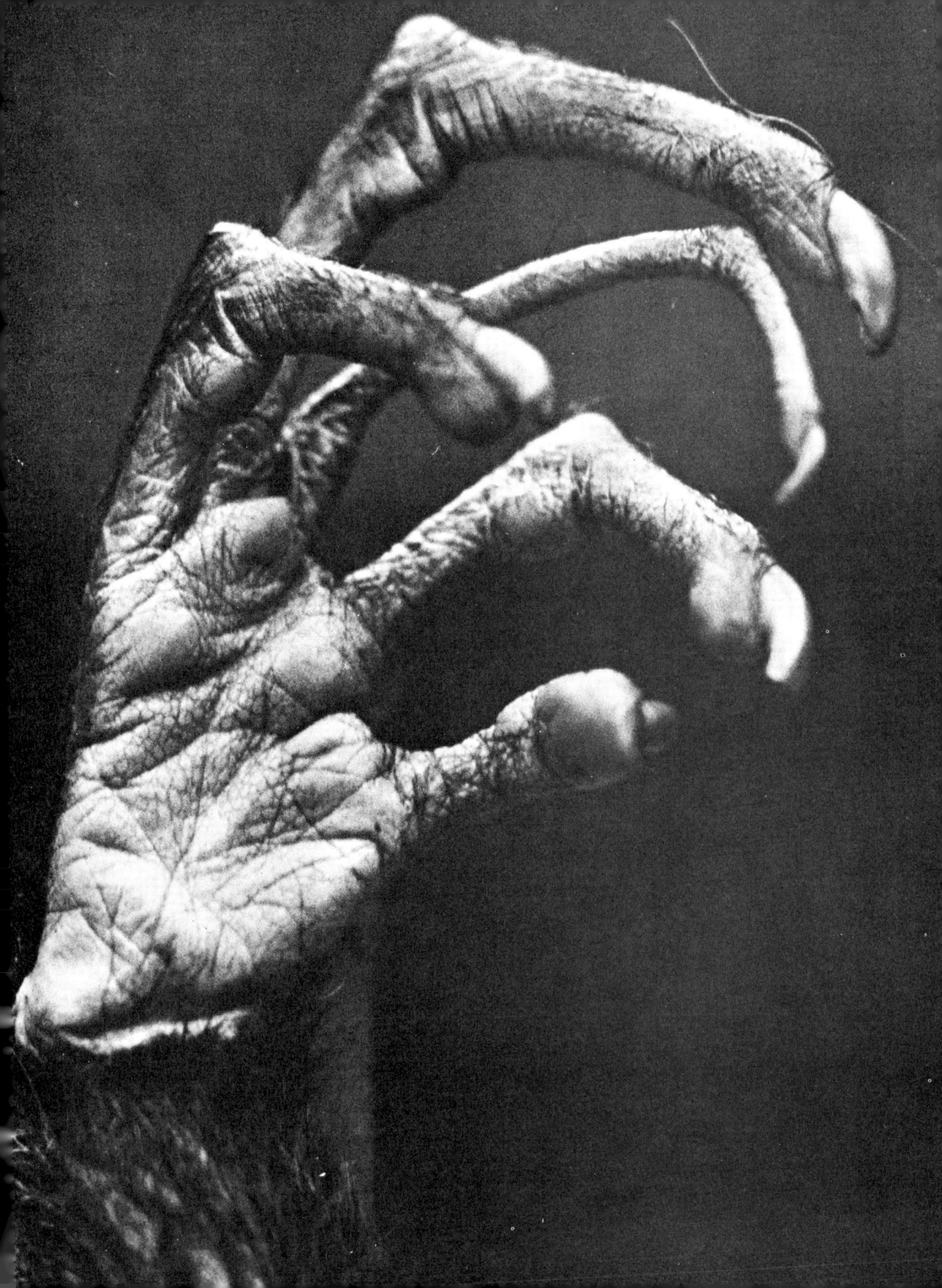

THE CAPUCHIN is the most familiar New World monkey, largely because of its winning way of soliciting coins for organ-grinders. It is also a popular entertainer in zoos—where it adjusts well to captivity.

2
The Monkeys: Success in the Trees

Second only to man, monkeys are the most successful of primates. From the viewpoint of evolution, success is judged by numbers, and monkeys exist not only in vast numbers—many species in Africa and South America have 100 specimens per square mile (40 per km²)—but also in a dazzling variety of forms. In South America there are monkeys no bigger than kittens—in Africa, monkeys that weigh about as much as great Danes. Some are as timid as antelopes, while others will oppose a hungry cheetah and make it turn elsewhere for its next meal. According to the best available estimate, there are approximately 30 genera of monkeys, divided into more than 130 species. By contrast, men, though they have spread farther than monkeys across the earth, all belong to one single species.

Why is there so much variety among monkeys? One can approach the question at several levels, but it is easiest to begin with the differences which separate one closely related species from another. A species may be defined as a group of animals which is reproductively isolated from all other animals and shares a common gene pool. This means that the members of the group must not only be the same kind of animals—physically capable of mating with one

THE MONKEYS: SUCCESS IN THE TREES

another and producing offspring—but also that they must have access to each other. It is this matter of access that sheds some light on the amount of variety among monkeys. Many of them are arboreal animals which never, or only rarely, descend to the ground. Suppose the forest thins out or a stream widens into a river too broad to be crossed in a single leap. Unable to travel across the ground, the arboreal monkeys in the isolated set of trees will be cut off from other populations of their species. Generations pass; changes occur through mutation and genetic recombination, and those which are favored by selection are passed throughout the isolated group, inducing perhaps a fresh dash of color or a lengthening of the tail. Through time, these processes continue to increase the differences between the physically isolated population and the rest of the species, until eventually reproductive isolation is complete and a new species emerges.

Variations caused by selection are usually comparatively superficial at first; in fact, most closely related species differ primarily in their coloring or in minor anatomical features. These superficial distinctions have, over the millennia, created the dazzling variations in design and in coloring, in browns and greens and whites and blues and yellows, that are typical of the arboreal monkeys. The names of some of the guenons, the common monkeys of Africa, suggest the picture: the red-bellied monkey, the moustached monkey, the yellow-nosed monkey, the white-nosed, the spot-nosed, the red-eared, the white-collared, the green, the blue, the owl-faced. . . . How many species of guenons there are depends on which expert is doing the counting—more than a dozen is probably the best estimate.

Such counting of noses among monkeys suggests an interesting tendency: A genus that is primarily arboreal will tend to have a greater number of species than one that is primarily ground-dwelling. The langurs, for example, the common arboreal monkeys of Asia, number over 30 species. By contrast, there are only about one third as many ground-dwelling Asian macaques, and some of these are island forms.

The earliest primates were undoubtedly very similar. But the farther up the family tree we come toward the present, the greater the differences we find among different genera in such characteristics as chromosomes, bone structure and digestive system. Time is a great divider, and its mere passage tends to operate like a wedge, driving deeper and deeper. Once one group of monkeys begins to diverge from another, the differences will inevitably be multiplied by selection as the millennia pass. One basic separation apparently took place somewhere along the ancestral primate line at least 30 million years ago—and perhaps much longer ago than that—to produce two separate groups today. One of these is found in Central and South America (the New World monkeys), and the other (the Old World monkeys) spread throughout Africa and Asia. Every living monkey belongs to one group or the other. The differences between the two are now very great, resulting partly from their long separation and partly from the effects of the environments in which they have lived.

If genetic change and selection are the father of evolution, environment and need are the mother. This combination has been responsible for every variety of life. For example, the most urgent problem an individual animal faces is finding food. It must be able to find enough food that it can digest or, alternatively, it must adapt internally so that it can digest the food that is available. Monkeys have solved this problem in a number of ways, and this provides a

---

NEW WORLD

OLD WORLD

A DIFFERENCE IN NOSES

Monkeys from the Old World and the New differ in several, often subtle, anatomical ways, but one simple method to tell them apart is to look at their noses. The nostrils of the New World monkeys, such as the woolly (top), are round and separated by a broad nasal septum. Old World monkeys like the macaque (bottom) have narrow septums. As a result, their nostrils are close together, comma-shaped and pointing downward.

second answer to the question: Why is there so much variety among them?

It is on the basis of their digestive systems that all Old World monkeys are divided into two subfamilies: one embracing the langurs and colobus monkeys, the other all the remainder of Asian and African species. The colobus monkey and the langur are primarily leaf eaters. Leaves, as a staple of diet, have both advantages and disadvantages. They are enormously abundant but they are not particularly nourishing. To extract the maximum nourishment from leaves, langurs and colobus monkeys have developed specialized digestive systems, including greatly enlarged stomachs. Both langurs and colobus monkeys have to eat such huge quantities of leaves to survive that after a full meal, the food and the voluminous guts together make up a fourth or more of their total body weight. At such times a langur's stomach is so distended that even a well-trained observer often cannot tell whether a female is about to give birth or is just well fed.

THE advantage of the colobus-langur alimentary tract is that it enables its owner to digest mature leaves that other Old World monkeys cannot survive on. These old leaves even provide liquids. The Indian langur can go for several months without drinking water, and langurs in general can survive in drought areas where almost any other monkey would perish. Colobus monkeys inhabit the same trees in the Central African forest as mangabeys and guenons, and their digestive systems give them a competitive advantage. Suppose a group of fig trees starts to bear fruit. They will very soon be filled with a veritable menagerie of birds and animals: chimpanzees and baboons, mangabeys and several species of guenons, all busily attacking the figs. As the number of figs dwindles and the competition grows more intense, the monkeys and the chimpanzees might leave until finally all are gone. All, that is, except the colobus monkeys, whose specialized adaptation would enable them to obtain sustenance from the mature leaves that are useless to all the other monkeys.

There is yet a third reason for all these variations among monkeys. Consider, for example, the quite remarkable differences in physical structure and in temperament that distinguish the colobus monkey and the langur from the baboon. Forgetting their digestive peculiarities for the moment, the colobus monkey and the langur are typical arboreal monkeys. Temperamentally, they are extremely timid, and their normal response to danger is either to hide or to flee. Physically, they possess a typical monkey face. They are lithe, long-bodied and slender, and their long limbs make them very agile. This agility is clearly an adaptation to arboreal life. A langur can run with ease along slender branches, race from top to bottom of a hundred-foot (30-m) tree in seconds, and clear a 30-foot (9-m) gap between trees in a single, sure-footed, arching leap.

Baboons of the savanna are very different. They are large, sturdy and powerful; full-grown males may weigh more than 100 pounds (45 kg). They are not slender, they are not graceful. They are built not to jump agilely in trees but to maneuver and fight. Their faces are much longer, with doglike muzzles and heavy ridges of bone over the eyes. Their trunks are thick, their shoulders heavily muscled and made to appear even more formidable by a thick ruff of hair. They are clumsy in the trees, and leaping long distances from one tree to another would be impossible for them. And as for their temperaments, they can be tough, aggressive, even bellicose, prepared if necessary to stay and fight against all comers except lions, leopards and armed men.

Why all the differences? The answer, in part, lies in the word "predators." If food is the first requirement for survival, defense against attack is the second.

THE MONKEYS: SUCCESS IN THE TREES

To arboreal monkeys, defense is not much of a problem. Their chief enemies are carnivores, snakes, birds of prey—notably the crowned eagle in Africa and the harpy eagle in South America—and, very recently, man. In the trees, arboreal monkeys can usually evade a carnivore or a snake and, by staying under the top canopy, they can avoid most attacks by birds. A sturdy body and heavy muscles, and all that goes with them, would be more of a handicap than an advantage, since these would reduce the agility that is so enormously valuable in the trees. Almost all arboreal monkeys are, consequently, like the colobus, guenon and langur—lithe, slender, long-limbed—and in most cases, timid.

To baboons, the qualities most suitable for life in the trees are of little consequence because they are essentially terrestrial animals. True, they sleep in the trees, often feed in them, and when threatened by lions, climb up into them for refuge. But most of their waking hours are spent on the ground, where they are in constant danger from predators: lions and jackals, cheetahs and hyenas. In adapting to terrestrial life, male baboons were able to use their long canines to defend themselves, their females and their young. But animals that have learned how to defend themselves with their teeth need more than just teeth. They also need to have sturdy trunks, strong jaws and powerful shoulder muscles. Male baboons possess all these physical characteristics, and what is more, frequently combine against a common enemy.

Still, hefty and muscular as they are, baboons cannot always be sure of winning a fight against, say, a leopard. Even if they do win, they are liable to get badly mauled in the process. Obviously they are better off if they can prevent predators from attacking, by bluff, perhaps—by giving the impression that they are more formidable than they really are. The ruff of hair around a male baboon's shoulders achieves exactly this purpose. It makes the baboon's whole body look wider and deeper, and thus helps keep enemies at a distance.

For the female baboon, the picture is slightly different. She, too, is aggressive compared to arboreal monkeys; she, too, after all, is a terrestrial animal. But she is not really a fighting animal, because she and her young are defended by the males. Accordingly, female baboons do not possess long canines and are much smaller and lighter than the males. In fact, they are often only a little more than half as heavy.

Now, many male mammals are bigger than the females—but twice the size? So vast a difference in bulk between the sexes—or sexual dimorphism, to use the technical phrase—can surely be no accident. And it is not. In some instances, it appears to be the result of living on the ground. This is clearly demonstrated among the apes. Male and female gibbons, which spend all their time in the trees, are almost identical in size. Chimpanzees spend some of their time on the ground, and the males are somewhat bigger than the females. Gorillas are primarily terrestrial, and the males can be twice as big as the females. Presumably, the need of ground-dwelling primates to defend the group against predators has been a major reason for the males to become bigger and bigger. (It should be borne in mind, however, that larger males have also evolved through the urge to compete with each other for dominance.)

Adaptation to environment also explains the existence of ischial callosities, those pads of toughened skin on the rump, just underneath the tail, in Old World monkeys. These callosities are related to sleep, and possibly to feeding postures. An animal is most vulnerable while sleeping, and even the trees are not a completely safe refuge against attack. Certain snakes and carnivores,

PADS FOR RESTING

Among the characteristic features of Old World monkeys are the tough, callous pads on the rump, adapted for the long periods of time when these monkeys sit or sleep on tree limbs. Called ischial callosities, these pads (arrow, above) are attached directly to the undersides of the haunch bones. Hence there are no nerves or blood vessels to be pinched, and a monkey's legs do not "go to sleep" when the pressure of the body bears down on the pads. Even if it wedges itself between a limb and the trunk of a tree, as shown above, a monkey can be comfortable.

notably the nocturnal leopard, are competent climbers, and they can move both swiftly and silently. Therefore, some monkeys prefer to sleep as far away from the tree trunks as they can, out on the most slender branches that will bear their weight, so that if a snake or a cat ventures out toward them, they will be warned by the swaying of the branch. But sleeping on a narrow branch presents its own problem: If a monkey just stretches out, like a man in bed, it is likely to fall unless it can anchor itself to a branch, as a few New World monkeys do with their prehensile tails. Old World monkeys avoid falling when they sleep by sitting on their rumps with their legs thrust upward at a sharp angle, clinging to another branch for support. Because the pads of toughened skin are attached directly to the haunch bones with no nerves or blood vessels between bone and skin, their owners can sit in one position comfortably for hours.

Apart from baboons and possibly gorillas, there are only a few other genera of nonhuman primates that, when threatened, stay and fight instead of fleeing or hiding. One of these, the macaques, lives in Asia; and although smaller, macaques resemble African baboons in many respects. They are also predominantly terrestrial and have acquired the same characteristics of body build and temperament for precisely the same reason: to defend themselves against predators.

THE close similarity between baboons and macaques was largely responsible for the creation of a myth about monkey behavior which won wide currency earlier in the century, and which continued to mislead anthropologists until its falseness was exposed by the field studies of the 1950s. The myth is instructive because it can stand as an exemplary demonstration of the best possible way to reach wrong conclusions about animal behavior: by studying them only in captivity. To understand why the myth blossomed so vigorously, it is necessary to recall for a moment the division of monkeys into the two groups of Old World monkeys and New World monkeys. Totally separated for at least 30 million years, the two groups may have evolved out of different prosimian ancestors or may have diverged from the same stock, probably in Africa. They all possess typical monkey characteristics—they are all quadrupeds, for example—so if they sprang from different ancestors their similarity is a remarkable example of parallel evolution.

Nonetheless, the similarity is far from absolute. For example, no Old World monkey has a prehensile tail, but several kinds of South American monkeys do have such tails. On the other hand, all Old World monkeys possess ischial callosities and no New World monkeys do. To a taxonomist, however, the most significant differences between the two groups are found in their blood, the patterns of their teeth, their skulls and the structure of their brains.

These important distinctions between the two groups provided a reasonable basis for the myth—which ran somewhat as follows: Since *all* New World monkeys are anatomically quite distinct from *all* Old World monkeys, an equally clear distinction might exist in the way they behave. This argument was entirely theoretical since no one at the time had made a thorough study of even one species of either Old or New World monkeys in its natural habitat. During the 1930s, however, the American psychologist C. R. Carpenter did carry out a study of a group of South American howler monkeys on Barro Colorado Island in Panama, where observation is comparatively easy. Howlers, as their name implies, are exceedingly noisy animals, but as Carpenter found, they are quite amiable by temperament and rarely, if ever, get involved in fights. Meanwhile, several other species of South American monkeys had been

A TAIL'S SENSITIVE TIP

The most dexterous prehensile tail of all the New World monkeys belongs to the nimble spider monkey (above). Truly an extra limb, this supple appendage seems always in use, strong enough to hang by and sensitive enough to probe for, feel, then pick up an object as small as a peanut (below). The tip, supremely adapted, has a hairless undersurface with a pattern of ridges to give it added purchase when holding on—and also to heighten its ability to feel—much as do the whorled fingerprints of a man.

studied in captivity and they proved to be equally mild and unaggressive. On the basis of this somewhat slender evidence, New World monkeys were judged to be friendly, peaceful and altogether admirable creatures.

We turn back now to the Old World monkeys. In the late 1920s, a group of about a hundred hamadryas baboons were placed together on an island in the London Zoo. Hamadryas baboons are distinguished from other baboons primarily by a particularly lush ruff of gray fur which encloses their shoulders like a cape and reaches almost to the ground when they sit. They are also different in their social behavior: They form persistent groups composed of one male and several females and their young. The hamadryas male herds his females and is always jealous of them, even if one is not sexually receptive—in estrus —he will punish her if she strays and will certainly fight off any intruding male.

GIVEN these characteristics, the situation on the island in the London Zoo was an impossible one. The place was overcrowded to begin with, but worse still, there were many more males than there were females. With no chance of forming their accustomed groups, the males were bound to fight; and fight the captive animals did, regularly and with such ferocity that within a few years more than half of them were killed.

Most of the fighting naturally took place over the females. Once a fight began, the female would remain completely passive, covered by one male, while the other males surged around the pair. Furthermore—as was their natural habit—they constantly punished the female, grabbing and biting any part of her body they could reach. Every male who managed to win even temporary possession of a female promptly mounted her. The females' suffering, however, did not end with the incessant sexual pressure or with the bites of the enraged males. As long as the fighting lasted, the object of it was unable to break free and obtain food. Eventually, almost all the females in the group were killed, but even the death of a female did not necessarily end the fighting, since the males frequently continued to grapple over her dead body until the keepers intervened and dragged the corpse away.

The way the male hamadryas baboons behaved inside their enclosure suggested two conclusions. One was that baboon society was built on sex and jealousy. The other was that the males were themselves engaged in a continual struggle for dominance over each other. There was plenty of additional evidence to support this assumption. Even when no females were in estrus and no fighting was taking place, some males showed themselves to be dominant over others, and they asserted their power with ruthless persistence. They seized food from the weaker males, threatened them, snapped at them sporadically, drove them into tiny corners of the enclosure and, in general, kept them in a continual state of terrified submission.

By an unfortunate coincidence, from the viewpoint of establishing the whole truth, the next detailed study of Old World monkeys was carried out with a group of macaques which were transported from their homes in India to the 37-acre (15-ha) island of Santiago, just off the coast of Puerto Rico. There, it should be noted, they were fed regularly by human keepers. The macaques did not seem to fight with the savagery exhibited by the captive hamadryas. For one thing, this island was much bigger. It had more room, permitting weaker animals to escape from the stronger ones instead of being hemmed in by them. Nonetheless, the males were obviously in competition and used their canines vigorously in battles for dominance. The most powerful macaques monopolized the sexually receptive females, hogged the food, and just as the dominant hamadryas had done, brutally imposed their will on the weaker males.

Both these studies appeared to prove that baboons and macaques are ruthlessly selfish and aggressive and so determined to domineer that they will gravely injure or even kill any rival who tries to challenge them. On the basis of these studies, they were compared most unfavorably to the monkeys of South America. What is more, it was further assumed that the captive baboons and macaques were typical representatives of the entire subfamily of Old World monkeys. The conclusion was that all Old World monkeys lived in rigid social hierarchies, with the males competing viciously for dominance and the females occupying a status little better than that of slaves. Behavior, it was supposed, ran hand in hand with taxonomy, and the whole world of monkeys was split neatly into two. The anatomically more advanced monkeys were all unpleasantly bellicose and existed in a state of permanent strife on one side of the Atlantic, while the more primitive but easygoing and peaceable South American monkeys lived together in serene harmony on the other.

The only truth in this delightfully well-ordered analysis is that some monkeys are more aggressive and concerned with dominance than others. But as the reader will presumably have guessed, the distinction does not lie between Old and New World monkeys; most African and Asian tree-dwellers are just about as amiable and benign as most South American ones. It does not even lie, as one might be tempted to suspect, between monkeys that are adapted to life in the trees and monkeys adapted to life on the ground. Aggressive behavior is actually related to many factors, including the availability of necessary resources and the distribution of competitors for those resources. Another important factor is constant exposure to predators, to which the baboons and macaques—to a greater degree than any other primates—have developed a special temperament, one that enables them to stand and fight.

How important this is—fully as important as long canines and big muscles—is evident from the numbers of baboons and macaques which populate the regions where they live. Numbers, let us not forget, are the mark of success in evolution, and in this respect the baboons and macaques are certainly the most successful ground-dwelling monkeys. There are, of course, other successful adaptations to terrestrial living: the gorilla, which makes up for its lack of aggressiveness by sheer size and strength, and the patas monkey, which instead of fighting runs away or hides. But the baboons and macaques are an illustration of how selection can work to favor not only a useful physical characteristic but a psychological one as well. And while this adaptation of temperament subsequently affected the behavior of the individuals of these species toward each other as well as toward intruders of other species, it must be remembered that they never behave in the wild with the ferocity just described.

The vastly exaggerated view of baboon and macaque ferocity which was inspired by these two studies and was widely accepted actually arose from a failure to appreciate just how much a monkey's behavior changes when it is kept in captivity. A captive monkey is simply not a normal monkey, and it does not even have to be kept in a cage for its behavior to become abnormal. Whenever monkeys are subjected to unnatural conditions—when they are fed, for example, by humans—they are liable to become unusually competitive and aggressive. It is not hard to see why. In the wild, every monkey forages for itself, and competition over food is practically nonexistent. But if a whole troop of monkeys is obliged to feed out of the same bin, any natural competitiveness they possess is inevitably exacerbated. The closer the confinement, the more aggressive they will be, just like humans, who are likely to be much more irritable in Manhattan than in Wyoming, and very much worse in jail. Even comparatively peaceful monkeys, such as Indian langurs, are noticeably more nervous and irritable in confined areas around villages than they are in the roomy spaces of the forest. It is therefore well to remember that all conclusions about monkeys based solely on the way they behave in captivity, or when they are under any form of artificial restraint, should be regarded with considerable reservation.

The London hamadryas baboons and the Cayo Santiago macaques were peculiarly aggressive for yet another reason. In the wild, a monkey learns its place in the group as it grows up. By the time it is adult, it has established a relationship with all the other monkeys. They are all old friends, or at least old acquaintances. Every monkey knows that it is dominant over some, inferior to others. It is, consequently, the less likely to get into fights. When a baboon or a macaque does join another group, it frequently gets involved in dominance battles, which continue until its status is established, much as young boys do when they first attend a new school. It was therefore inevitable that scores of strange hamadryas baboons suddenly thrown together should have behaved viciously; just as in humans, when aggressive animals find themselves in a power vacuum, a struggle for power is unavoidable.

The adaptation of the baboons and macaques which makes it possible for them to stand and fight where others might run has enabled them to spread over much of the Old World—over a far larger area, in fact, than any other genus of monkey or ape. Adaptation to local conditions in this far-flung area, moreover, has led to the formation of well over a dozen species in the two genera. This is a dramatic illustration of how aggressiveness may be related to the ability of an animal to extend its habitat; and it brings us back to the curious point, mentioned at the beginning of this chapter, that all of the more than 130 species of monkeys between them have not been able to spread over as much of the earth's surface as the single species of man.

M AN has been able to range so widely for four main reasons. He is a terrestrial animal, not restricted to the forest. He can cross any natural barriers, such as deserts, oceans and mountains. He can live off a very wide variety of foods. Most important of all, he has developed culture, he has learned to make clothes and build fires which allow him to live in climates where he would otherwise perish. To a considerable degree, he shares the first three advantages with the ground-living monkeys. They, too, can move over unforested land. They, too, can cross natural barriers such as rivers, because they can swim, which they do by paddling, rather like a dog. And they, too, can digest many kinds of food. Possessed of these advantages, a single species of baboon has spread across Africa from Dakar in the west to Ethiopia in the east, and south all the way to the Cape of Good Hope. Macaques have done at least as well. One species, the rhesus macaque, is equally at home in forests, in open cultivated fields and inside heavily populated cities. Another species, the crab-eating macaque, inhabits the mangrove swamps of Indonesia. Macaques range high in the Himalayas, and in Japan, they dig for plants under the winter snow and pick up shellfish in summertime on the beaches. Were it not for the cold in some areas, for the oceans and the presence of competitors, they might well have spread over as much of the earth as man himself has done.

THE RARE WHITE-FACED SAKI OF THE AMAZON RAIN FOREST IS HUNTED BY MAN BOTH FOR ITS MEAT AND FOR ITS BUSHY TAIL, USED AS A DUSTER

Two Worlds of Monkeys

The most numerous and diversified of all primates, monkeys are grouped into two great divisions: New World and Old World species. They may have shared a common ancestor before they became divided. In any case, they resemble each other both physically and behaviorally. Fossils show that they once ranged into temperate latitudes, but today they live almost entirely in tropical habitats.

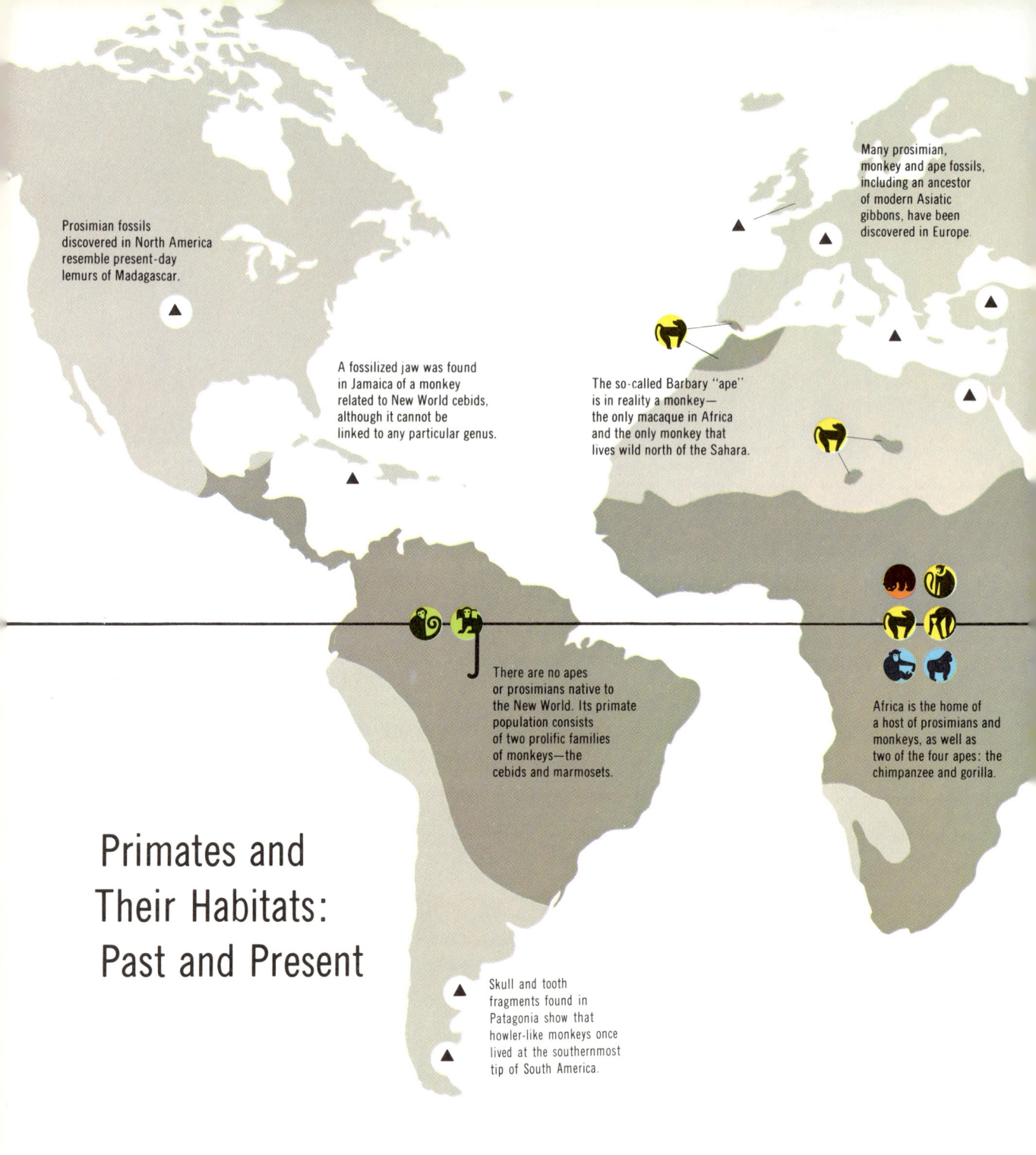

Prosimian fossils discovered in North America resemble present-day lemurs of Madagascar.

A fossilized jaw was found in Jamaica of a monkey related to New World cebids, although it cannot be linked to any particular genus.

Many prosimian, monkey and ape fossils, including an ancestor of modern Asiatic gibbons, have been discovered in Europe.

The so-called Barbary "ape" is in reality a monkey—the only macaque in Africa and the only monkey that lives wild north of the Sahara.

There are no apes or prosimians native to the New World. Its primate population consists of two prolific families of monkeys—the cebids and marmosets.

Africa is the home of a host of prosimians and monkeys, as well as two of the four apes: the chimpanzee and gorilla.

Skull and tooth fragments found in Patagonia show that howler-like monkeys once lived at the southernmost tip of South America.

Primates and Their Habitats: Past and Present

Monkeys are traditionally tropical animals. As this map shows, almost all of them are found living in a broad belt of hot rain forest or savanna running right around the globe roughly between the Tropics of Cancer and Capricorn. The key identifies the principal kinds of living Old World and New World monkeys, together with living prosimians and apes, each group given its own key color. Closely related genera, even though they may live on different continents, are represented by the same symbols. Thus, the baboons of Africa share a symbol with their cousins, the Asian macaques and the Barbary "apes." Similarly, African colobus monkeys and Asian langurs share a symbol, as do African pottos and galagos with Asian lorises. The small black triangles denote places where important fossil finds have been made outside the tropics, indicating how much more widely spread primates once were than they are today.

This once-wider distribution is due, of course, to the much warmer climate that prevailed in ages past and which permitted tropical forest to spread over much of the earth. But about

44

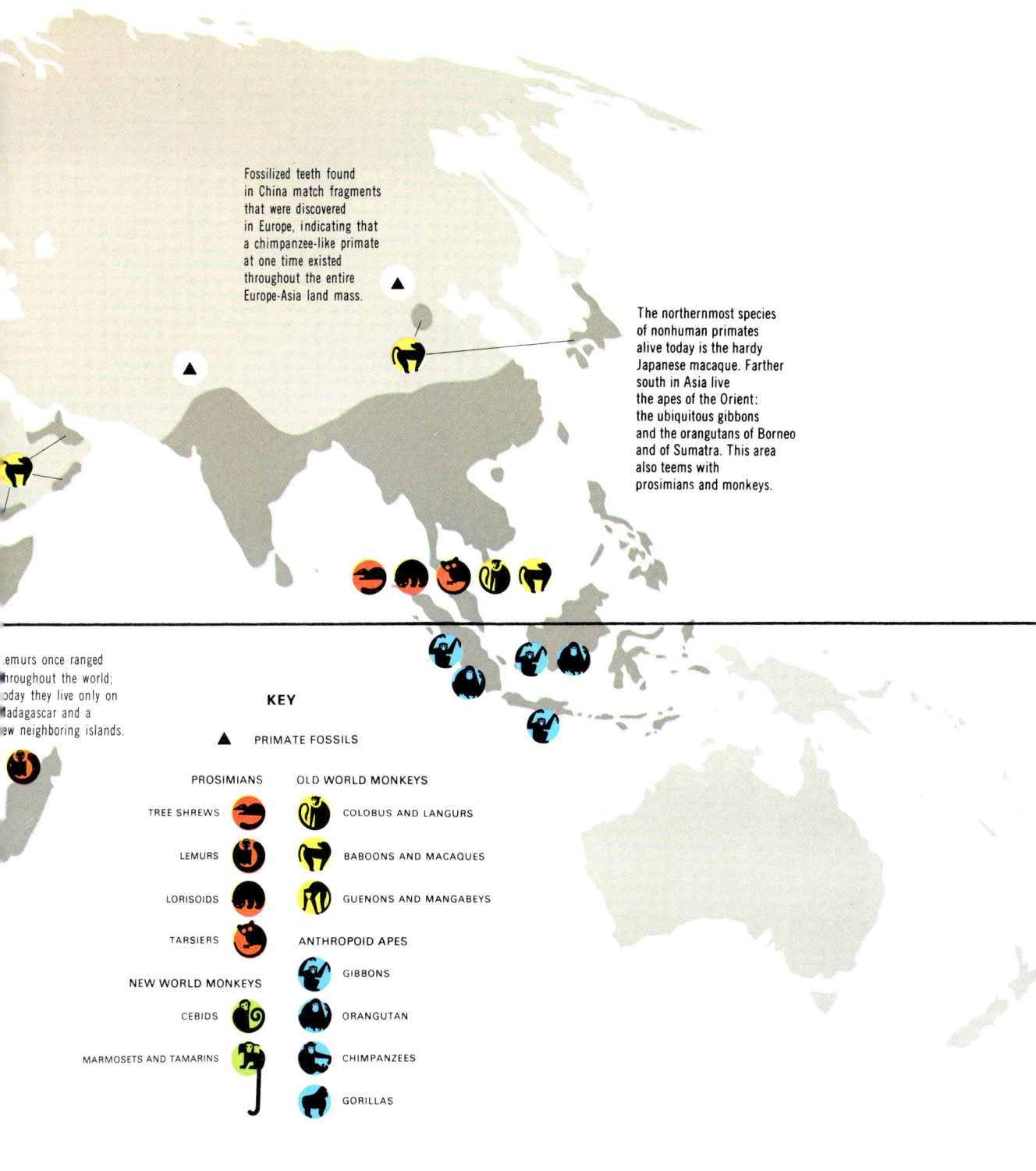

Fossilized teeth found in China match fragments that were discovered in Europe, indicating that a chimpanzee-like primate at one time existed throughout the entire Europe-Asia land mass.

The northernmost species of nonhuman primates alive today is the hardy Japanese macaque. Farther south in Asia live the apes of the Orient: the ubiquitous gibbons and the orangutans of Borneo and of Sumatra. This area also teems with prosimians and monkeys.

Lemurs once ranged throughout the world; today they live only on Madagascar and a few neighboring islands.

KEY

▲ PRIMATE FOSSILS

PROSIMIANS
- TREE SHREWS
- LEMURS
- LORISOIDS
- TARSIERS

NEW WORLD MONKEYS
- CEBIDS
- MARMOSETS AND TAMARINS

OLD WORLD MONKEYS
- COLOBUS AND LANGURS
- BABOONS AND MACAQUES
- GUENONS AND MANGABEYS

ANTHROPOID APES
- GIBBONS
- ORANGUTAN
- CHIMPANZEES
- GORILLAS

35 million years ago the weather began to change. In response to long periods of cold and dryness, the tropical forests shrank until they were restricted to the essentially equatorial position they occupy today. During this period a few of the monkeys—notably the baboons and macaques—left the heavy forest and gradually became adjusted to living on the open savanna. But where the forests survived, most primates stayed in the trees.

Scientists are hoping that the climatic changes of the ancient earth will, as they are better understood, help explain the distribution and relationships of the various different kinds of primates. It is clear, for example, that the African forests that contain colobus monkeys were once connected to the Asian forests that contain their close cousins, the langurs. What is unclear is when the ancestors of the New World monkeys and the Old World higher primates became separated—though this certainly took place before the evolutionary divergence of Old World monkeys and apes. While no true apes live in South America, some New World monkeys fill the niches occupied by apes elsewhere.

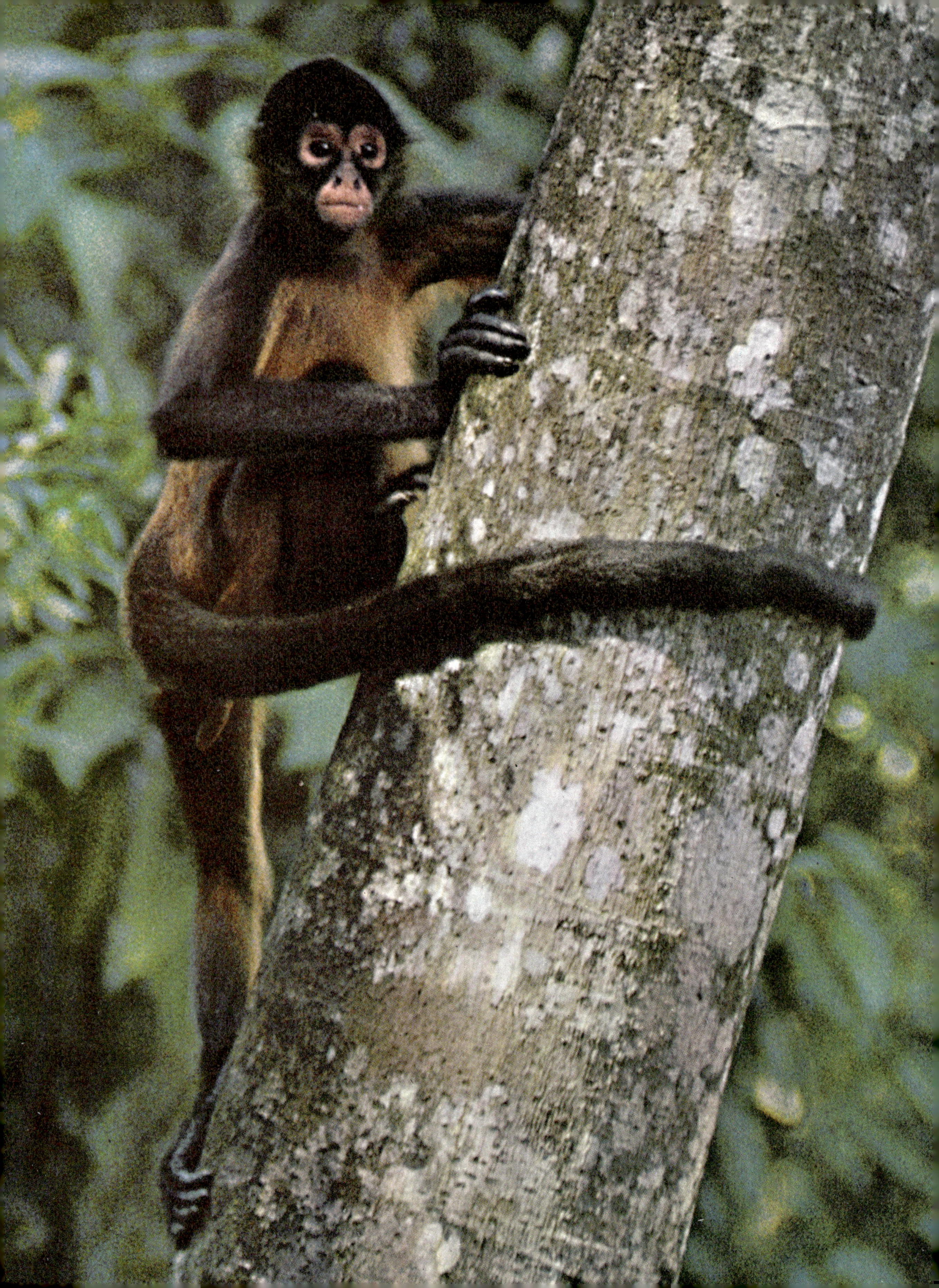

NEW WORLD MONKEYS
The Long Tails of the Jungle

There are more than 50 species of New World monkeys. Many of these have a very useful anatomical adaptation lacking in their Old World counterparts: that curious "fifth hand," the prehensile tail. In a few species, like the spider monkey *(left)* and the woolly monkey *(right)* bare spots like fingertips have developed on the end of the tail. While such a tail is not equipped with fingers, it can sometimes be even more useful than an arm or a leg. The spider monkey's tail is longer than its head and body combined, and is frequently used instead of a hand to grasp distant objects. Primates like the squirrel monkeys *(below)* are not so specially equipped and have ordinary long, heavy tails that are mainly useful as balancers when leaping or jumping. Without prehensibility they must relegate at least one limb to help support them while feeding, whereas the spider monkeys can hang by their tails while they enjoy a good meal with both hands and feet.

A WOOLLY MONKEY BALANCES ITSELF BY USING HIS "FIFTH HAND"

SQUIRREL MONKEYS SWARM OVER A FOREST TREE TO SEARCH FOR FOOD—FRUITS, FLOWERS, INSECTS AND EVEN SMALL BIRDS

A SPIDER MONKEY GRASPS A TREE TRUNK WITH ITS LONG AND POWERFUL PREHENSILE TAIL

IN A RARE ACROBATIC MOMENT, A UAKARI LEAPS ACROSS A FOREST ABYSS. IT USUALLY GOES SWIFTLY ON BRANCHES ON ALL FOURS

AN INVERTED UAKARI hangs by its feet from a branch. This posture, which it uses while searching for fruits and nuts, makes up in some ways for its lack of a prehensile tail.

NEW WORLD MONKEYS

The Mysterious Uakari

One of the rarest of the New World monkeys is the uakari, a cat-sized creature with a short, nonprehensile tail. It lives in swamp forests along remote Amazonian rivers and has adapted to life in the forest canopy, rarely if ever descending to the ground. Uakaris are hunted by Indians of the area; the adults are eaten, but the young ones are occasionally kept as pets.

With short tails and long, shaggy hair, they move rapidly in the trees. Their faces always seem to express sorrow, but their emotions show through in a variety of behavior patterns such as shaking branches, arching their backs and raising the hair on their backs in order to look bigger and fiercer.

A BABY UAKARI clings to its mother. Despite their surprising habit of emitting what sounds like hysterical laughter when annoyed, these creatures are reputed to make delightful pets when they are young—so loyal to their owners that if deserted they refuse all food and ultimately pine away. As adults, however, they are less tractable and do not adjust well to captivity.

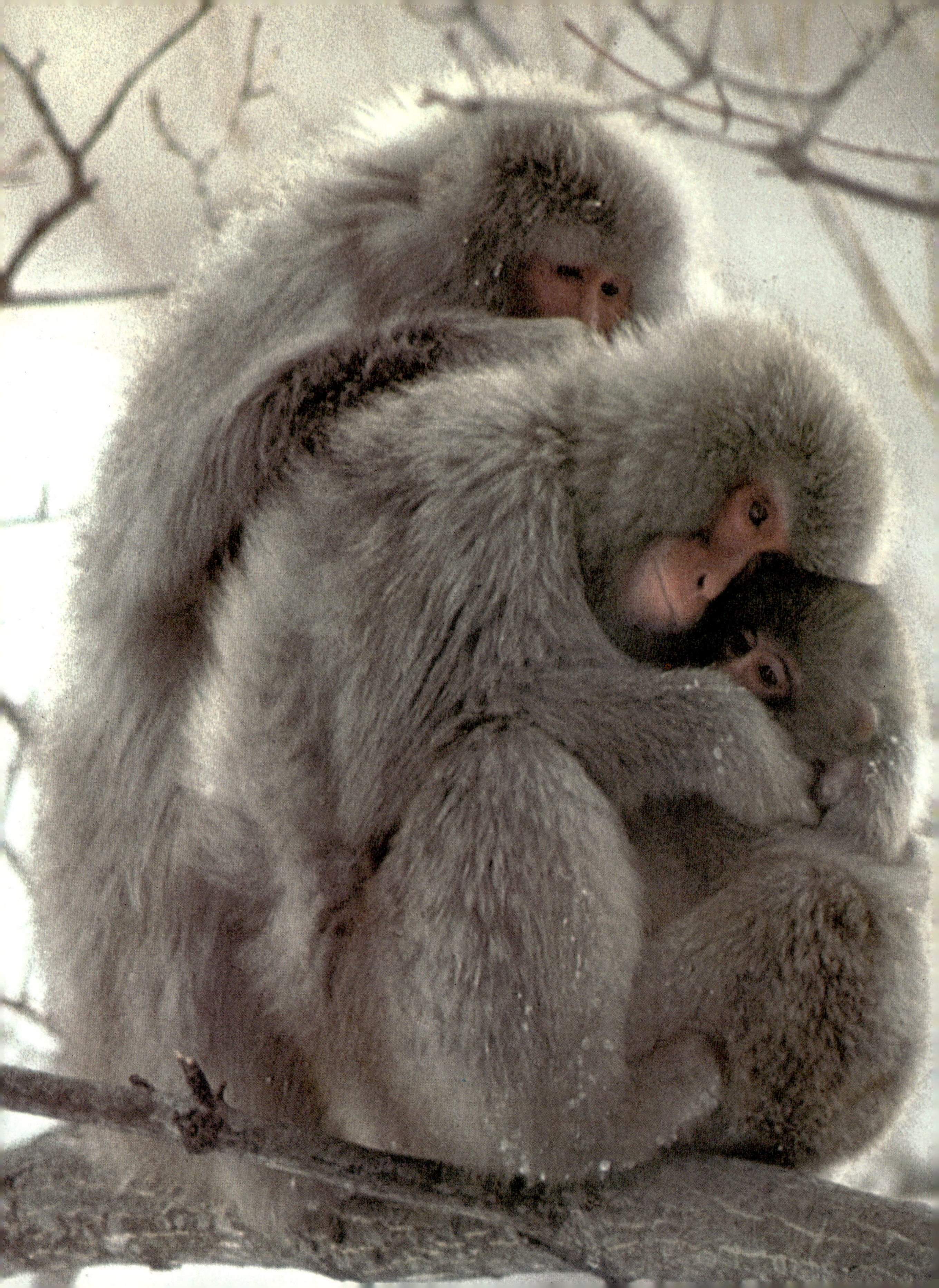

OLD WORLD MONKEYS
Snow Monkeys of Japan

Strange as it may seem, there are a few monkeys which have learned to live with snow and ice. These are the Japanese macaques, aptly called snow monkeys. Thousands of years ago when the climate of Japan was warmer, macaques were a common sight in the country's mountainous areas. Today there are only a few colonies left in what has become a freezing wilderness during the harsh winter, when snow monkeys scrounge for food and huddle together for warmth. However, one troop living high in the rugged Japanese Alps has found a real boon to its existence—a hot-springs pool. Snow-capped monkeys can be seen regularly luxuriating in the soothing steam bath.

A BABY CLINGS TO ITS MOTHER—SOURCE OF FOOD, WARMTH AND TRANSPORTATION IN EARLY LIFE—AS SHE LEAPS ACROSS A FROZEN RIVER

AN ATTENTIVE MOTHER SNOW MONKEY CUDDLES HER INFANT, WHILE A COMPANION SOLICITOUSLY GROOMS HER

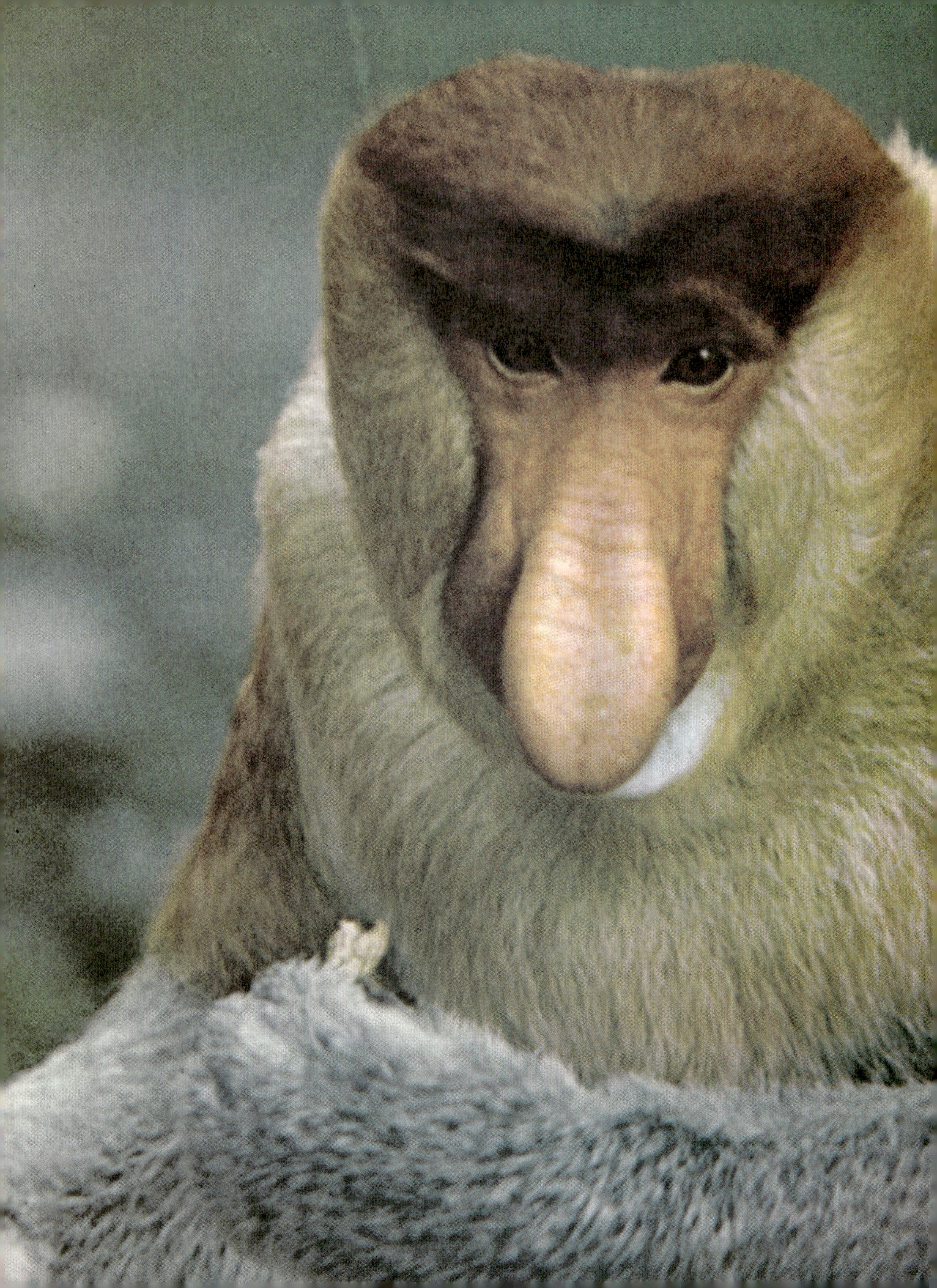

SECURED BY ONE HAND, A PROBOSCIS MONKEY SCOOPS WATER WITH THE OTHER

OLD WORLD MONKEYS

A Primate Pinocchio

Old World monkeys vary greatly in behavior and appearance. One of the most bizarre is the proboscis monkey, an aptly named genus of langur found in the forests of Borneo. Both sexes have large, fleshy noses, but the male proboscis, considerably bigger than the female, has a correspondingly larger and longer nose, which it uses to give loud warning "honks" when there is danger. These odd monkeys are excellent swimmers but apparently swim only when necessary—not for pleasure. They often live in large troops. Individually, they are calm of temperament. Another member of the family, the snub-nosed langur, has a nose permanently upturned.

THE BULBOUS NOSE of a proboscis monkey surprisingly does not get in the way while its owner eats. Like all langurs, these are leaf-eaters, but they also eat palm shoots and fruit.

THE STRIKING PELT of the black-and-white colobus monkey was coveted by Abyssinian natives and European ladies alike. Two million were killed before the rage declined—just in time to save the species from extinction.

THE GOLDEN LANGUR changes its color with the seasons. It is creamy white in summer, but in cold weather it turns to a light chestnut or golden hue.

OLD WORLD MONKEYS

The Gentle Leaf-Eaters

The colobus monkeys of Africa and their Asian cousins the langurs are generally retiring creatures. Most of them live in the trees, although some langurs spend a major part of their time on the ground. The entire subfamily of colobus monkeys and langurs, which includes the proboscis monkeys, exists solely on vegetation. The enormous quantity of leaves that they eat has led to the development of a specialized labyrinthine stomach that can extract the greatest possible nourishment from the unnutritive bulk.

The golden langur is such a recluse that, although in 1907 it was rumored to exist, nobody was able to track it down and obtain specimens and photographic proof until 1953. Its Indian relatives, the common langurs, however, are not such strangers to mankind. They are notorious for raiding crops and entering houses. Because they are held sacred to the monkey god, Hanuman, they are permitted to live on the grounds of Hindu temples.

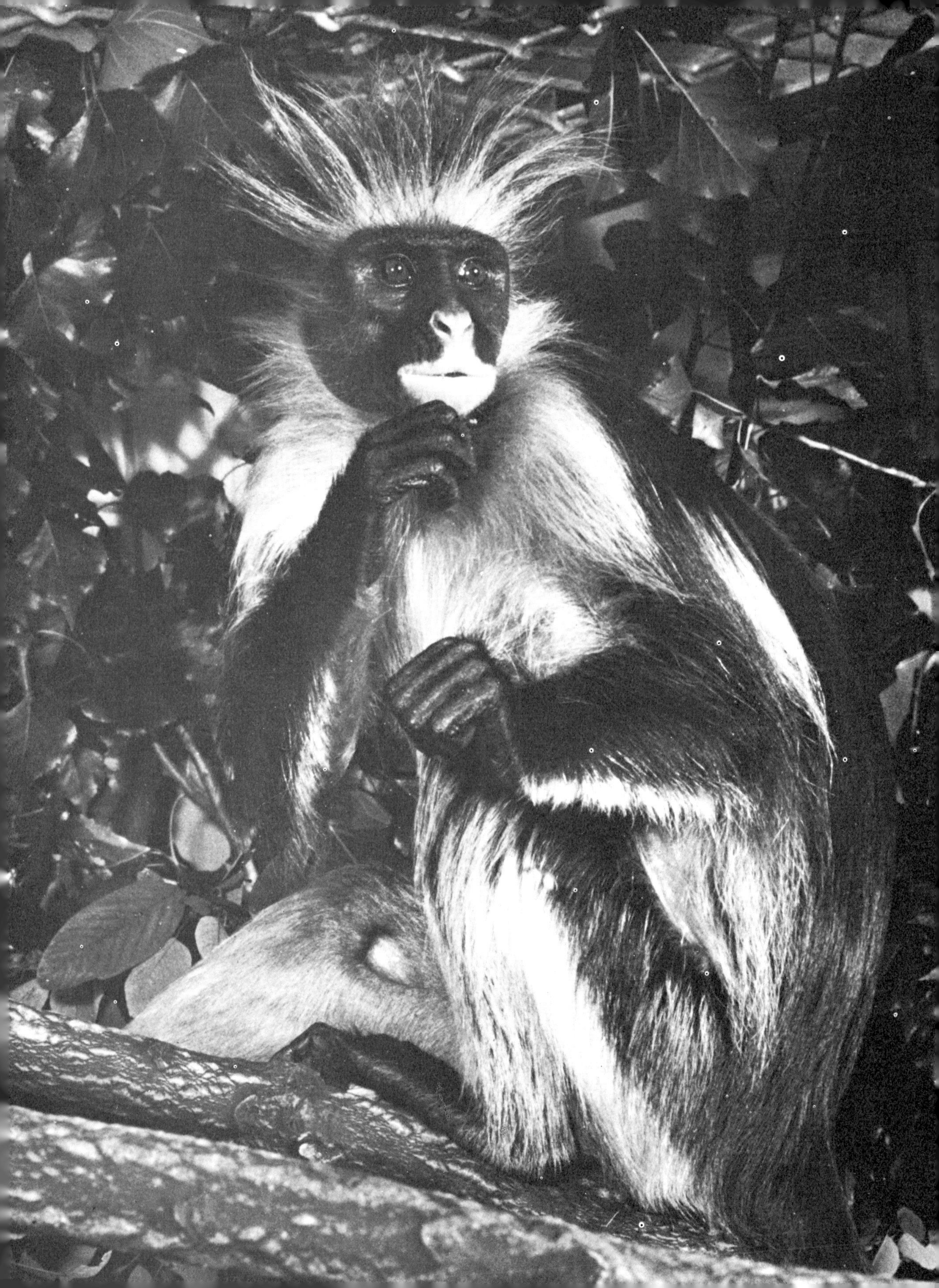

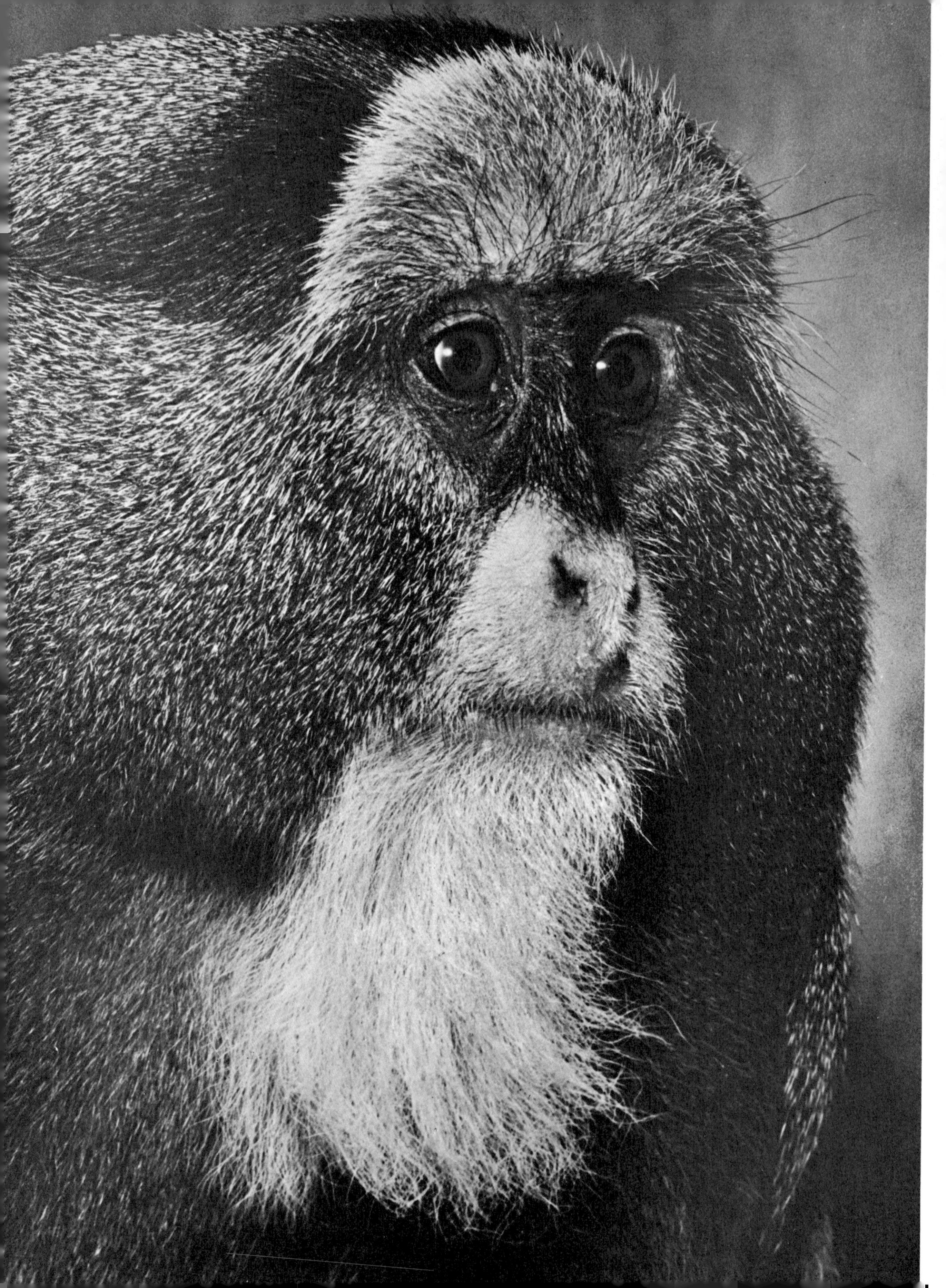

RED-EARED GUENON

SCHMIDT'S WHITE-NOSED MONKEY

OLD WORLD MONKEYS
The Madcap Guenons

The guenons of Africa make up one of the largest groups in the primate world. All told, they include about 80 different varieties, with tremendous diversity in coloration and fur patterns. All are characterized by long tails, cheek pouches and digestive tracts that can handle a quite omnivorous diet. Guenons, except for the vervets, are mainly arboreal monkeys that wander through the forest in groups of variable size. The vervets live in a variety of habitats that range from tropical rain forests to arid grasslands. They spend much of their time on the ground, moving in well-organized troops to protect themselves from predators.

The canopy-dwelling guenons, like other forest monkeys, have attained remarkable prowess in treetop locomotion. Their style, however, is markedly different from that of other monkeys: Instead of leaping from one particular branch to another, they appear to dash into space, aiming at the center of a dense clump of foliage. When they land they scramble through the small branches onto a large limb; from there they hurl themselves at their next objective. Though this performance sometimes resembles a slapstick comedy, guenons can move through the trees as fast as a man can run on the ground.

OWL-FACED GUENON

THE GUENON KNOWN AS DE BRAZZA'S MONKEY IS EASILY IDENTIFIED BY THE DIGNIFIED GOATEE

THE GELADA BABOON lives high in the mountains of Ethiopia, usually making its home in rocky ravines. It can be distinguished from other baboons by its snub nose and short upper jaw and the heart-shaped patch of bare red skin on its chest.

OLD WORLD MONKEYS
The Powerful Ground Dwellers

Baboons and macaques, the most numerous of the ground-dwelling monkeys, are strong creatures; most are well equipped to stand their ground against predators, and their own kind as well. They range from Africa to Japan, but nowhere do the genera overlap—convincing evidence that they are members of a single continuous radiation of monkeys. Further proof of this is found in their striking physiological and behavioral similarities. In fact, no other primate except man has ranged so far with so little change in physical structure. Hamadryas baboons *(opposite)* were among the most common animals in ancient Egypt—revered as companions and oracles of the god Thoth. This status also gained for them the honor of being mummified at death.

A HAMADRYAS BABOON BARES ITS CANINES IN A TYPICAL THREAT POSTURE

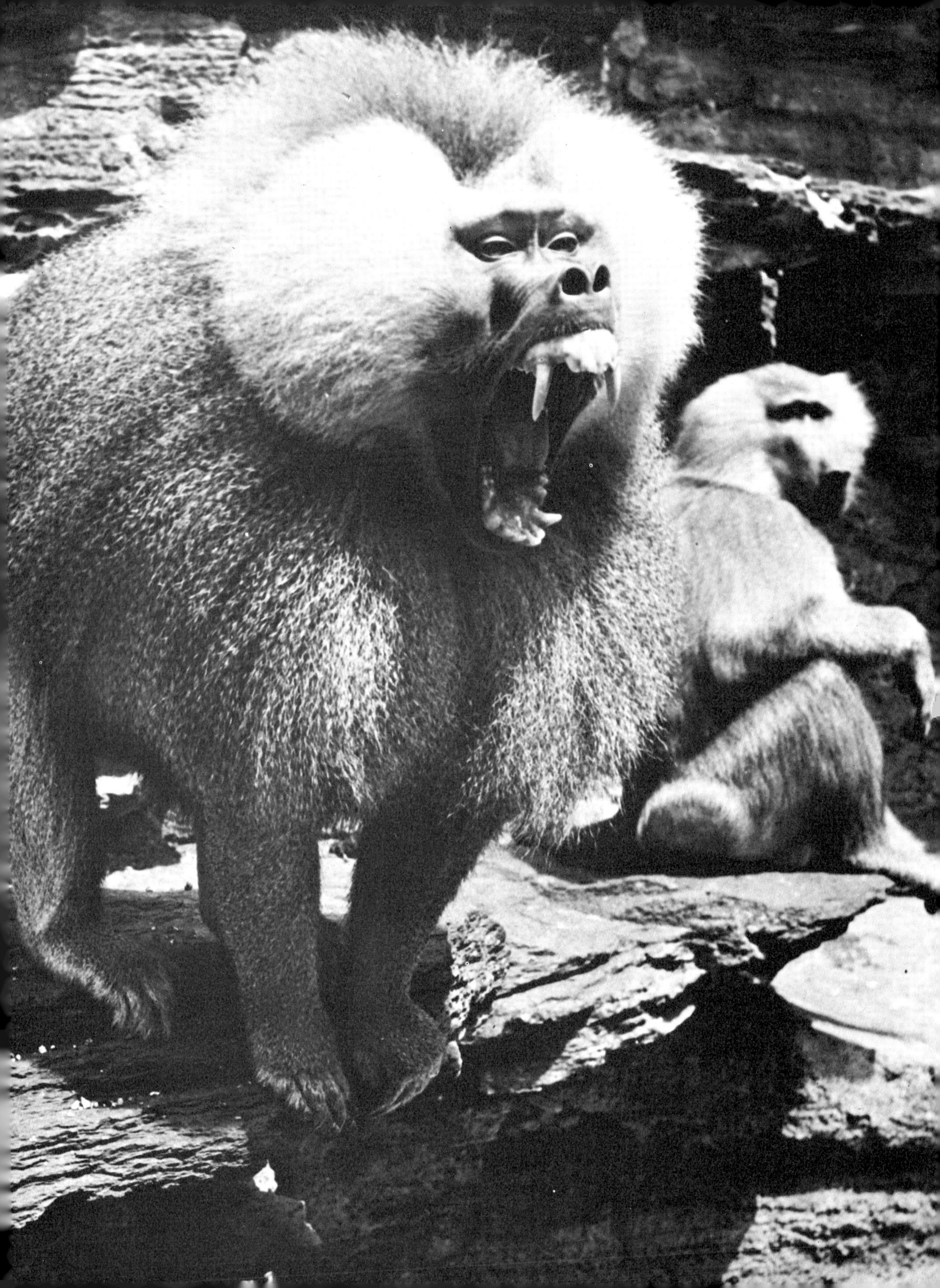

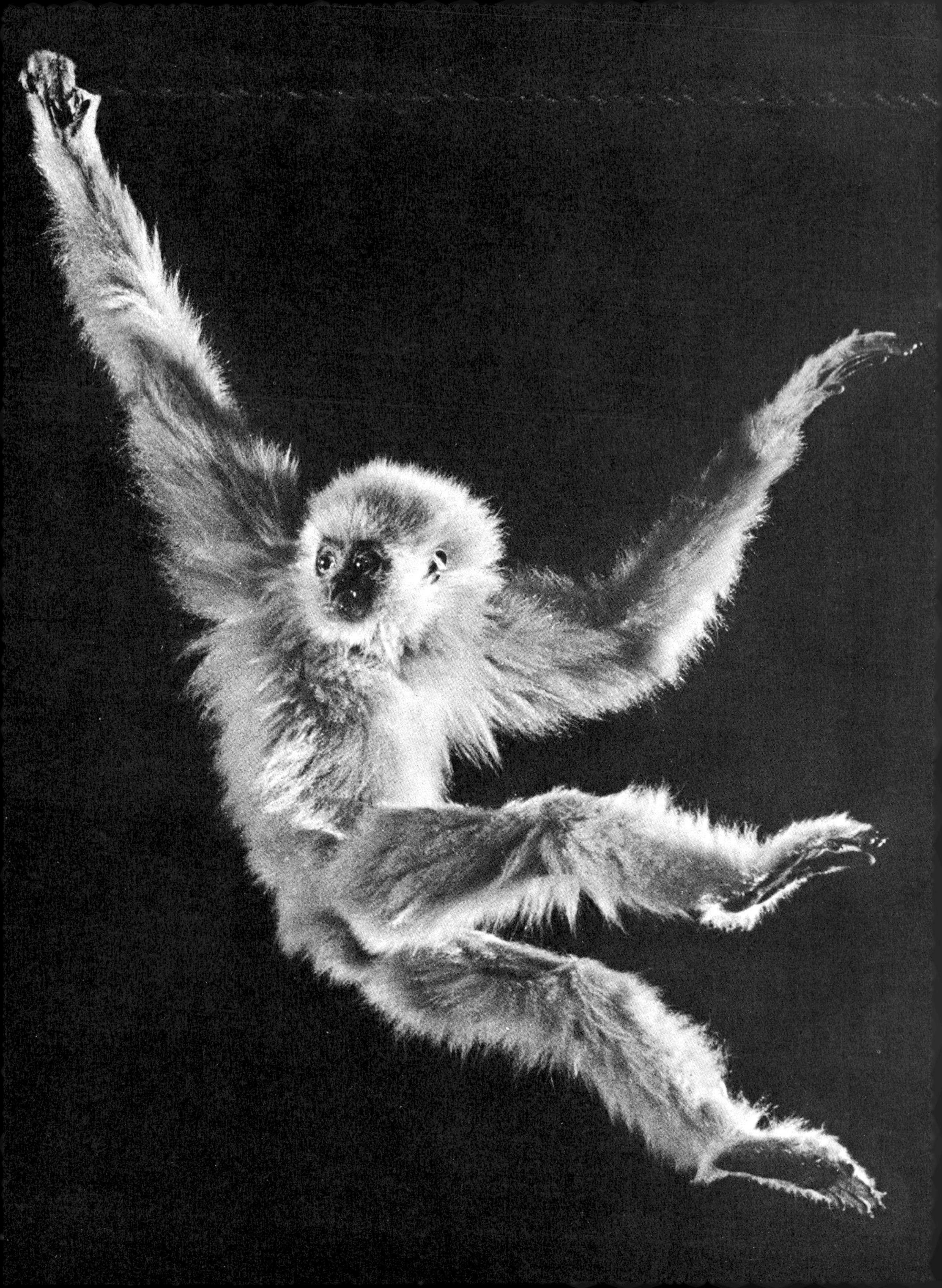

A HANDY WAY TO GO, brachiation is the favorite means of locomotion for gibbons. This two-year-old female exhibits the long arms and graceful style that make gibbons the best aerialists among the apes.

3

The Apes: Pioneers on Two Legs

"IT is almost impossible," the English naturalist William Charles Martin wrote of a female gibbon in 1840, "to convey in words an idea of the quickness and graceful address of her movements: They may indeed be termed aerial as she seems merely to touch in her progress the branches among which she exhibits her evolutions." No one since has suggested more vividly the sense of flowing, careless rhythm which makes a gibbon in the trees one of the most graceful spectacles nature has to offer. The gibbon is the arborealist supreme. It moves by swinging itself from branch to branch—or brachiating, as this movement is known—clutching briefly with alternate hands, before again hurling itself forward.

The precision of the gibbon's judgment is breathtaking; its dexterity and coordination are almost unbelievable. A gibbon can pluck a bird out of the air with one hand in the midst of a jump, then grasp the branch at which it is aiming with the other. C. R. Carpenter, who has devoted a lifetime to primate studies, once observed a branch break under a gibbon just as it launched itself into the air for a long leap. Turning in midair, it reached back, grasped the remaining stump, swung around it, over the top, and then, with almost no break in

THE APES: PIONEERS ON TWO LEGS

momentum, made the long outward jump of up to 30 feet (9 m) to the next tree.

The gibbon, as already stated, is an ape—a member of the superfamily that also contains the orangutan, the chimpanzee and the gorilla. This picture of the gibbon as a superlative acrobat flying through the treetops forms a sharp contrast to the popular conception of apes in general as large, clumsy, blundering creatures. But then apes, like monkeys, are infertile ground for generalization, and most attempts to categorize them run into difficulty. Take the question of how they are related to each other. One obvious way to answer it is to start with geography, putting the gibbon an orangutan of Asia into one category and the gorilla and chimpanzee of Africa into another. Such a distinction does have its points. Gibbons and orangs are predominantly arboreal; gorillas and chimpanzees are quite at home on the ground. Gibbons and orangs live in very small groups; the African apes in much bigger ones. Yet the impression this distinction conveys is misleading. Taxonomically, gibbons are different enough from other apes to be placed in a family of their own. They stand only about three feet (0.9 m) tall, and none weighs more than 25 pounds (11 kg), far less than many monkeys. Unlike the other apes, they are apparently no more intelligent than monkeys. And in their agility and speed in the trees, they resemble arboreal monkeys far more closely than they resemble the gorilla or the orang.

Hurtling around just below the top canopy of densely clustered trees that reach more than 100 feet (30 m) high, gibbons are difficult to study, and we know much less about them than we would like. We know about their anatomy. We know they live in small groups of a male and female together with their young. We know that both males and females are so jealous of members of the same sex that the young are forced by the hostility of one or the other parent to go off on their own as soon as they are sexually mature. We know that each group warns intruders by issuing loud hoots.

Although the heavier orangs are fully as arboreal as gibbons, they are as slow and deliberate as gibbons are rapid and daring. In the trees they normally move with great care, testing branches and distributing their weight on as many as possible on the chance that one might break. When they are frightened or disturbed, however, they forget their caution. At such times, they have been seen to descend a tree by allowing themselves to fall, fleetingly gripping a branch with a hand or foot as they descend. When they are at ease, they hang from a branch by their feet, but with their bodies upright, their legs reaching up on either side above their heads, and their hands resting on their bellies. On the ground, they walk very awkwardly; although they go on all fours, their arms are much longer than their legs, and as a result their bodies are raised up as they move, giving them the look of an old man, bent by age and making his way with the aid of two sticks. Both hands and feet are so curled that they resemble hooks; and the old-man look is further enhanced by the fact that they cannot walk with their soles flat on the ground but rather must walk on the outside edges of their feet.

Actually, orangs have a number of unusual characteristics. Consider their faces for example. Orangs have a marvelous command over their facial muscles, especially around the mouth and nose. They can move parts of their big lips to produce a variety of expressions that would make any human television comedian envious. Presumably, these twitches are a form of communication. The cheeks of an adult male bulge out in fleshy lobes, unique among primates; below them, large air sacs connecting with the larynx can be blown up like

GIBBON

LIMBER FORELIMBS

One of the basic differences between apes and monkeys is in the greater freedom of movement that the former have in their forelimbs. Apes are brachiators; they can swing by their arms and move them freely in all directions (gibbon, above). Most monkeys, by contrast, are true quadrupeds. Since they travel on four limbs, they need only move their front legs backward and forward (macaque, below) and just a little bit to the side.

MACAQUE

enormous goiters. These sacs also play a part in communication. Although orangs are usually quiet animals, males use the sacs as resonators to make calls that can be heard a mile (1.6 km) away. Generally, the calls serve to establish an orang's location. Since males are solitary travelers and prefer not to associate with each other, the vocalization helps to keep them apart.

It also serves another purpose—to attract sexually receptive females. In competing for females, the largest males usually win. Apparently it is this competition—and the outcome—over thousands of years that explains why male orangs today are about twice as large as females. In other words, the reason for the sexual dimorphism among orangs seems to be somewhat different from that for ground-living species, whose males have become larger partly in order to defend females and young against predators. Orangs once ranged over a much wider area than they now occupy. Scattered through the dense forests of parts of Borneo and Sumatra are an unknown number of these rare apes.

Until fairly recently the number of gorillas was not known either. What is worse, the gorilla was thoroughly misunderstood. Any man as maligned as the gorilla could have collected heavy damages for libel from all the travelers who have so reviled it in their memoirs. To zoologists and laymen alike, the gorilla had traditionally stood as the representative of man's primitive savagery, killing for killing's sake, tearing limb from limb any innocent human unlucky enough to venture within range.

The misunderstanding was natural enough because nature, one might say, has typecast the gorilla for the villain's role. It looks ferocious. A full-grown male stands about six feet (1.8 m) tall and weighs more than 400 pounds (180 kg), much of it in its mighty chest and arms, which suggest irresistibly the possibility of a deathly hug. Its face is, if anything, even more scary, with huge teeth enclosed in a massive jaw and supported by a heavy ridge of bone around the skull. More than that it beats its chest and pretends to charge when alarmed—a terrifying spectacle to anyone suddenly confronted by it. What the gorilla's appearance suggested, the travelers' tales confirmed. In 1856, the explorer Paul Du Chaillu ventured into the dark and cavernous forests that stretch inland from the West African coast and house what is now called the lowland gorilla. Du Chaillu was actually a perceptive observer, but like other explorers he tended to shoot first when he came across a gorilla and do his observing later. His report that the gorilla reminded him of "some hellish dream creature—a being of that hideous order, half-man half-beast," lent support to the equally terrifying accounts given by the Africans. When in 1892, another explorer, R. L. Garner, ventured into the West African jungle to study gorillas and chimpanzees, he thoughtfully built himself an iron cage to sit in so that the gorillas could not get at him. Waiting for the animals to come to him, Garner found out very little about lowland gorillas.

To this day less is known about lowland gorillas than about another group, usually referred to as mountain gorillas. Their range lies in the center of Africa where the eastern part of Zaïre (formerly the Congo) joins Uganda and Rwanda. Here, in thick forest, mountain gorillas live in danger of extinction and are forced by man's encroachment to retreat steadily farther up the mountains and squeeze into ever-smaller pockets of jungle. In 1971 there were probably less than 1,000 and within five years the figure had dropped to around 500.

This is the area where, early in 1959, the distribution of the mountain gorilla was surveyed by two zoologists from the University of Wisconsin, John Emlen

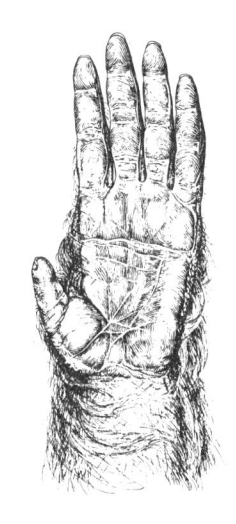

ORANGUTAN HAND

LONG, HOOKING FINGERS

The most arboreal of the apes, the brachiating gibbons and orangutans, have specialized hands with extraordinarily long, strong fingers that can be flexed into hooks for hanging and swinging. Their thumbs, however, are different. That of the orang is short and stumpy and does not get in the way during brachiation. The gibbon's is longer, and although sometimes used in climbing, can be neatly tucked alongside the palm when its owner is using its other fingers to travel by swinging from branch to branch.

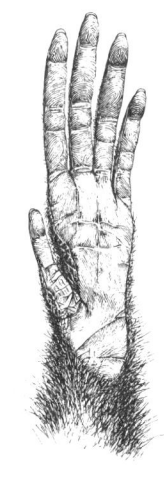

GIBBON HAND

GIBBON

LONG LIMBS FOR TRAVEL

The more a primate depends on a single pair of limbs for locomotion, the longer and stronger these limbs become, as is shown in these two drawings. The gibbon, enlarged here for comparison with man, travels from branch to branch by swinging from its arms which have become so elongated that their span easily exceeds the total length of its body and legs. Man, by contrast, having developed the ability to walk upright, has long legs. His arm span, unlike that of the gibbon, is no greater than his height.

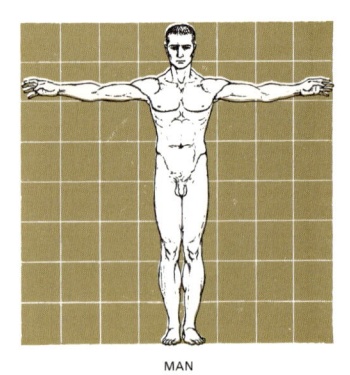

MAN

and George Schaller. Emlen returned home after six months, but Schaller, accompanied by his wife, established himself on the mountain slopes of the Virunga National Park and stayed on until September 1960. For much of the time the two lived in a small hut in a meadow near the forest where each day Schaller ventured out to follow and observe the gorillas. He has described what he found in two magnificent books, *The Mountain Gorilla* and *The Year of the Gorilla*. Schaller's classic work has since been supplemented by that of Dian Fossey, an occupational therapist from California who began her extensive study of mountain gorillas in 1967.

Both Schaller and Fossey quickly discovered that, far from being the ferocious beasts of legend, gorillas are actually mild-mannered vegetarians who like to mind their own business. According to the reports of both observers, the gorillas were at first startled by the presence of humans. Usually an adult male would rise and give a roar of alarm or beat his chest threateningly before fading into the trees after the females and the young. But once they realized they were not in danger, curiosity replaced fear. Young gorillas watched their observers with open interest, the adults more covertly, like suburban wives peering through the curtains, as if embarrassed to let anyone see they cared. Occasionally Schaller blundered into a gorilla emerging from the trees. Having already noticed that some of the individuals he had been studying would shake their heads almost in an appeasing way—as if to relieve embarrassment—when he stared at them too fixedly, he decided to try the same thing in the tense moment of a sudden, too-close confrontation. So, whenever he did accidently come face to face with a male gorilla, Schaller would shake his head vigorously, whereupon the gorilla would turn and move off back into the forest.

Dian Fossey, too, found that acting like a gorilla and avoiding actions that could be misinterpreted were invaluable to her work. Not only did she imitate feeding and grooming habits, but she became so expert in making feeding noises that she was able to elicit a round of belchlike vocalization in a group she had quietly joined. Fossey eventually won the gorillas' confidence to the point that younger members of the study groups came close enough to touch her boots and equipment.

The gorillas' acceptance of her, as well as their docile nature, was proved beyond a doubt on one occasion when she made contact with a mature young male of a group she knew. As usual, she sat down in the ground foliage before she began to reassure him with feeding sounds. After supplementing these with some vigorous scratching of her scalp, Fossey this time slowly extended her hand, palm side up, since this part most resembles a gorilla's. Continuing in slow motion, she next turned over her hand, allowing it to rest on some foliage. Interested and unafraid, the young gorilla studied this somewhat unfamiliar sight. Then, moving a step closer, he reached out and—for just an instant—softly touched her fingers. Nothing like this had ever happened before in the three years that Fossey had been studying gorillas. But she needed no further proof of the gentleness of her ape friends.

Actually gorillas have little reason not to be gentle. While their ancestors were probably in danger from predators when they first descended from the trees, today's males are so large and powerful that a group is never attacked except, very rarely, by a leopard turned gorilla hunter. Because they need enormous quantities of food, the adults spend from six to eight hours a day eating, and much of their bulk is due to their large digestive tract. The gorilla's sheer size and bulk, however, make climbing trees an awkward business for an adult, especially a full-grown male. While the young nip around with ease in the trees, the adults climb with caution. Even so, branches do break under their weight and they may fall several feet before gaining a fresh, secure hold. Actually the adults spend about four fifths of their time on the ground and they ascend trees only for some specific purpose: to eat, to obtain a longer view or to sleep. Like orangs and chimpanzees, they build nests to sleep in, but while chimpanzees may sleep 100 feet (30 m) up in the trees, gorilla nests, if built in trees, are rarely more than 10 feet (0.3 m) above the ground.

When building a nest in a tree, a gorilla picks a firm site in a fork or along a stout branch and then bends or weaves in adjacent branches and vines to form a secure platform. Chimpanzees and orangs normally refine the technique by adding a final layer of leafy branchlets to make their nests more comfortable. The reason why the great apes build nests in trees is obvious: They are too big simply to balance all night in a fork or on a branch without severe danger of falling. As nest builders they are also gradually losing the toughened skin pads on their rumps—possessed by all Old World monkeys, which characteristically sleep sitting on branches. Gibbons do not build nests and have retained the skin pads. However, not all chimpanzees have them, nor do the majority of orangs and gorillas. A behavioral adaptation, in other words, has replaced a biological one: The nest has replaced the rump pads.

The gorilla's sleeping habits are very curious. Other primates sleep in trees to avoid predators, but gorillas are not afraid of predators and often sleep on the ground. Their tree-sleeping proclivities are presumably vestigial—a holdover from earlier times when they had to build arboreal nests for their own protection. The same may be said of the way they still build nests on the ground. Under some circumstances, these seem to be quite useless—scarcely nests at all. For example, they are often located on a slope so that the occupant rolls out during the night and wakes up in the morning several feet away. This illustrates how a habit like nest building may be maintained by a species even though it is only useful in certain locations.

W ITH nothing to fear—except man—and plenty of food available, the gorillas Schaller and Fossey encountered lived in a state of mild and amiable serenity. Most of them lived in groups of five to 20, each one led by a powerful silverback male, so called for the saddle of grizzled silver hairs that begins to sprout up among the black males when they reach the age of 10. His dominance over the group is absolute, but normally genial. Occasionally a young gorilla will get too frolicsome and be silenced by a glare or a threatening slap on the ground from an adult. Sometimes a couple of females will begin to scream at each other until the leader glares at them and they promptly calm down. The leader, however, is no stern paterfamilias. When he wants quiet, he gets quiet, but except for one or two particularly irascible silverbacks, the leaders are usually quite approachable. Females nestle against them and infants crawl happily over their huge bodies. Amity reigns. When a band of gorillas is at rest, the young play, the mothers tend their infants, and the other adults lie at peace and soak up the sun.

Like men, gorillas yawn and stretch when they awake in the morning and sit dangling their legs over the sides of their nests. They pick their noses, scratch themselves when puzzled and, if nervous or excited, they often begin to eat vigorously, much as a man might pull at a cigarette. Though there is great

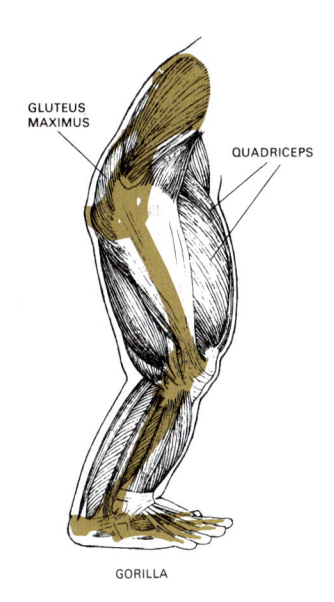

WHY MAN WALKS BETTER

Why can't a gorilla walk and stand like a man? Because of differences in leg bone and muscle. Man has a strongly developed buttock muscle, the gluteus maximus, which pulls his body forward and over his leg with each stride. In the gorilla, the gluteus maximus is relatively underdeveloped, so the best it can do bipedally is a shuffle. But man also has the ability to lock his legs at the knee so that when he is standing erect he does not need to use his quadriceps to hold himself up. The gorilla, unable to lock its legs, can stand up only in a tiring crouch.

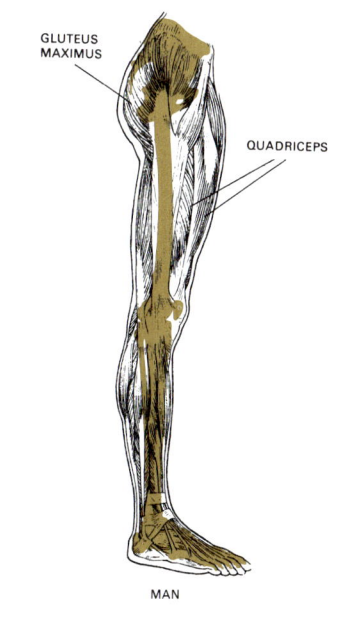

A GORILLA'S EMOTIONAL DISPLAY

The famous chest-beating display of a mountain gorilla is actually just one phase in an elaborate ritual. As shown here, it begins with hooting and builds up in a sequence including symbolic feeding, standing and chest beating, ending with a climactic thumping of the ground. A display by one male may start an entire group on a chest-beating spree. Infants at play may perform parts of the ritual, and sometimes adults do a little languid chest beating while lolling on the ground.

HOOTING

SYMBOLIC FEEDING

STANDING ERECT

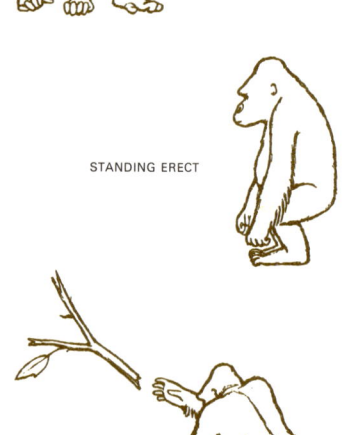

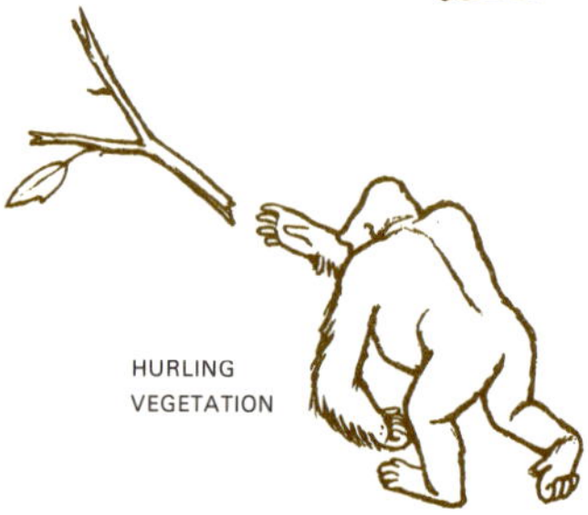

HURLING VEGETATION

individual variation of temperament among gorillas, there is about them a curious reserve, as if they are reluctant to show their feelings. It is almost as if they were shy, unwilling to reveal themselves to the inspection of the curious, or perhaps so self-assured that they disdain to show their emotions, out of indifference to the opinion of others.

Nonetheless, gorillas can exhibit strong feelings, especially when they feel threatened. They scream in alarm and as a warning to other members of the group. They toss leaves in the air. They also beat their chests. All gorillas, even the very young ones, do this, rising up on two legs on the ground, or popping up amid the foliage of a tree to give a few brief slaps before fading out of sight. The full performance, however, is put on only by the silverback males, and it is as formalized as the entrance of a fighter into the prize ring. It begins inconspicuously with a series of soft, clear hoots that gradually quicken. Already, the silverback apparently expects to command attention because, if interrupted, he is liable to look around in annoyance. As he continues to hoot, he may stop, pluck a leaf from a plant nearby and place it between his lips. This curiously incongruous and delicate gesture is a prelude to coming violence and, when they see it, the other gorillas get out of his way. The violence is not immediate. First the gorilla rises to his full height and slaps his hands on his chest or his belly, on his thigh or on another gorilla, producing a sound that can be heard a mile (1.6 km) away. The chest beating over, the violence erupts. He runs sideways for a few steps, then he drops down on all fours and breaks into a full speed dash, wrenching branches from trees and slapping at everything in his way, including any other members of the group who do not have the wit to keep clear. Finally, there comes the last gesture: The silverback thumps the palm of his hand violently on the ground, and then sits back, looking as if he is now ready to hear the applause.

THE chest-beating display seems to serve a variety of purposes. It may be self-assertion, threat, challenge—or all three rolled into one. And probably it originated as a form of displacement activity, an action performed when an animal is torn by conflicting emotions and avoids decision by doing something quite irrelevant, as a man may beat the table instead of hitting his boss. But from this simple beginning, it has entered now into a highly complex and ritualized form of bluff. Although his pracice of beating his chest has contributed to the gorilla's reputation for fearsomeness, it is not so much an act of aggression as a substitute for it. An angry gorilla may bluff and threaten another gorilla but he rarely fights. Schaller describes one incident that illustrates the point to perfection. Normally, two strange groups of gorillas will pass each other, and even intermingle, without any signs of hostility. But once, when two such groups came together, one leader apparently felt that his position was threatened and he tried to assert it by cowing the leader of the other group. Several times he rushed at his rival, stopping only an inch (2.5 cm) away, head thrust forward, trying to stare the other silverback down. His supreme effort was to throw a handful of leaves in the air in a gesture of challenge. But when the other male refused to be intimidated, the silverback gave up his attempts and retreated. His actions were actually intended to avoid a fight, but from evidence of several tufts of hair pulled out by the roots and found on the trail the following day, Schaller concluded that "a tussle probably occurred."

Almost inevitably, one finds oneself comparing the gorilla to his fellow African ape, the chimpanzee. It is an intriguing exercise and full of paradoxes.

At first glance, they look physically very different. A full-grown chimpanzee male is much smaller than a male gorilla, 10 to 12 inches (25 to 30 cm) less in height and barely a third the weight. And apart from his smaller stature, the chimpanzee looks less ferocious. He possesses neither the gorilla's huge teeth nor his massive facial musculature. Nonetheless, the two apes are anatomically very similar. What distinguishes them most is their diet, behavior and temperament.

Gorillas eat mostly ground plants. Chimpanzees feed mostly on fruit, and they are predominantly arboreal. They travel on the ground as easily as gorillas and in much the same manner, supporting their weight on the soles of their feet and on toughened skin pads below their knuckles. Still, they spend some three quarters of their time in the trees; they are much more arboreal than gorillas but less so than orangs. And where orangs are slow and deliberate, chimpanzees are often fast and impulsive, climbing around a hundred feet (30 m) above the ground with the ease of a monkey.

LIKE most monkeys that live in trees, chimpanzees are noisy. They seem to love noise for its own sake, and very little is needed to provoke them into a chorus of hoots and high-pitched screams that transform the forest into bedlam. They may hoot when they come across a rich supply of fruit, when they wake up and when they make their nests at night, and when two groups meet or a large group breaks up. Frequently their calls are backed up with a great stamping in the trees, a shaking of branches and a reverberating drum roll produced by pounding on the buttresses of ironwood trees.

Africans have told of "carnivals" that last for hours, the noise rising to a crescendo in one part of the forest after another. Chimpanzees seem especially sensitive to the intrusions of humans. Frequently they greet visitors with a few opening hoots, then, after a few moments of quiet, they start up again, but this time at full volume, complete with shrieks and hoots and drum rolls. Strangers to the forest have admitted being terrified by the sudden stunning uproar rendered all the more scary by the fact that the noisemakers remain invisible, concealed high in the forest canopy. Chimpanzees can be very dangerous, but if given a choice they will flee from man in the wild. From the safety of a tree, they will brandish branches they have torn off, a behavior also practiced by orangs and several kinds of monkeys. Probably chimpanzees screech and shake branches for much the same reasons that gorillas throw leaves in the air or beat their chests: not so much to inflict actual damage but as a form of defiance or challenge, or out of anger.

Most of our basic information about chimpanzees in the wild comes from a husband-wife team, Vernon and Frances Reynolds, who studied chimpanzees in the Budongo Forest, Uganda, and from Jane Goodall, who studied them in northern Tanzania. After graduating from high school in England, Goodall took a job in East Africa as secretary to the distinguished prehistorian, the late Louis Leakey. Noting that she showed real promise as a field researcher, Leakey promised to give her a chance to study chimpanzees in the wild if she would get some university training. She worked under primatologists in England for a year, and in due course was established on a field station in a remote part of Tanzania. Her principal research weapons were an intense determination and a deep affection for chimpanzees. There were between 100 and 200 of these animals in the Gombe Stream Chimpanzee Reserve where Goodall launched her study—all of them wild, afraid of humans and as anxious to keep away from her as she was to get close to them. It took her about 14 months of patient,

CHEST BEATING

LEG KICKING

RUNNING SIDEWAYS

UPROOTING VEGETATION

GROUND THUMPING

daily tracking before she could approach to within 30 or 40 feet (9 to 12 m) without disturbing their normal activities. Ultimately she broke down their fear of her entirely and became accepted as one of the group—thus she was able, for instance, to pick burrs from their hair, a service which they reciprocated.

Jane Goodall has witnessed one of the most puzzling chimpanzee displays, a performance she has entitled the "rain dance." Describing one such occasion, she tells how she was watching a group of chimpanzees in a tree halfway up the side of a steep valley. When rain started falling, the chimpanzees came down from the tree and started walking up the grassy slope in two groups. At the skyline, the females and juveniles climbed high into the trees. Then, as the rain turned into a violent tropical deluge, the males, amid crashes of thunder, began their spectacular display. One, turning suddenly, charged diagonally down the slope, slapping the ground as it went, and as though this were a signal, all the other males joined in. Some charged down hitting at vegetation, others sprang into trees, tore off great branches, hurled themselves to the ground and raced down the hillside at breakneck speed dragging the branches behind them. At the bottom, each chimpanzee swung up into a tree to break its headlong flight. There it sat for a moment before climbing down and plodding up the hill again to resume, with wild cries, its downward rush. Then, as suddenly as it began, the show was over; the spectators climbed down from the trees and the whole group disappeared over the horizon.

WHAT provokes the chimpanzees to put on such a performance? Possibly it is an expression of irritation at the rain. Possibly it is also a form of sexual display. The males exhibit their strength and prowess, and the females, one trusts, are properly impressed. But—and this again is only suggestion—there may be more involved than mere irritation or sexual braggadocio. Activities like football and dancing, including even chimpanzee "dancing," are expressions of exuberance practiced most vigorously by extroverts—and extroversion is always tinged with the hues of exhibitionism. Chimpanzees are the extroverts among the apes, and the most unabashedly exhibitionistic. They revel in applause; they love attention. They shine at the tea parties that are a traditional form of entertainment in some zoos. Indeed, chimpanzees give the impression that they positively look forward to displaying their table manners, unlike gorillas or orangs who are acutely uncomfortable at such affairs.

Any animal that wants an audience must be ready to please it. So, as one might expect, chimpanzees are the most compliant of the apes. That is to say, young chimpanzees; old ones, especially old males, often become thoroughly intractable and even dangerous in captivity. But young chimpanzees do very well in laboratory intelligence tests, both because they are intelligent and because they are willing to oblige their masters. One could fill pages with examples. Chimpanzees have learned to ride bicycles, smoke cigarettes and put on evening dress. As part of a publicity stunt, they have been trained to work on assembly lines, stuffing foam rubber into pillows and putting Hollywood beds into cartons. They can drive tractors and they can steer automobiles, and, in fact, they can do the latter in so human a manner that some years ago a Florida police patrol picked up a chimpanzee for speeding.

Actually, he was only steering. His owner, a carnival showman, was operating the pedals. Still, it would be hard to imagine a gorilla steering a car or driving a tractor, or performing on television. This is not because a gorilla lacks the intellectual capacity to perform such feats. His brain, so far as we can tell, is as developed as a chimpanzee's. But how far can we tell? Professor Robert M. Yerkes, one of the founding fathers of primatology, who carried out many classic studies of captive apes, came to the conclusion that his test gorilla, a young female, was slow at intelligence tests because she was timid and introverted, and lacked the chimpanzees' interest in winning her keepers' good opinions. Since Yerkes' early studies, however, at least one gorilla, Koko, has mastered the art of communicating intelligently with humans.

Laboratory tests, unless they are really sophisticated and well planned, can be misleading in the conclusions they suggest about the intelligence of nonhuman primates. All too often in the past, they tested abilities that might have seemed important to humans but did not happen to be at all important to monkeys or apes. Suppose a New Yorker were to be trapped by a group of chimpanzees, shipped to Africa and stuck up in a tree a hundred feet (30 m) above ground. Almost all his abilities—his mastery of language, his skill at fixing a disabled fuel pump, his aggressive salesmanship—would be irrelevant to his situation. Hanging on for dear life, frequently confusing edible with poisonous plants and, no doubt, experiencing grave difficulties in distinguishing one chimpanzee from another, he would appear to his captors to be an exceedingly stupid animal. Their judgment, of course, would be unfair, since it would arise from a failure to appreciate that New Yorkers are not used to living in trees.

Odd as it may appear, many of the early laboratory psychologists who first began to try to appraise the intelligence of monkeys and apes fell into precisely this kind of error. Take, for example, the famous box-stacking test. A chimpanzee, say, is placed in a cage where a banana is hanging a few feet above his reach. The only way he can get it is by stacking up the boxes that have been left scattered around the cage. If he stacks three boxes on top of each other and then climbs up and grabs hold of the banana, he is given a certain rating. Then the banana is placed higher. If the chimpanzee can then stack four boxes and get the banana, he is rated very highly. If, on the other hand, he commits the blunder of dragging out the bottom box to put on top of the others, so that the whole pile collapses, he is considered to have failed.

Then there is the food-and-sticks test. A monkey is chained to a spot a few feet away from a food reward, with a short stick left lying within his reach, and another, longer stick just beyond it. His task is to use the short stick to draw in the long stick, and then to use the long stick to draw in the food. The quicker he learns to do it, the brighter he is judged to be.

THE trouble with these tests is that they actually tell us almost nothing about the intelligence of monkeys and apes because they are conducted with objects and in situations which are abnormal to the animal concerned. Monkeys are not adapted to manipulating objects; chimpanzees do not encounter boxes in the wild which they can stack to bring an inaccessible banana within reach. Yet in the wild both monkeys and chimpanzees—or all apes, for that matter—can be extremely intelligent in learning the things that matter to them: obtaining food, avoiding or overcoming enemies and, in the case of many species, getting along with the group—a truly significant ability which had not been tested in laboratory experiments at all.

Actually, the chimpanzee is a very gifted animal, not much inferior in intelligence, one might guess, to the apelike ancestors from which the first bipedal men emerged. A young chimpanzee is as intelligent as a human child before the child learns to talk. Like children, young chimpanzees are also extremely inquisitive, and in captivity they will work diligently at a problem, apparently for the pure satisfaction of solving it. Chimpanzees, like all the other apes and monkeys, even learn to control their emotions. In the wild, a young chimpanzee learns as it matures not to irritate the adults. As a juvenile, it learns to control its natural exuberance in play with infants of the group so as to avoid injuring them. In fact, so far as control of the emotions is concerned, the principal difference between an adult monkey or ape and an adult human being is one of degree: Contrary to Freud, repression of emotions is by no means a monopoly of man.

The fact of the matter is that intelligence is not a single thing. What is really important is an animal's ability to learn. What has evolved in animals is the ability to learn those things which are of importance to them, and to survival of the species. In the course of evolution, furthermore, certain abilities have decreased while others have increased in efficiency. A blindfolded man, relying on his sense of smell alone, would fail at making many distinctions which would be easy for a lemur. The lemur, testing human intelligence, might mark out a scent trail through the branches of a tree, only to discover that "moron man" could not follow the trail at all. In the same way, chimpanzees are different from men in their ability to communicate and use tools. Their skills with tools are very limited, and though researchers have taught chimps and gorillas to understand spoken works and sign language, they can learn the meaning of only a very few words and cannot enunciate any. The animals are able to reply only in sign language or by selecting symbols on a keyboard.

INTELLIGENCE, then, is not something general but a series of specific abilities to learn and perform. This is what the far more sophisticated tests of today are aimed at—and not in comparison to human standards, either, but in comparisons of one animal species to another. And by these standards—the relative learning abilities of a lemur, a rhesus monkey and a chimpanzee—we can get some measure of the change from the primitive to the advanced types.

What the field studies of recent times have contributed to our understanding of intelligence among apes and monkeys is an awareness of the rich and complicated lives which these creatures normally learn to live. They learn to distinguish many different kinds of food plants, they learn all the intricacies of a complex and variegated range, they learn the problems of predators, the social hierarchy and the way of life of the troop. And from troop to troop this whole complex of behavior varies not only according to the biology of the species but to the history of the troop concerned.

We tend to think of apes and monkeys as creatures without the power of conceptual thought, although trained chimpanzees and gorillas indicate they have it to some degree. Furthermore, we know they have the ability to plan—can we say they do not reflect upon the past and the future? Certainly they learn from the past. And if we think of them as concerned only with their immediate needs—obtaining food, avoiding danger, getting along with their fellows, raising their young; in short, living only in the present—is this not largely true of humans too? Professor Adriaan Kortlandt has described how he once watched a chimpanzee gazing at a sunset for a full 15 minutes, sitting quietly and watching the changing colors until the western sky grew dark. Anthropomorphic romanticizing? Perhaps. Yet it would be very arrogant of man to assume without question that only he can experience the sensation of awe or find pleasure in the beauty of an African twilight.

THOUGH IT IS ESSENTIALLY A QUADRUPED, A CHIMPANZEE CAN AND DOES WALK UPRIGHT. ALOFT, IT CAN BE NEARLY AS AGILE AS A GIBBON

The Anthropoids

Man's closest relatives are the apes—gibbons, chimpanzees, gorillas and orangutans. They vary greatly in appearance and behavior, from featherweight gibbons that spend their lives in the branches to massive gorillas that are most at home on the ground. But these expressive, intelligent creatures have many anatomical and behavioral features that link them to each other—and to man.

THIS MULTIPLE PHOTOGRAPH SHOWS A BRACHIATING GIBBON IN PERFECT FORM. RELEASING ONE HAND, IT SWINGS SWIFTLY FORWARD AND GRASPS

A Swinging Primate

The ability to brachiate, or swing hand over hand through the trees, is a characteristic of the apes, although not all of them make frequent use of it. The undisputed king of the art is the gibbon, whose slight body, elongated arms and fingers make it beautifully suited to arboreal locomotion. The gibbon's wrist, arm and shoulder are especially adapted for mobility as it reaches, grasps and changes its holds; proportionately, its arms are longer than those of any other ape. When a gibbon is peacefully brachiating along, it usually travels at about the speed of the average human walk. But when it is excited or frightened, it can plunge through the forest canopy at astonishing speeds, sometimes cov-

THE ROPE AHEAD OF ITS OTHER HAND, THEN REPEATS THIS IN A SERIES OF FLUID ACTIONS RESULTING IN CONTINUOUS FORWARD MOVEMENT

ering 30 feet (9 m) or more in a jump without a break in its "stride." With each leap gravity carries it closer to the ground; after two or three leaps, it clambers high into the branches again for a fresh series of leaps. Although great bursts of high-speed brachiation are short-lived, they are quite sufficient to put hundreds of yards between the gibbon and one of its predators. On rare occasions, a gibbon has been seen to seize a long vine and swing Tarzan-like to another tree. Even if a gibbon is surprised by a predator on open ground, it can usually flee to safety, running on two feet like a man, but holding its arms up at a dainty angle for balance and to keep them from dragging on the ground.

73

CLUTCHING HER INFANT PROTECTIVELY, A GIBBON SHOWS THE INTENSE MATERNAL CARE GIVEN THE YOUNG UNTIL THEY ARE WEANED

At Home with the Gibbons

Why has the gibbon alone remained small and agile when the rest of the apes have evolved toward ever-increasing size? One answer is that, for their specialized way of life, natural selection favored the smaller individuals: The gibbon's light weight and agility ensure it virtual freedom from predators and a limitless food supply. The greatest portion of its diet is made up of fruit—figs, mangoes, grapes and plums. Sometimes, as though for a treat, a gibbon will steal a bird's nest and carry it cafeteria-fashion to a comfortable perch, where it will devour the eggs. At night the gibbon sits or curls up on its side in the branches to sleep—it is the only one of the apes that does not build nests. At birth, a gibbon is just about as helpless as its human counterpart, but in a few weeks it awakens to the world around it: It smells flowers, plays with its feet and eagerly tastes anything it can get into its mouth. By the time it is about a year old it has an established social life revolving around its parents and siblings.

ONLY A GIBBON WOULD EVER WALK A VINE LIKE THIS; EVEN THE NIMBLEST MONKEYS WOULD USE ALL FOURS

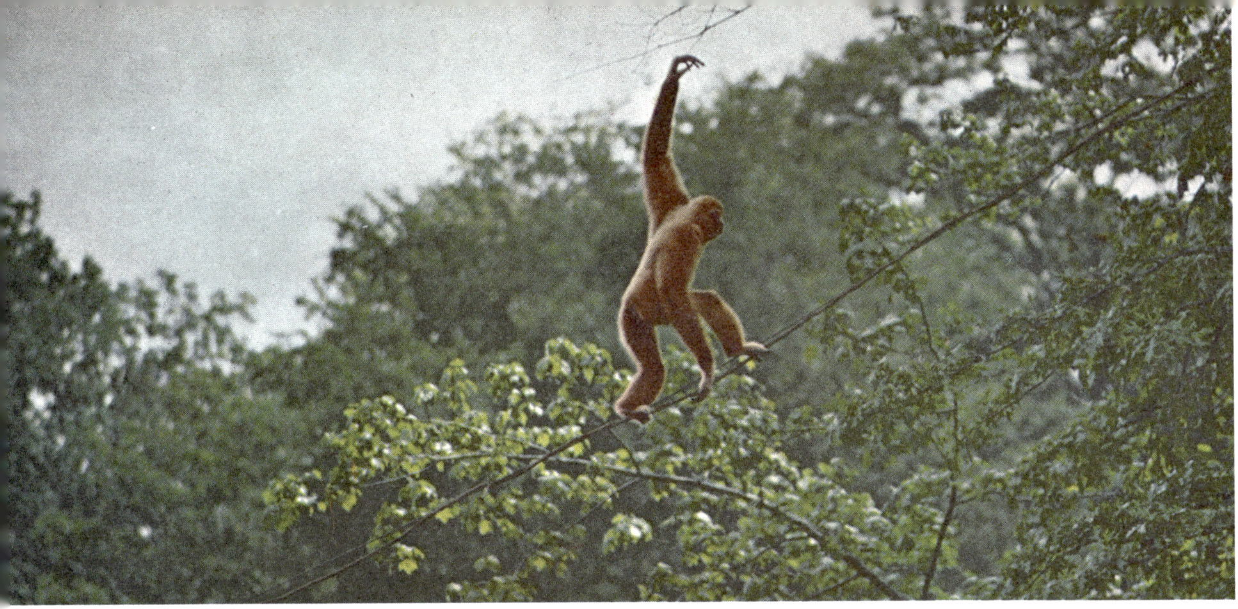
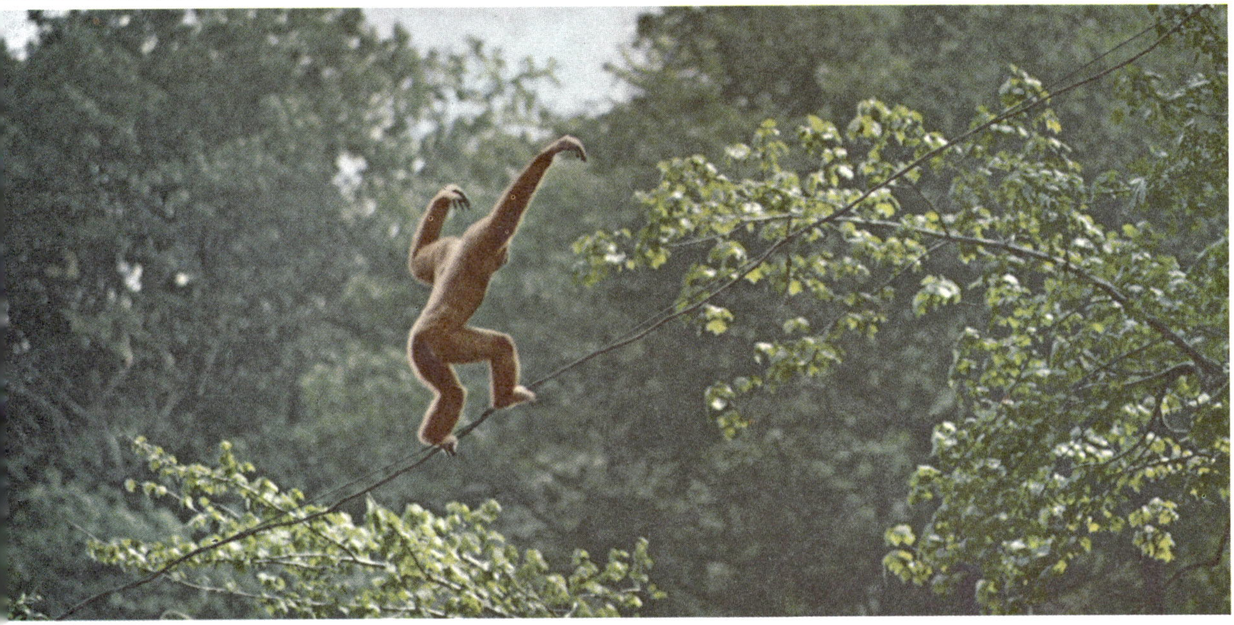
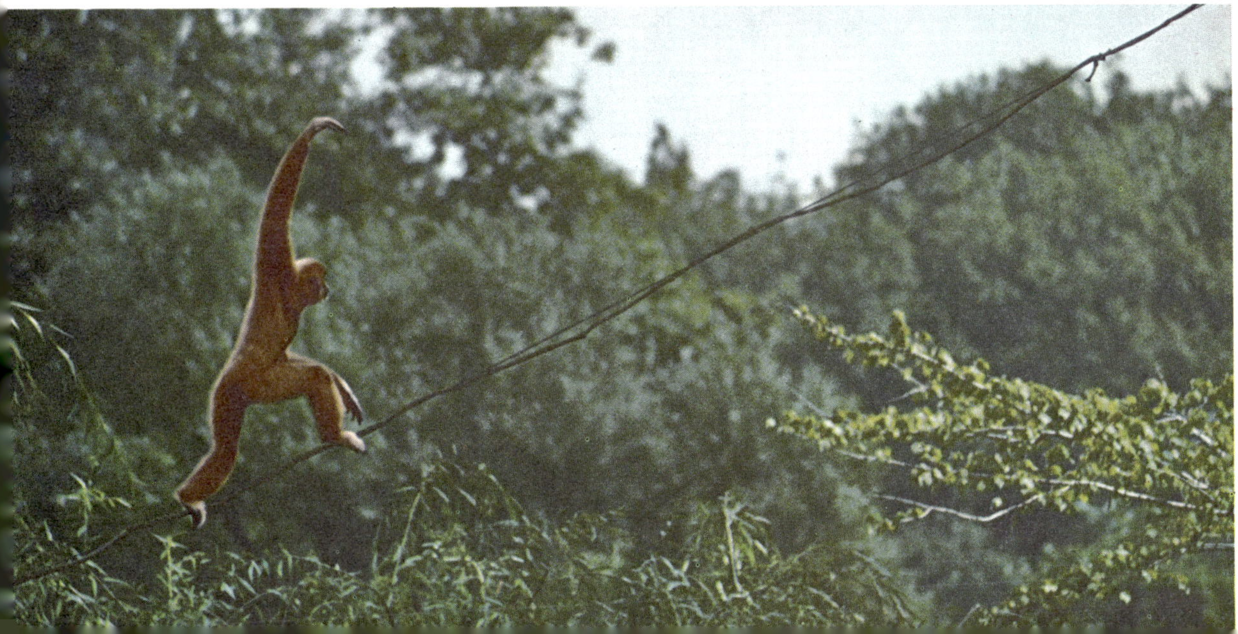

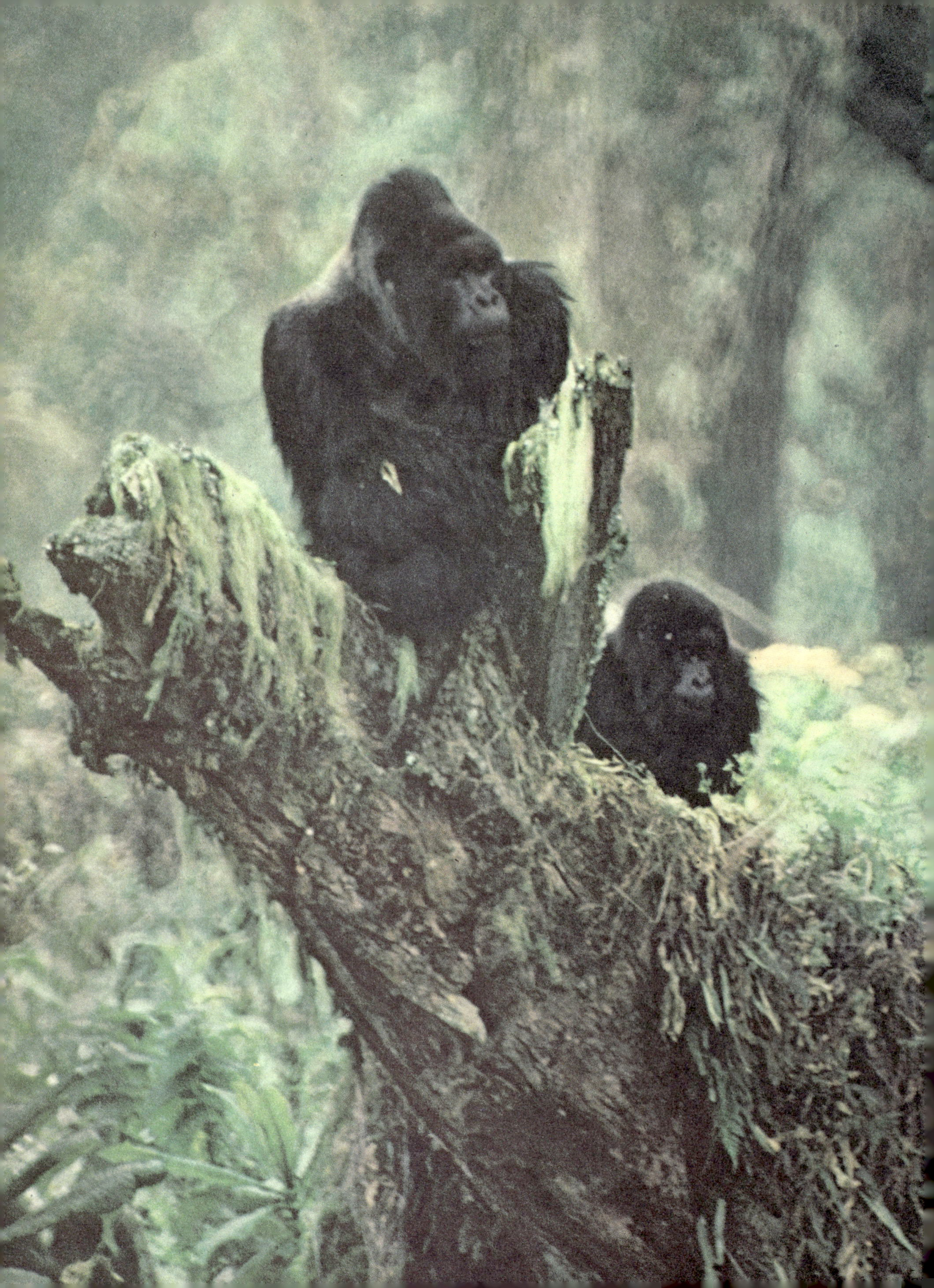

A BABY GORILLA chews tentatively on a tender shoot. Its elders are always nearby, ready to defend the baby if necessary from any predator brash enough to attack.

The Gentle Giants

Despite all the atrocities falsely attributed to it, the gorilla is essentially a peace-loving creature that would rather retreat than fight except in circumstances when its life is threatened and retreat is impossible. In the wild it has never been seen eating meat, although individuals have learned to do so in captivity. Nor do gorillas seem to drink water in the wild; they apparently get what moisture they need from their diet of greenery and fruit. Their gentle nature is evident at an early age: At play, the juvenile gorillas are markedly solicitous of the often turbulent infants. Females mature at about seven and males at about 10 years of age. Females have only one infant at a time and usually about one every three years.

THE GROUP RELAXES after a morning devoted to eating. A few groups may contain as many as 30 gorillas, but the majority are around a dozen.

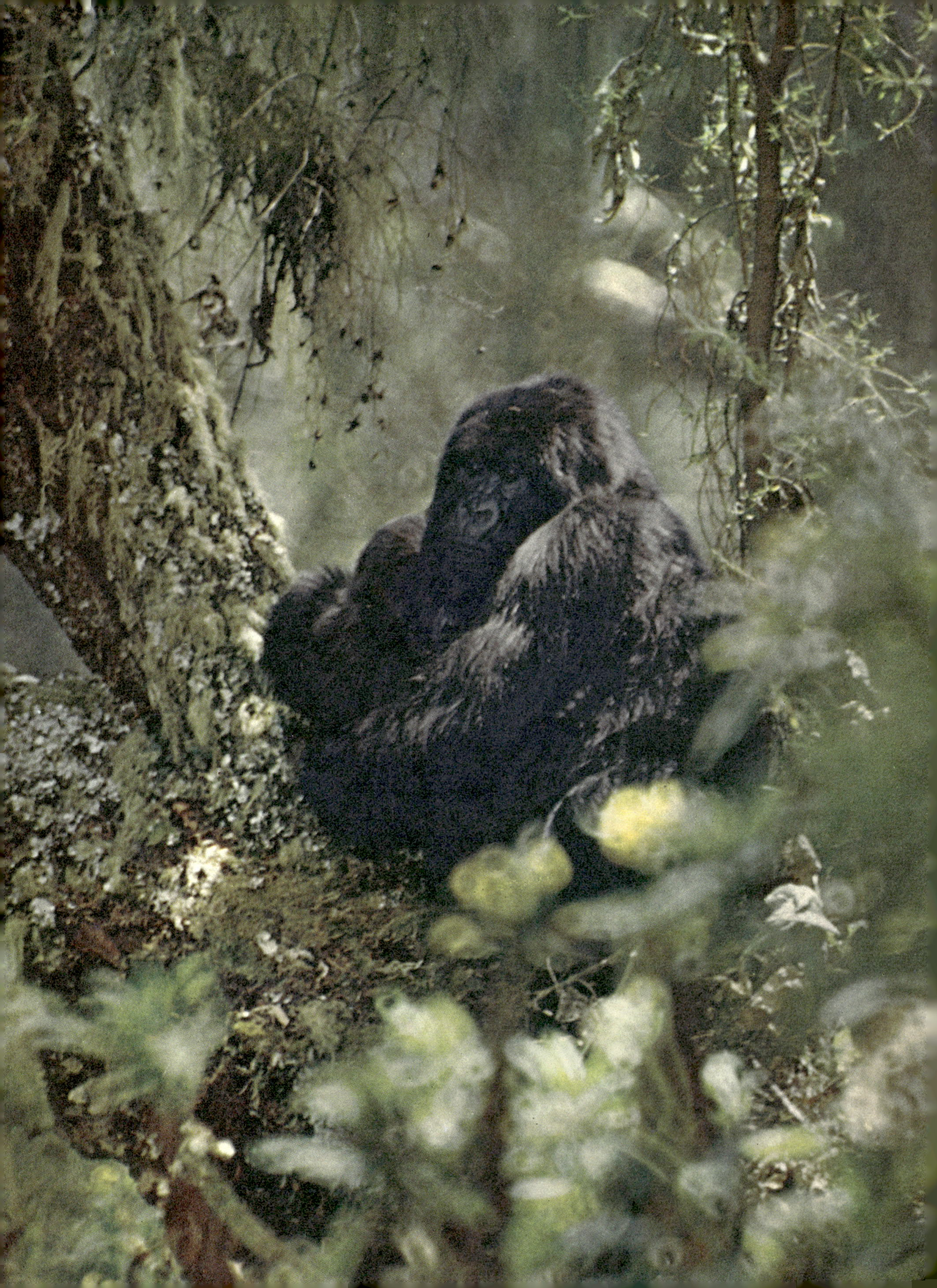

THE POWER OF INSTINCT leads a captive female gorilla to collect a pile of leaves to serve as a nest. This is a holdover from habits of the wild, where it is usual for gorillas to make simple, makeshift nests in the afternoon for resting and in the evening for nighttime sleeping. The young and occasionally the females go to sleep in trees. The others sleep on solid ground.

79

FIERCELY MATERNAL, A FEMALE GORILLA CLASPS HER TINY INFANT IN HER ARMS AS SHE GLARES AT THE INTRUDING CAMERA

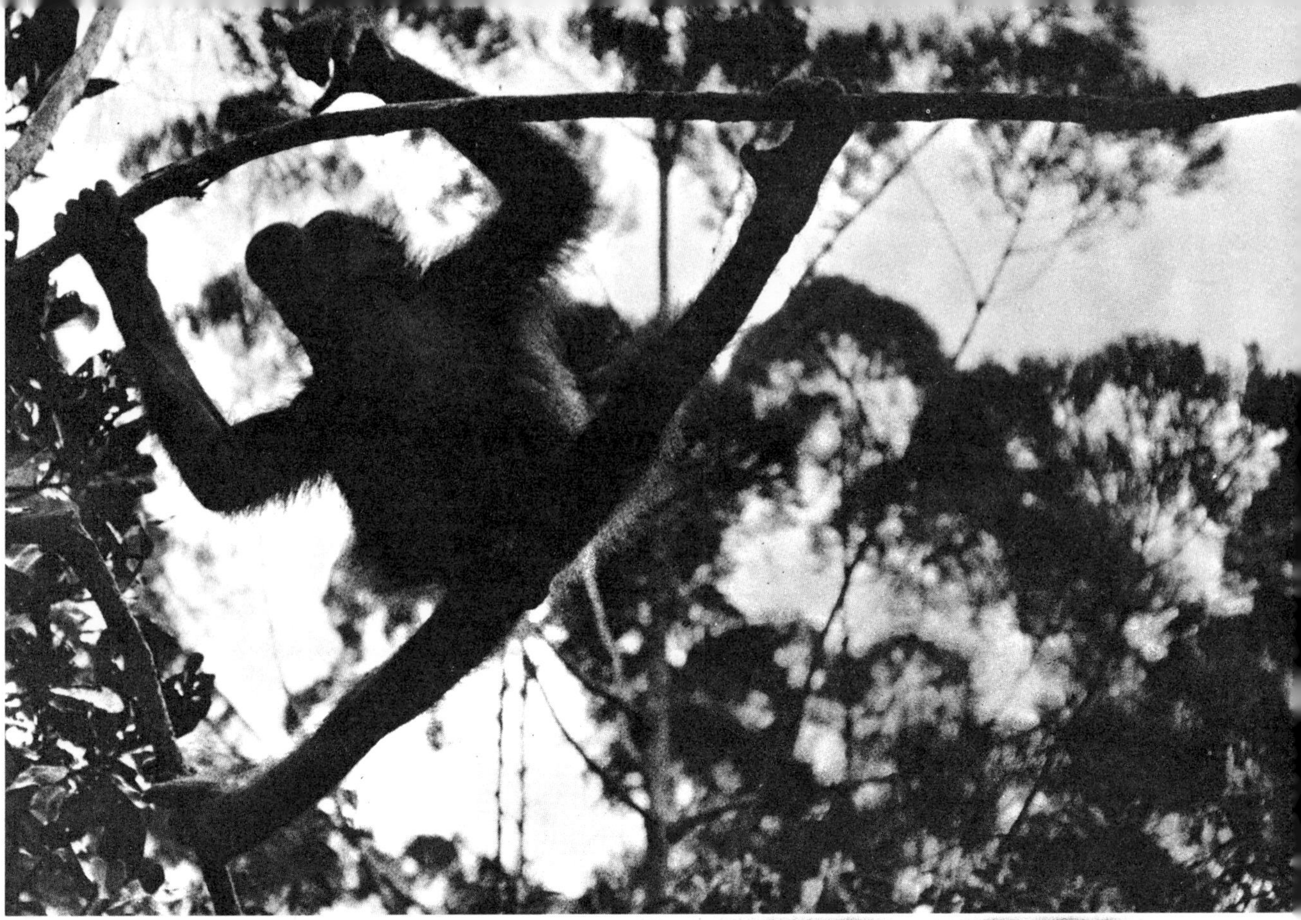
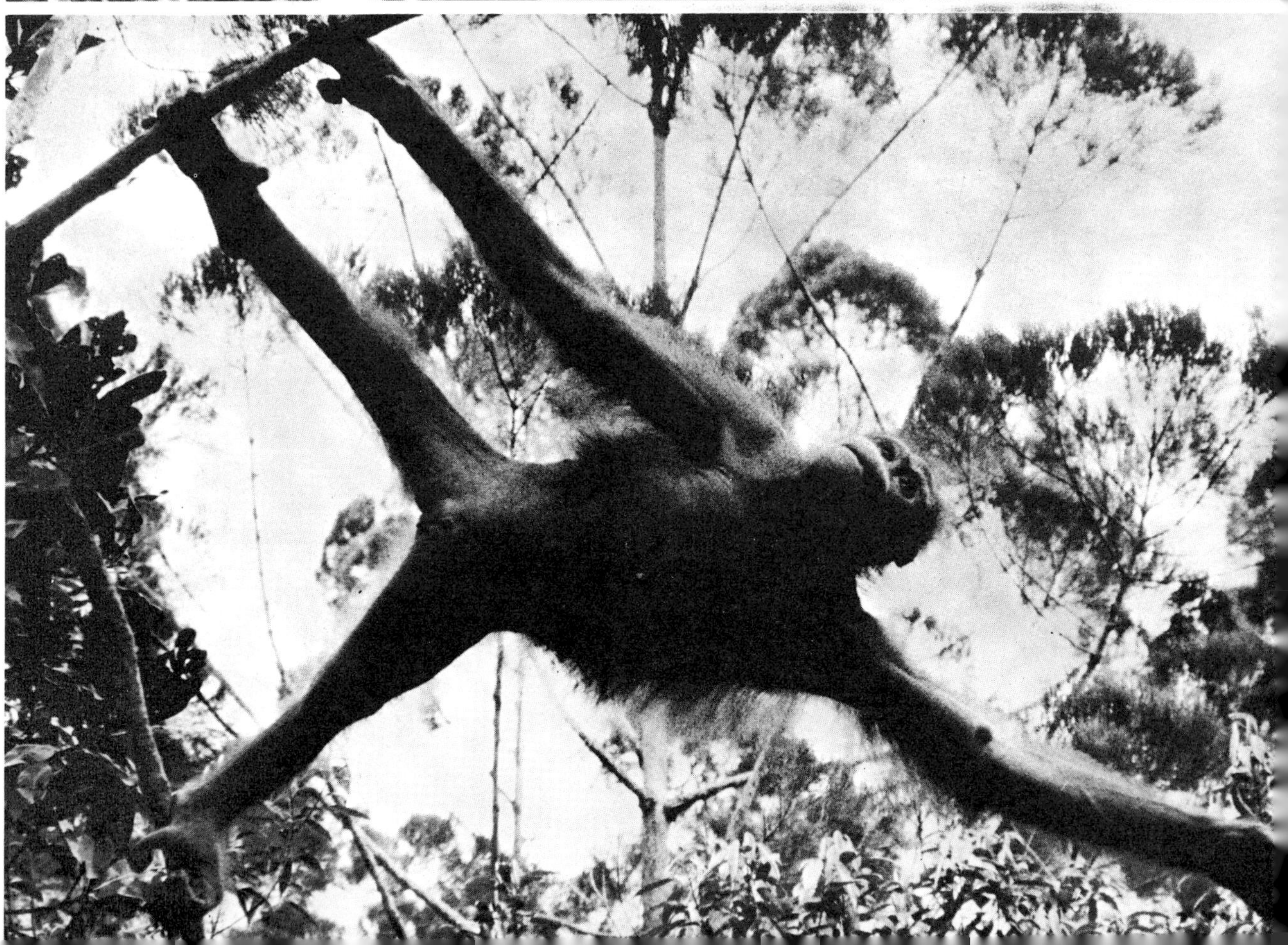

A 20-YEAR-OLD WILD ORANG PEERS AT AN INTRUDER IN BORNEO, WHERE LOCAL INHABITANTS CALL HIM "THE PERSON OF THE FOREST"

The Solitary Orang

Unlike the other big apes the orang has been characterized as lethargic and unsocial, a judgment based in part on its abject demeanor in zoos. But studies in the wild are beginning to round out a much more interesting picture of the red-furred ape. Found in the forests of Borneo and Sumatra, the mature males travel alone and compete with each other for females that live either alone or with offspring. The basic reason for such small family groups or loners seems to be largely due to the orangs' diet —figs, rambutans, mangosteens, bees' honey— which is scattered throughout the area. Therefore they cannot afford to group together, but do their searching independently. While the mature orangs tend to be serious-minded loners, the juveniles welcome any chance they get to be exuberant acrobats.

AN ORANG CLIMBS WITH CHARACTERISTIC CAUTION, HANGING ON WITH HANDS AND FEET WHILE IT HUNTS FOR FRUIT

Skeletons from Monkey to Man

Because of their separate evolutionary development over the past millions of years, monkeys, apes and men have today a variety of skeletal forms which, in part, reflect their different modes of locomotion. The monkeys are slender with slim hips, compressed rib cages and the longest spinal column, ideally flexible for rapid climbing and leaping. The apes are basically constructed as brachiators, even though the gorilla shown here spends nearly all of its time on the ground. They have long, powerful arms with hooklike hands adapted for grasping overhead limbs, and their shoulder blades and arm sockets are positioned and designed to allow for a wide range of arm movement above their heads. Their backs are relatively inflexible—an adaptation that reflects their ability to hang by their arms. Man possesses a moderately flexible spinal column and has developed long legs for walking bipedally.

THREE PROFOUND CHANGES in structure from monkey to man are in the shoulder, the lumbar region of the spine and the pelvis. The monkey's shoulder blades are nearly parallel to each other on opposite sides of its rib cage; man's are on his upper back, and a gorilla's extend upward with a great bony collar. Lumbar vertebrae—those with no ribs attached—usually number six or seven in monkeys, but most apes have only three. Man normally has five. In its quadrupedal stance, a monkey's tilted pelvis provides an anchor for its leg muscles. The gorilla's pelvis provides a base for muscles to support its heavy, stooped torso. Man's pelvis not only supports the upper body but is an excellent base for the powerful muscles used in walking.

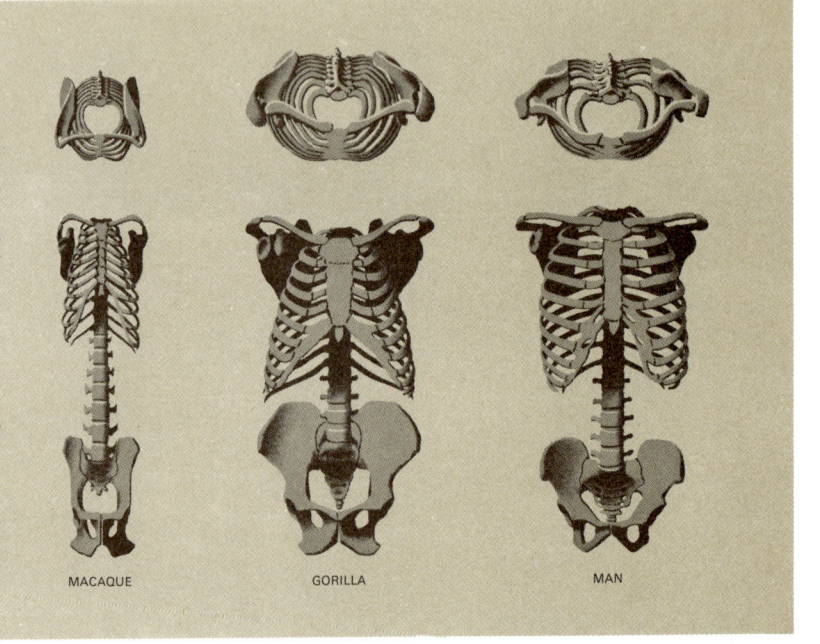

MACAQUE   GORILLA   MAN

COMPARATIVE SKELETONS from a macaque monkey, gorilla and man illustrate the anatomic progression from four-footedness through arm-swinging to two-legged walking. The monkey's arms are somewhat shorter than its legs; it can walk with its hands palm down, an impossible feat for a gorilla. On the other hand, the monkey's down-turned shoulder sockets prohibit brachiation in the true sense of the word. Man is less specialized and thus more adaptable: As an infant he can crawl palms down; as a youth he can brachiate—if clumsily—and he stands on two legs.

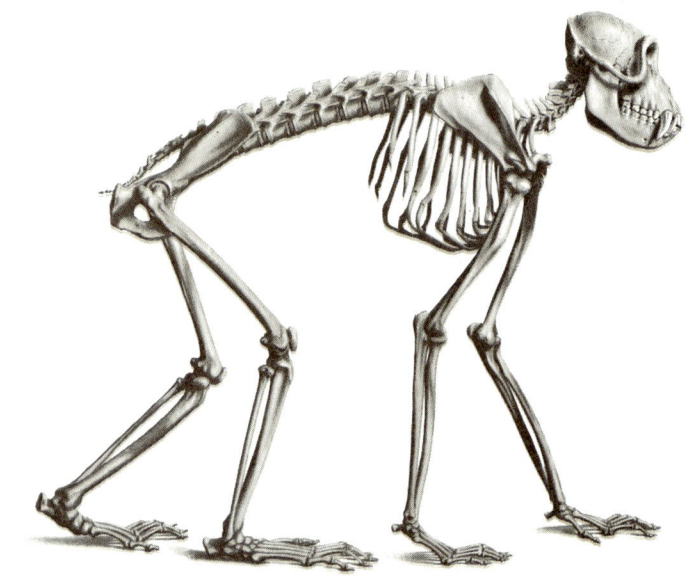

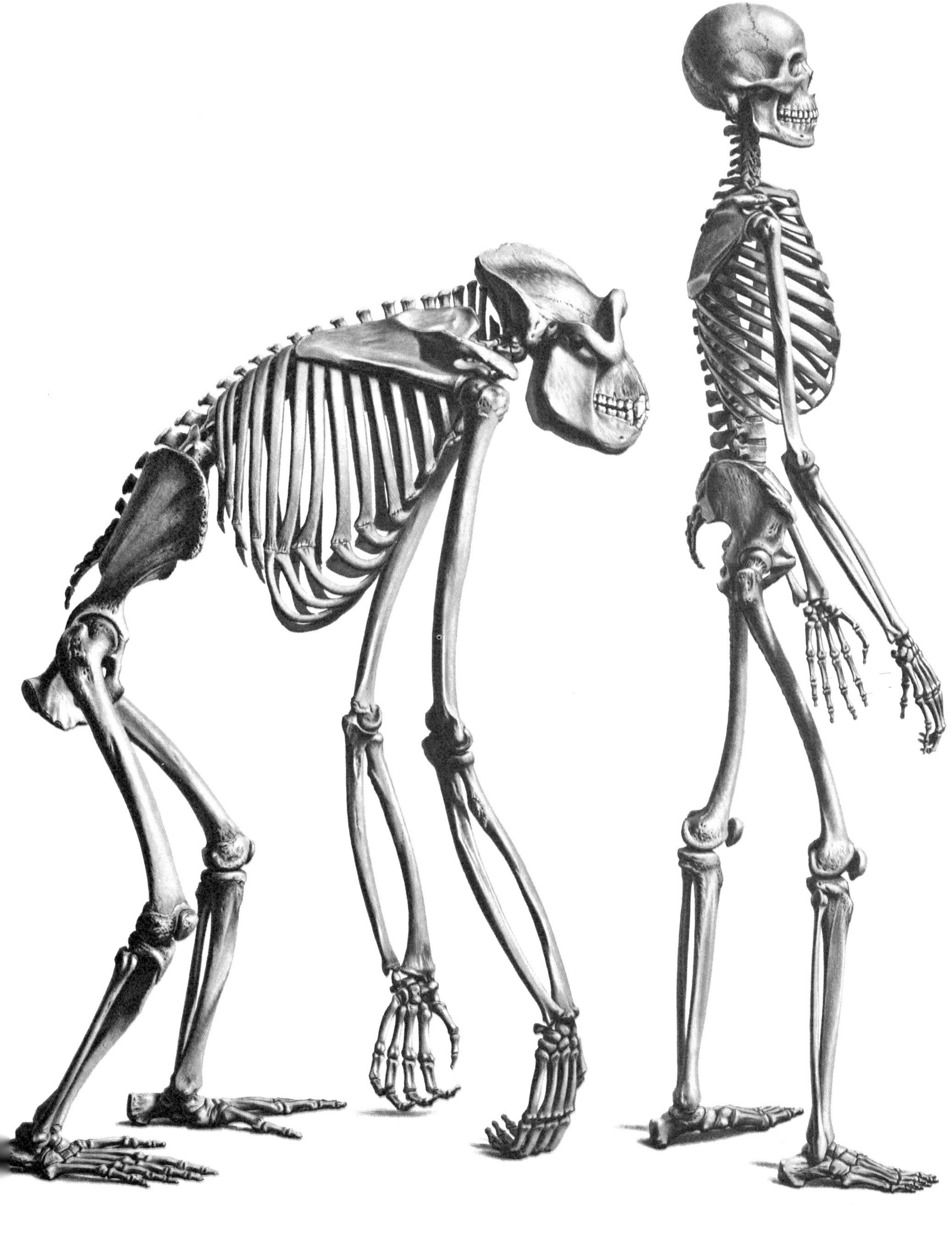

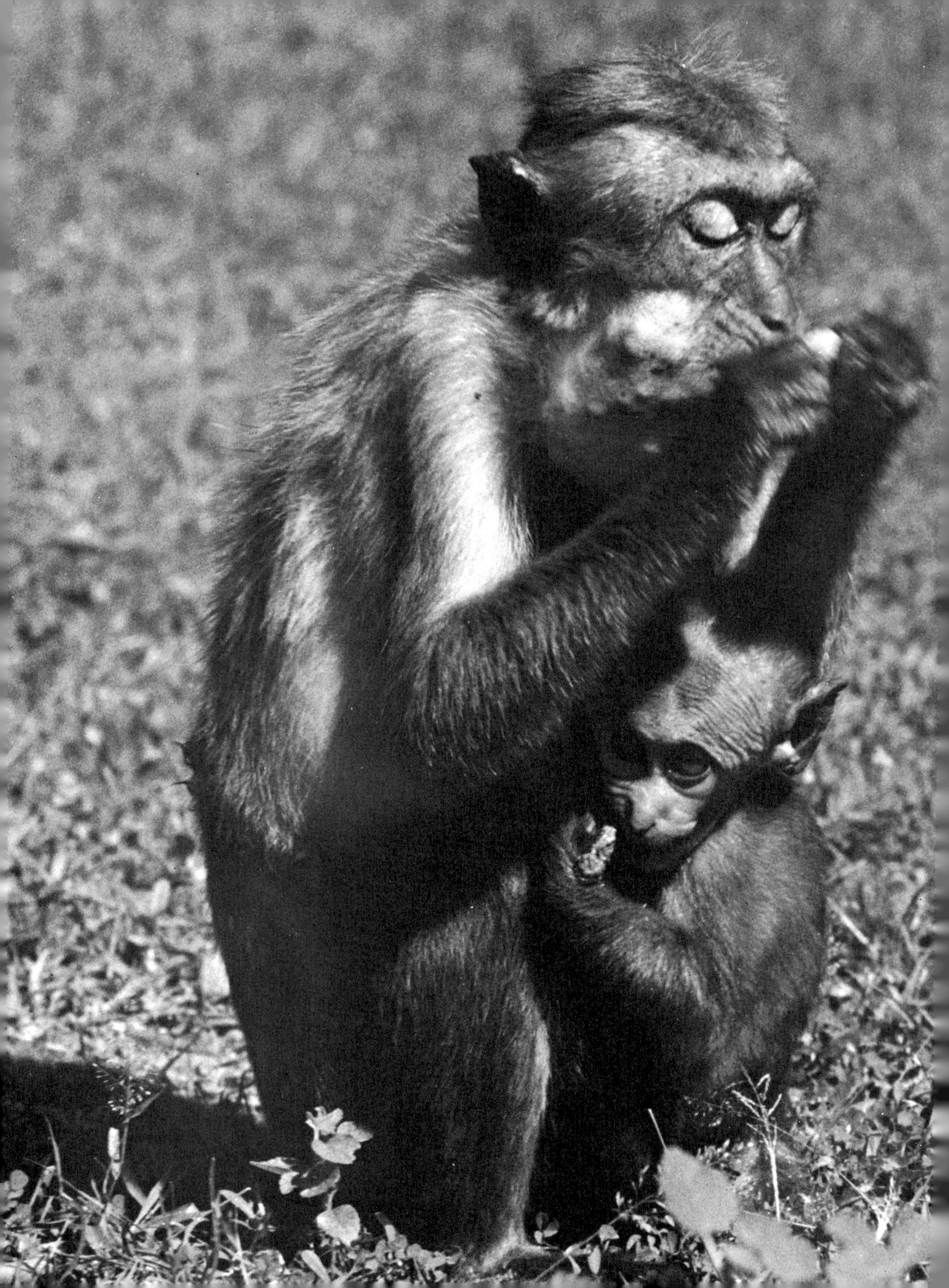

CRAMMING HER CHEEKS with peanuts, a toque macaque mother from Sri Lanka seems oblivious to her clinging infant but nevertheless is providing it with one of the necessities of life: a sense of security.

4

The Rewards of Childhood

Any event that happens with sufficient regularity is accepted by us as a matter of course. That is why we never question the normal human practice of bearing one infant at a time. Today multiple births are no longer so rare, due to the use of fertility drugs, which tend to produce twins or even quintuplets. But in natural human pregnancies, twins are still the surprise and triplets an astonishment. Yet multiple birth is common among most other mammals, and the multiplication sometimes runs as high as two dozen or more babies at a time. Why are human twins born only once in 90 natural pregnancies, triplets once in 8,000, quads once in 700,000, quints once in 65 million? Why do human females experience multiple births about as rarely as monkeys and apes?

The form of the latter question supports the answer. There is much of the monkey inside us still. Unlike many prosimians, most monkeys came to bear their young singly as a part of their adaptation to life in the trees. It is not possible to say precisely why or when they acquired their birth pattern, but it probably came at the beginning of monkey radiation. Single births must have been advantageous, and one can say that both the pattern and the close physical relationship between a monkey female and her newborn infant were acquired

THE REWARDS OF CHILDHOOD

at least partly as a solution to the problem of transportation. Throughout the day, monkeys are continually on the move from one feeding area to another, and the mother of a newborn infant is able to move quite freely and comfortably, using all four limbs, only because she has a single infant and because that infant clings to the hair on her belly.

To infant monkeys and apes, an effective grasp is almost as vital as breathing. They have to cling to mothers who are likely at any moment to perform some violent feat of acrobatics, either to escape from sudden danger or in the normal course of feeding. A gibbon, for example, even with a newborn infant clinging to her, remains an extraordinarily agile animal. She will feed at the end of a long branch, swaying perhaps in a high wind. Suddenly she will drop to another branch, run along it, and then start to swing again in the long, characteristic gibbon leaps, spanning perhaps 20 feet (6 m) at a time. The infant cannot afford to relax its grip on her hair for a second because if it does and it is shaken loose, it is a dead gibbon.

W HAT impels it to grip so firmly? It is not enough to dismiss the infant's tenacious grasp as due simply to an instinct necessary for survival. To do so is to misunderstand the forces which provoke apes—or monkeys or men —to action. People do not eat because they need food to survive, nor do they practice sex because copulation is essential for the preservation of the species. Nor does a human mother hold and fondle her infant because if deprived of her attentions it would die. We eat, we copulate and, if we are mothers, we look after our babies because such activities are pleasurable—which is simply another way of saying they satisfy a need.

So it is with infant monkeys. While the simple act of clinging may not seem very rewarding, it happens to give infant monkeys an enormous amount of gratification. Emotionally, they prefer an object to which they can cling to one they can suck on. And if the reader is surprised, he will find himself in much the same frame of mind as did Professor Harry Harlow of the University of Wisconsin, when he made the discovery as a result of his well-known series of experiments with infant rhesus macaques and two simple types of dummy mothers. These were cylinder-shaped objects made of wire mesh and equipped with wooden heads and artificial breasts. Harlow named them "surrogate," or substitute, "mothers." Half of these dummies he left with their wire bodies bare, the others he covered with terry cloth. Then he set up a number of cages with a pair of dummy mothers accessible to each. For half of the cages he connected the "breasts" of the wire dummy with a milk supply, for the other half the terry cloth mother was the one who had the milk. Finally he put a newborn baby rhesus macaque into each cage and sat back to see what would happen.

There were several things the babies might have done. They might have ignored the dummy mothers altogether, only going to them to feed. Or they might have developed a special attachment to the dummy whose breast they fed from and remained near it between their meals. This presumably is what they would have done if suckling is the strongest tie binding an infant to its mother. Actually the infants followed a third course. All of them, including those fed from the wire mother, showed an unmistakable preference for the cloth-covered mother, and passed hour after hour huddled against her, clinging to the cloth. The cloth, in brief, gave pleasure, security and emotional support to the infant monkeys; the nipple satisfied only when they had to suckle. It is significant that the infants displayed so strong an urge, not just to grasp

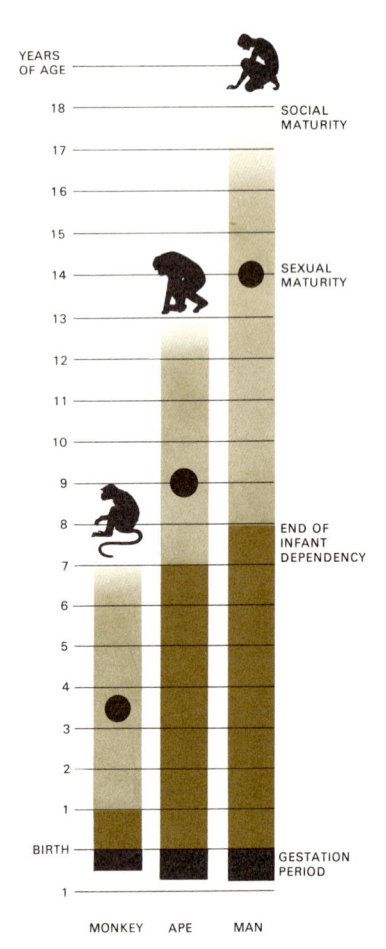

LIVE AND LEARN

Compared to other animals the primates grow up very slowly. This is because they have much to learn and need a long childhood in which to absorb it. The one that needs to learn the most (man) has the longest childhood of all. This chart shows how long a guenon monkey, a chimpanzee and a man stay in the womb and at what age each achieves token independence of mother, then sexual maturity and, finally, adult social maturity. These stages are shown by different color tones in the graph; lightening tone indicates increasing age and independence.

but also to huddle against the cloth. For this urge also reflects the situation an infant monkey confronts in the wild. It must obtain food, it must have protection. The source of both benefits is its mother, and therefore the closer it stays to her, the safer and better fed it will be. Not only that, it *likes* to huddle against her because this makes it feel secure. Does this good feeling come because it has learned that the mother's presence means protection? The truth is not so simple. As Harlow showed in another classic series of experiments, the sense of reassurance an infant monkey obtains from its mother is not derived from her living, breathing, loving presence alone; it is derived in large part from the texture of her body.

Both the ability to cling and the pleasure of touch provide the newborn monkey with an early sense of security. How strong this need is to the developing infant depends in part on the kind of upbringing it has. And as psychiatrist Charles Kaufman has shown, the nature of a monkey's care and training depends on the species. In observing the behavior of two closely related species, bonnet and pigtail macaques, Kaufman found that pigtail mothers are much more protective of their young than are bonnet macaques. The pigtails, who tend to be clannish, isolate themselves with their newborn. In contrast, the more sociable bonnets quickly rejoin the group. As a consequence of this early lack of group contact, pigtail infants are brought up to be far more dependent on their mothers than are the bonnet infants that are thrust into social interchange with their neighbors from the time of birth.

To test the mother-infant bonds of the two species, Kaufman removed the mothers from their infants. Even at a period when the young normally spend increasing amounts of time away from their mothers, the pigtail infants went into severe states of agitation and depression before adapting themselves to their loss. Bonnets too showed a sense of agitation at first, but quickly managed to find acceptable substitutes for their mothers; in some instances they were even nursed by other females. In Kaufman's study, mothers and infants were reunited. Harlow's experiments, however, measured long-term deprivation. When permanently separated from their mothers, a group of young rhesus monkeys grew up to be alarmingly abnormal.

THE laboratory work of Harlow, Kaufman and many others has been amplified in recent years by extensive observations of monkeys in the wild. Take, for example, the common Indian langur. We know a great deal about it from field studies in India, pioneered by Phyllis Jay, an anthropologist at the University of California. During the 1960s a team of Japanese primatologists, and S. M. Mohnot of India also studied the Indian langur, and further studies were made in the 1970s by Sarah Blaffer Hrdy of Harvard University.

Over a period of two years, Phyllis Jay lived in various regions of India in order to concentrate on four separate groups of langurs, three of which lived in forest areas. Being unused to humans, they promptly disappeared whenever Jay appeared. Once lost, they were hard to find again in the forest, and she spent a great deal of time merely trailing them around, trying to keep them in sight, before they began to get over their fear of her. Because of the problem of maintaining communication with a troop, she would keep an eye on it until its members had gone to sleep for the night, then return before dawn in order to be on hand when it woke up and began moving again. Eventually the langurs got so used to her presence that her daily arrival did not disturb them at all. Most of the adults ignored her, but many females would huddle against her, hoping to be stroked, and the infants would snap at her ankles or pull at her skirt, trying to lure her into joining in their play.

A good field student gets to know each of the monkeys he is watching. He becomes so familiar with their individual temperaments and quirks that quite often he can anticipate how each monkey in a group will react to almost any situation. This is the basis for understanding monkey behavior. For once an observer can anticipate a gesture or a movement, he is well on the way to understanding what it signifies. Through months of continually observing the same langurs, Jay came to know how each of the females and juveniles and adults would behave to the infants and how the infants would respond. The following account is drawn entirely from her acute and intensive study.

All male langurs inside a group are organized in a dominance hierarchy. So are the females though to a much less marked degree. As soon as she gives birth, however, a female moves out of the dominance structure. Concentrating exclusively on her infant, she ceases to participate in the group's dominance relationships. If, for example, a squabble breaks out over precedence, she quietly picks up her infant and moves away. So long as the infant requires all her attention, she makes no attempt to impose her will on any other monkey and the others, in return, usually make no attempt to impose their will on her.

Motherhood, in other words, replaces status. As she holds the baby, cleaning and inspecting its body, the other females gather around. Their curiosity is intense and their desire to hold the infant so impelling that they wait in line for their turn to do so. A few hours after it is born, the mother allows other females to take it, but her attention rarely wanders from it for more than a few seconds. She will take it back at the first signs of distress or whenever she just feels like holding it. Her right to do so is unquestioned. She can take it away even from a female who is normally her superior in the hierarchy. If ever the group is alarmed, she dashes to the infant, scoops it up and races into the nearest tree. She is able to do this the more easily because the infant is so eager to have her hold it. Soon after its birth, it learns to recognize her and will stretch out its arms toward its mother whenever it sees her approach.

The other females are not merely curious about the newborn infant; they are also extremely protective. Their claim to hold it depends largely on whether they can keep it contented. If it begins to squeal or shows the least sign of discomfort, and if its mother is not nearby, another female will take the infant from whoever is holding it. The female's very strong protective feelings are evoked by, among other things, the infant's movements and cries. But hair color of the baby also plays its part. For the first three to five months, a langur is distinguished by its dark coat, which contrasts with its pink face, hands, feet and ears. Even if its tiny size did not command the attention of the females, its distinctive coloring would. This becomes clear from the way a mother reacts to her infant's death. Apparently nonhuman primates do not appreciate the significance of death, or so their behavior suggests. George Schaller once saw a female gorilla carry a dead infant for four days before she abandoned it, and Phyllis Jay saw a langur mother repeatedly trying to make a dead baby cling to her body by placing it under her body and then standing up. When the infant fell, she continued to stroke it gently. But because the mother's behavior is also a reaction to the infant's movements, the mother of a dead infant gradually gives up. She cleans and inspects it less often, makes less and less effort to retrieve it from other females and, at last, abandons it completely.

Once the infant's coat alters color—from dark to light—the attitude of the other females changes. They still come to its aid if it is mistreated, perhaps by a too-vigorously playful older infant, but they no longer have the desire to hold it. Its mother, of course, continues to remain tender and protective, and the infant is never far from her. When the troop is on the move it rides, clinging to the hair on her front, and when it stops to feed or rest, the baby still stays very close to its mother's side.

All the while, the infant is learning. There is a popular assumption that all animals know by instinct what to eat, where to wander and which enemies they must avoid. So far as monkeys are concerned, this assumption is completely wrong. The infant must learn all that is essential to its survival, such as what it can eat and what it cannot. Just as a young child copies its mother's actions, so does an infant monkey. When foraging, it stays close beside her, picking the same plants and leaves that she does. Actually, juvenile monkeys spend comparatively little time eating. They are enormously active, and work off steam in running, climbing, chasing and wrestling. It is the daylong practice at these skills during an extended adolescence that helps shape the young monkey into what he will become. As Sherwood L. Washburn and David A. Hamburg have stated in *Primate Behavior*: "The rich social life and environmental exploration by the young monkey or ape is the result of its doing far more than it needs to do for immediate utilitarian purposes. Prolonged youth would have no advantage unless the inner drive to activity led to knowledge and skills."

Observation of others—including mistakes and misfortunes of others—produces a kind of group knowledge among monkeys which is very useful to them. Valuable information is quickly passed around, as is well illustrated by a group of baboons living in Nairobi Park. They had long become used to automobiles, but when two members of the group were shot from a car, all of them became extremely suspicious of all cars. Eight months later it was still impossible to get near them by car. In the same way, other groups of baboons have learned to flee into trees when threatened by lions, but to come down out of them and run away when threatened by men—although it may be years since the group was shot at. The younger members have learned what to avoid, and the behavioral adaptation persists.

The mother monkey must learn, too, how to be an effective mother. Though females are born with strong maternal tendencies, the tendencies are only potentials. To be realized, they have to be developed. Long before they are mothers themselves, they learn, by observing their elders, how infants should be treated. Moreover, as juveniles, the females of some species, such as langurs, gain practical experience by holding and looking after the infants of other females. This does not mean that all monkeys are good mothers. Experience helps, of course. A mother who has had four infants is likely to be a thoroughly competent mother. Relaxed yet firm, she holds her baby almost as if she were oblivious to its frequently violent struggles. But there are some females, nervous, uncertain or irritable by temperament, who never make good mothers. In baboons these tend to be the mothers who are low in the female hierarchy and are constantly under pressure from their social superiors. They are continually jogging the infant around, either because it annoys them or because they simply cannot learn how to handle it properly. The unfortunate infant, it need hardly be said, is liable to grow up insecure and irritable just like her. Among monkeys as among human beings, the child is "mother" of the man.

3 WEEKS

5 MONTHS

10 MONTHS

THE BABOON COLOR SHIFT

A baboon is born with a pink face, pink ears and a black coat of body hair. This color combination stirs strong reaction in adult baboons; a baby receives intensive care from its mother, and the males of the troop are fiercely protective toward it. Then at four months its face starts to darken and its coat becomes predominantly brown. At this point the females' interest is rapidly waning, but the males are still strongly protective. By the time the young baboon is 10 months old it has all the coloration of an adult. It leaves its mother frequently and seeks out the company of its peers.

As soon as it can walk with ease, a langur infant starts to venture away from its mother and to play with other infants. In most monkeys, births are not evenly spaced through the year but tend to occur at certain seasons so that, in a group of any size, there will be several infants in the same age group. While they play, their mothers sit calmly by and watch, like human mothers in a park, intervening only if the play gets too rough. Then they will bring the offenders to order with a mild threat. And, occasionally, some of them will wander away to take a break, leaving one or two behind who watch the babies.

It is hardly possible to exaggerate the importance of play to an infant monkey. It seems obvious that it is through play that the infants learn to adjust to their fellows and become effective members of the society. Being a social animal, a monkey has to learn the rules. Only by trial and error, constantly repeated, does it learn how far it can go in asserting itself—in threatening or attacking others before drawing punishment down on itself. And the play group is the perfect instrument for such learning because its members are young and their teeth are neither sharp enough nor long enough to inflict serious damage.

INSIDE this protected environment, the infant learns how to mix. By playing with its peers, it also develops a fully integrated personality. The word personality may appear somewhat inappropriate when applied to a monkey, but no other adequately suggests the complexity of a monkey's nature. Like humans, they can be social, antisocial or, in captivity, positively unable to cope with society. They can be well adjusted, neurotic or psychotic. Lower mammals, such as rats, can be driven insane if subjected to sufficient stress. What distinguishes monkeys—and probably apes—from other nonhuman animals is that artificially imposed stress is not necessarily needed to turn them into neurotics or psychotics. If they do not receive enough of the right kind of care in early infancy, they will never be able to mix properly with other monkeys.

This, too, has been established by Professor Harlow in another classic series of experiments which demonstrates once again how useful the laboratory can be in confirming or elucidating the observations of field students. It is obvious, from watching monkeys in the wild, that they play a great deal. As practically every major activity a monkey indulges in serves some useful function, it follows that play, too, must be important to it. But how important? The only way to answer that question is to deprive monkeys of the opportunity to play and see what happens; and that is exactly what Harlow did.

First he raised several groups of monkeys from birth without allowing them any chance to play. Some groups were brought up in total isolation. The others were raised, each in its own cage, in sight of other monkeys but without any physical contact with them. The results were utterly disastrous. All the infants in both groups developed severe neuroses, or perhaps psychoses. Some sat blankly in their cages, staring fixedly into space. Others clasped their arms and rocked and swayed hour after hour, or sucked compulsively at their thumbs or fingers, or pinched repeatedly at their skins. And some, when approached

YOUNG GORILLAS AT PLAY

Play is important to young gorillas as a way of gradually learning the skills necessary to adult gorilla life. It goes on until about the age of six and has been intensively studied in the wild by George Schaller, whose drawings of young gorillas at play are shown here. In the first picture a 15-month-old infant places a spray of lobelia leaves on its head. The juveniles in the center are performing a sort of snake dance. Schaller has also observed games of follow the leader and king of the mountain. The three acrobats at right are engaged in the commonest type of solitary play exercise—which builds up muscles and improves coordination. Besides climbing and swinging from branches they also delight in jumping, sliding, running and somersaulting.

by human beings, chewed and tore at their bodies in terror until they bled.

We shall consider in a later chapter the bearing of this behavior on the genesis of human neuroses and psychoses. For the moment, we are concerned only with the monkeys. After varying lengths of time, Harlow brought them into contact with other monkey infants. Those raised in isolation were simply terrified, completely unable to make any kind of social contact. The infants raised in sight of other monkeys did a little better: They did succeed in establishing some kind of social relationship, but the relationships were thoroughly unsatisfactory. The infants fought savagely, they showed almost no sign of friendliness and, most curious of all, they were unable to copulate.

Why should these monkeys have been unable to perform an act, normally considered instinctive, which is essential to the survival of the species? Two possibilities at once offer themselves. The first is that an infant monkey needs proper maternal care if it is to grow up normal enough to copulate. The second is that monkeys may learn how to copulate in the wild by observing their elders. Harlow, a great believer in testing theoretical assumptions by practical experiment, proceeded to do just that. He raised many infants, males and females, each one alone in a cage with its mother. After several months, he brought the infants together and found that they had absolutely no inclination for making effective social contact. It seems that the presence of the mother is not enough.

That disposed of the possibility that proper mothering is the essential prerequisite for effective sex. Meanwhile, Harlow had also been raising two groups of four other infant macaques. Each was brought up alone in his own cage, except for the presence of a cloth-covered mother. These infants, however, were allowed to play with each other in a large room for 20 minutes a day. The effects of just this brief play period were surprising. After a brief, initial uncertainty, each group of four infants played together with all the confidence, vigor and liveliness of monkeys born in the wild. Nor was that all. Before a year was out, the males and females began to take on their normal roles. The males started to display dominance, the females submission, and all adopted sexual postures which indicated that sex was going to be absolutely no problem.

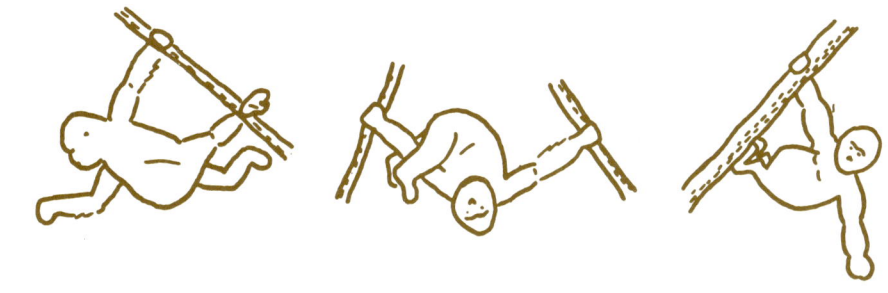

THESE experiments suggest some intriguing conclusions. To a monkey in the wild, a mother serves as the initial teacher as well as protector. But, so far as its mating and its adult social life are concerned, playing with its peers is vitally important. Being allowed to play with the other kids, one might say, is what ultimately produces a well-adjusted adult monkey. How far this might also hold true of human children, the reader must be left to judge for himself—remembering always that humans have the ability, through language, to communicate to each other things that animals can only learn by actual performance. But if we restrict ourselves to a discussion of monkeys only, one further conclusion can be drawn. The four infants that were allowed to play together had never seen adults copulate. Then obviously they do not learn to copulate by observing their elders. Actually, it is not just the specific physical act of copulation a monkey has to learn, because he is born with a tendency to perform it. Basically what he does have to learn is how to get along with other monkeys. For that ability is apparently an essential prerequisite for effective copulation and it can be acquired by a monkey only through play, at an early age, with other young monkeys.

To think of monkey play in human terms inevitably creates a false impression. This play is incomparably more vigorous. By the time a langur is a year old, it can run up a tree trunk, race along a branch and leap over to another tree with more ease than a human acrobat will ever command. In its vigor, and in some of its forms, the play of infant monkeys resembles that of 10-year-old children. They wrestle; they chase each other. They play follow the leader, climbing up to a height, perhaps, to jump down into a pool, as infant macaques do. Young chimpanzees play tug-of-war, using a twig as the rope, and George Schaller observed infant gorillas playing king of the mountain with enormous zest, the king kicking his adversaries and stamping on their fingers as they struggled to dethrone it, though without inflicting any real damage.

All this tremendously energetic scampering around is more than just the natural exuberance of youth. It prepares monkeys and apes to cope with sudden emergencies that one day might mean the difference between life and death. The English research virologist A. J. Haddow has described what happened once when an eagle, flying below the level of the treetops, swooped without warning onto a tree where guenon and colobus monkeys were feeding. In a flash, the monkeys raced down to safety near the bottom of the tree. No one knows how often eagles attack or how successful they are. But the monkeys' reaction showed that such attacks must occur often enough for them to have learned to flee—and flee instantly, for an eagle attacks so suddenly that the monkeys have only a second in which to escape. In their sudden flight, they must take jumps far more daring than those they would normally essay, and females with young must reach and snatch them up before escaping. Descending with such speed, the monkeys must move with extremely acute agility and judgment, for the slightest error would mean a fall, and possible death.

The ability to react with extra speed and precision in emergencies is essential to the survival of any monkey species, and it is acquired through the long hours of play in which monkeys indulge when they are young. Playfulness, of course, is common among many kinds of mammals, but probably none of them spend as much time at playing as monkeys do. Much the same as athletes who are preparing for the one big event that they know is going to demand their maximum strength and effort, so do monkeys prepare to meet those sudden moments of crisis which may end in safety or in death.

S<small>TILL</small> such crises do not occur too often. Until it is about a year old a langur's life must be an extremely pleasant one. There are some members of the group it must not approach, and if it gets too obstreperous, it will be disciplined. On the whole, however, permissiveness is the rule. The infant is protected and carried by its mother, and treated with tolerance by the adult females. The process of being weaned must therefore come as a profound and unpleasant shock. Certainly the youngster's behavior suggests so. At first it reacts as if it simply cannot believe that its mother—that loving, protective mother—is actually rejecting it. Indeed, after a preliminary repulse or two, she does allow it to suckle. But gradually, her rejections become more decisive. When it runs after her she runs away. When followed, she keeps her breasts covered. If it persists she may, if passive discouragement fails, slap it. The infant throws tantrums. It screams, returns her slap and even beats its head on the ground.

For several months the struggle continues, quietly ignored by the rest of the group. Though the infant's cries of distress sound, to human ears, exactly like those which at an earlier stage would have brought an adult racing to its aid, they now evoke no response. Inevitably the mother wins, but having to resist her infant's indignant and persistent claims seems often to impose a severe strain on her nerves, making her exceedingly irritable and very bad company for the rest of the group. Weaning an infant, it seems, can be a strain on mother and child whether monkey or human.

Because a langur female may resume her estrous cycle before her infant has been weaned, she may attract males while the baby is still with her. This can precipitate a most trying domestic situation. While she is copulating, her infant is liable to stand close beside her, in obvious distress, sometimes slapping impotently at the intruding male. Presumably it feels rejected; possibly it is reacting to what must look like an assault on its mother.

The weaning period, in any event, is decisive. It signals the end of childhood. For a while the young langur, now about 15 months old, continues to follow its mother around and may even still ride on her, clinging to her belly. Its size makes it look faintly grotesque, like a very big man trying to fit himself into a very small car, because its arms and legs are so big that it hardly has room to pack them into the space between its mother and the ground. Still, try as it may, these attempts to remain a baby are doomed to fail. Several months after the weaning is over, its mother gives birth again and her young juvenile must make its own way in the group.

From this stage on young langurs become segregated by sexes in a way that, once again, irresistibly recalls human society. The female juveniles stay near the center of the group, close to the adults, mixing more and more intimately with the adult females and their infants. Holding the infants and sometimes tending them while the mothers are away, they are gaining experience toward their own future role as mothers. The male juveniles, meanwhile, spend most

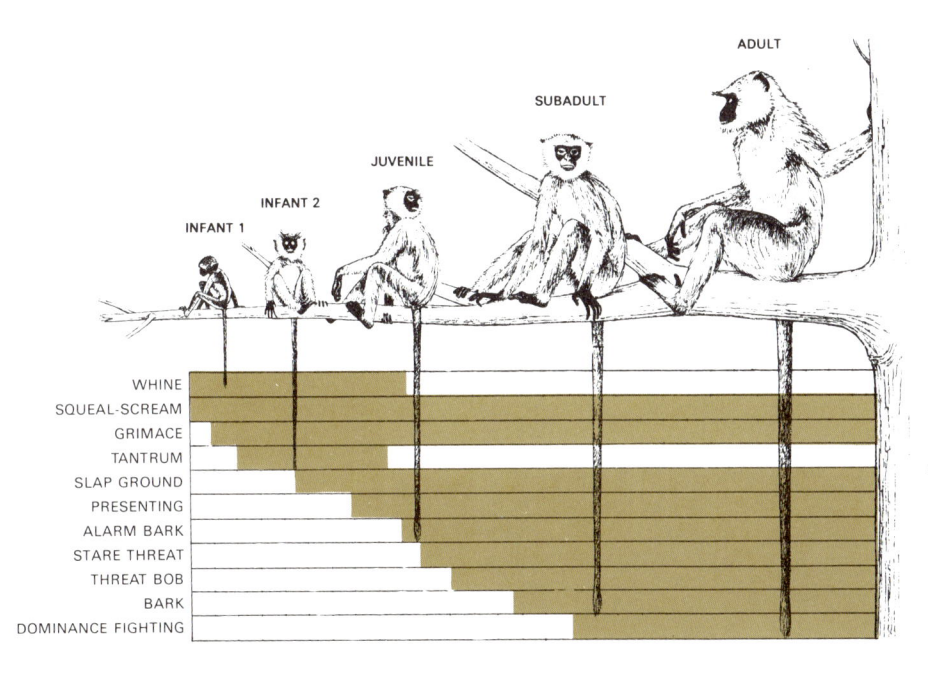

HOW LANGURS COMMUNICATE

As a langur grows up, the kinds of noises and other social behavioral activities that it is capable of keep changing. As a newborn infant all it can do is whine, squeal and scream. At the Infant 2 stage (from five to 15 months) it begins to be able to throw tantrums and grimace. As a juvenile it gradually gives up whining and infantile rages and begins to pick up more adult activities such as alarm barks and bobbing its body as a threat. Truly aggressive dominance fighting is behavior that is reserved for subadults and adults.

of their free time playing. As they grow older, their play becomes ever more vigorous and mobile, and, needing more room, they drift toward the periphery of the group, away from both the adults and the infants.

Through their play, the male juveniles establish the close social bonds that will later help to keep the group unified. As they compete, for food or for the best sleeping positions or the easiest passageways through the trees, they gradually establish the order of dominance they will carry with them into adult life. Gradually, too, they begin to have more contact with the older members of the group. One by one, each male subadult fights his way up the female hierarchy, dominating one female after another as he grows stronger and more confident, and eventually he will find a position among the adult males. When their period of adolescence finally ends, both females and males are equipped to take their places as fully adult members of the group. Without any formal course of instruction, simply by allowing their own tendencies to develop within the context of the group, they have learned all they need to know.

THE youthful developments of several other genera of monkeys—baboons, macaques, tamarins and squirrel monkeys, among others—have also been studied. The pattern they follow illustrates interesting social differences in the male attitude toward infants. In a langur group adult males are inclined to keep themselves apart from young children. Since langur females are normally sexually unreceptive while nursing their young, dominant langur males may even murder infants in order to gain immediate access to the mothers. On the other hand, Japanese macaque males have been observed to cradle one- and two-year-old infants during the birth season. And among many marmoset species fathers carry and groom their newborn offspring, returning them to the mothers only for nursing. Paternal attention of this nature, which may persist for some time, is close to that of hamadryas baboons. The subadult or young adult hamadryas male in fact acquires females for his eventual one-male family unit by first "mothering" infant females. For months, and often a year or more, a young female enjoys a protective relationship with the male that is similar to the protection she received from her mother. The male readily carries a young female on his back, helps her over difficult terrain when she walks and lets her huddle next to him at night. In savanna baboon groups, adult males also show an intense interest in infants. They do not, however, assume responsibility for individual infants. Usually an adult male will approach a mother, smacking his lips to show he means no harm, in order to enjoy the pleasure of playing with the mother's infant.

Why these differences? They are adaptations acquired in the interests of survival. Comfortable as some langur species are on the ground, none ever ventures more than a few yards from trees. The females do not require the male's protection and they usually do not get it. If a langur group is alarmed, it is every monkey for itself. Baboons are organized differently, since they frequently move far from trees, and, if a predator approaches, females and infants alike depend on the adult males for protection. But an animal is hardly likely to risk its life to save an infant for whom it feels no emotion. In the course of their adaptation to life on the ground, baboon males have acquired a tendency to feel affection or at least a strong protective urge toward all infants, and it is this urge that, in an emergency, will give males a motive to defend them. And this is true not only for baboons; the urge to protect their babies must also have evolved in men before they could successfully adapt to life on the ground.

A BRIGHT-EYED, INFANT CEYLONESE GRAY LANGUR HAS THE OVERSIZE EARS THAT UNMISTAKABLY SET OFF THE YOUNG FROM THE ADULTS

Growing Up to Be a Monkey

From their birth to around the time of their weaning, infant monkeys receive the solicitous care of their mothers, who provide them with nourishment, protection and even transportation. Thus made secure, they come playfully to maturity, learning about life through a fascinating process of adjustment and adaptation, in a range of interactions with their mothers, other adults and their age-mates.

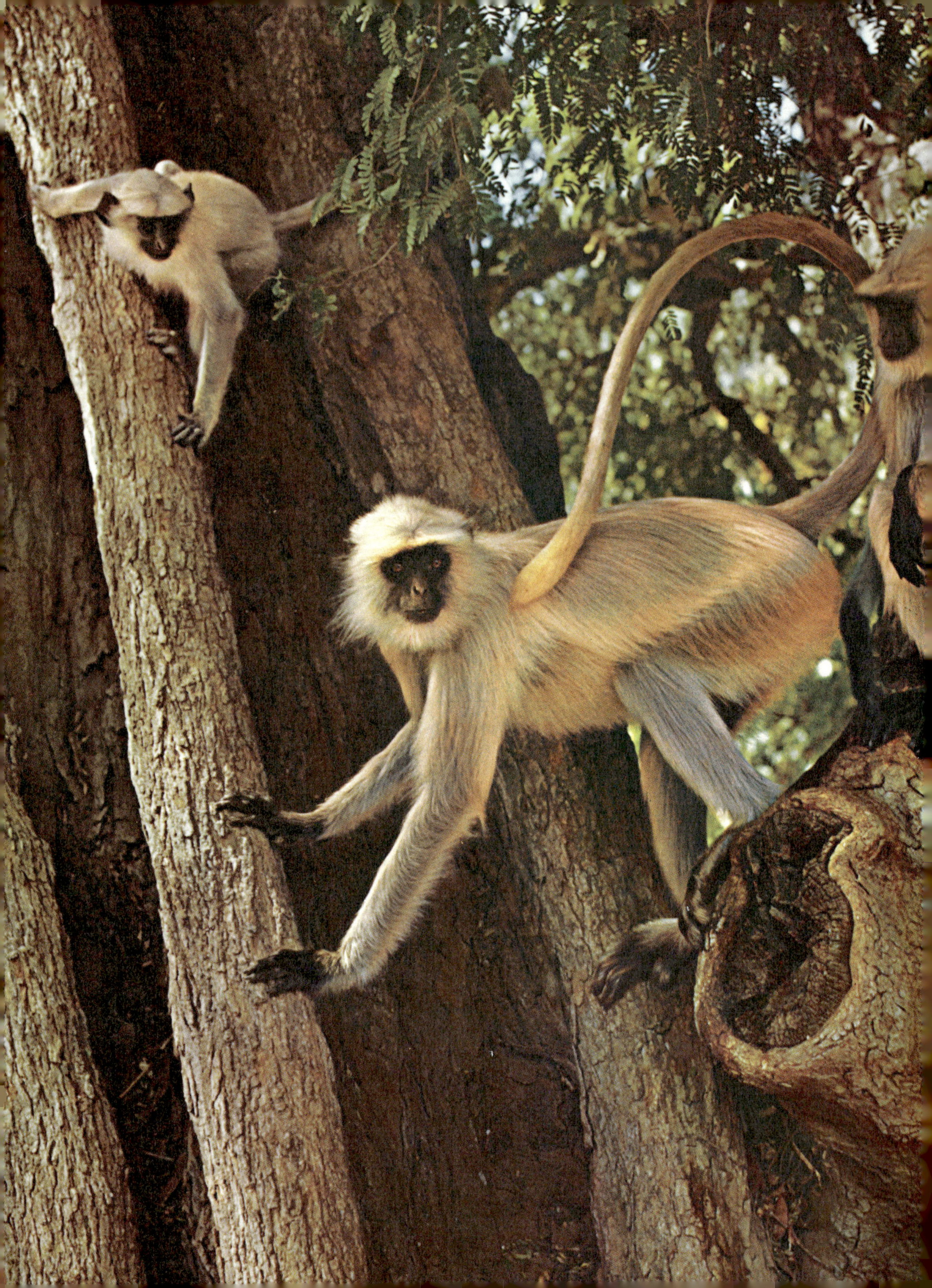

FLINGING OUT ITS ARMS, a gray langur leaps to another feeding tree. Able to get moisture and nourishment from mature leaves, langurs can live in a variety of vegetation zones.

The Importance of Being One of the Group

For animals as slow to mature and with as much to learn as the monkeys and apes, there are advantages in living together in groups, which, of course, is what most primates do. Whether the members number only a few or several hundred, the group becomes the repository of their experiences, which are then passed on to the new generation. The infant born into a group would thus seem to be at an advantage. During its prolonged youth, it not only has the protection of other members but time in which to learn from them, as well as to rehearse, through play, what it has learned. The arboreal gray langurs of India and Sri Lanka *(opposite and above)* offer prime examples of the benefits accruing from life in a group. Some aspects of their free and easy existence are shown in this picture essay.

PERCHED IN A TAMARIND TREE, Indian langurs display their sleek lines. Although adapted to an arboreal way of life, they often spend as much as 80 per cent of the day on the ground.

TIRED OUT, an infant gray langur leans against its mother. One month old, it still spends most of the day either touching or clinging to her, occasionally climbing onto her shoulders or her head.

IN A RELAXED MOOD, two langur mothers groom each other, while their infants—a male on the right, a female on the left—explore their immediate world, licking, smelling and touching strange objects.

In Mother's Shadow

Nothing could be more important to the development of an infant Indian langur than its relationship with its mother. During its early weeks, it depends almost completely upon her, and she, in turn, fastens her attentions upon it—although from time to time she will allow the other females to hold and fondle it. Secure in this maternal haven, the infant gradually comes to widen its horizons. Though its first week is spent sleeping and nursing, by its second it is already stumbling about and being restrained by a yank of the tail or leg. At four weeks, tripping over itself, it ventures forth and discovers the world—or at least that part of it within a safe three or four feet (0.9 to 1.2 m) of its mother.

CLUTCHING A DEAD INFANT, an Indian langur shows how strong the maternal drive is in a monkey mother—this one carried the corpse around with her for at least two days.

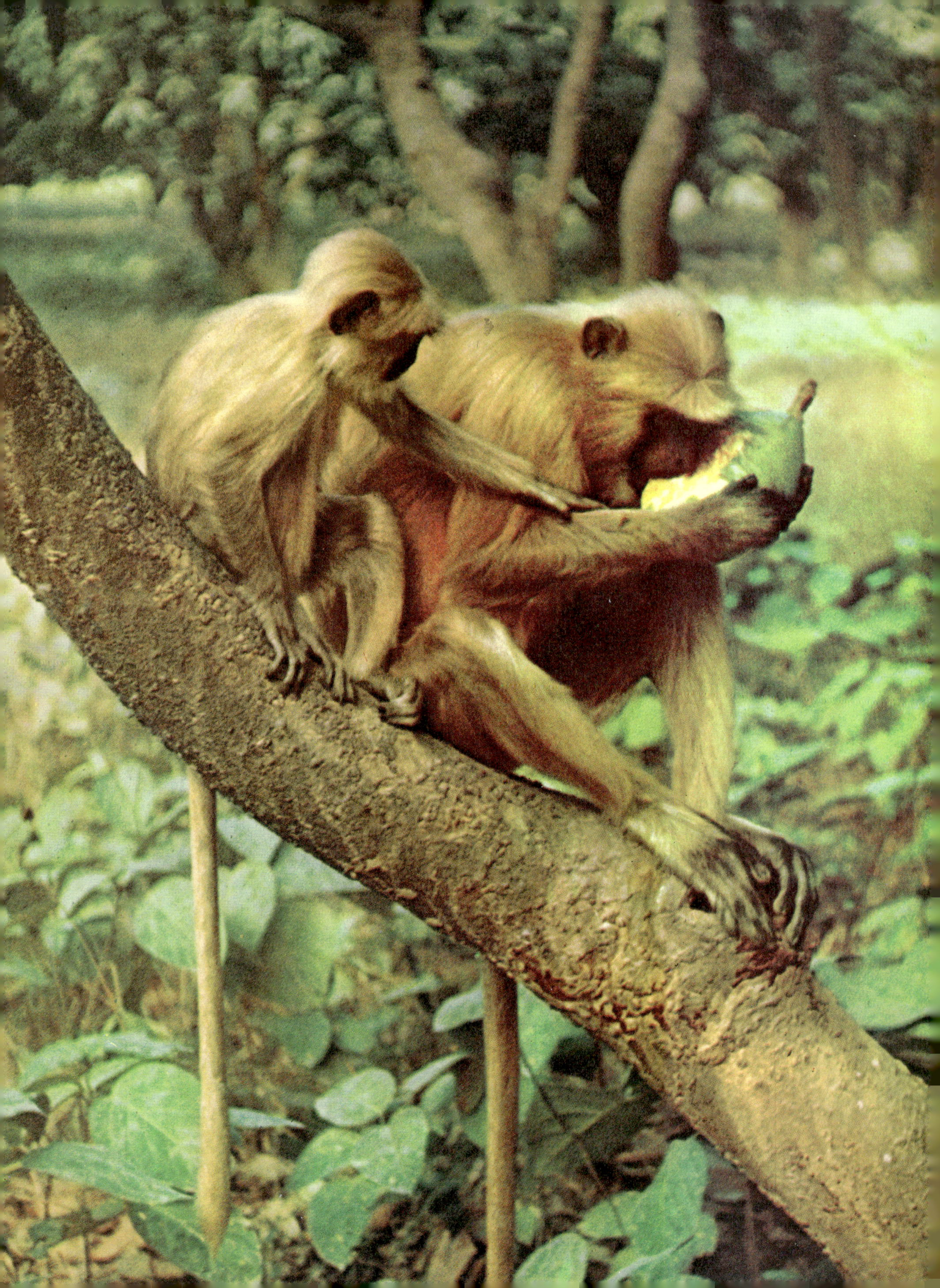

An Ever-widening Circle

As its excursions into the world grow bolder, the maturing infant Indian langur begins to encounter age-mates. At first, with its attention span still short, its coordination still imperfect, it retreats from such social contact, scampering "home" for a swig of milk before settling down to play by itself. But by its third month it need no longer rely entirely on its mother. It now learns how to eat solid foods by sampling those the mother consumes *(opposite)*, and in a demonstration of its increasing freedom, spends more and more time away from her side in the company of other young monkeys. This loosening of ties corresponds to a change in the color of the infant's coat, from brown to light gray. At five months it ranges 20 to 30 feet (6 to 9 m) from its mother for 20 minutes or so at a time, climbing tree trunks and branches and playing. But despite its new-found independence, the infant still is under its mother's care, still under her watchful eye.

AN ALOOF MALE eating alone on a branch reflects the separation the adult males maintain from the infants. Even in times of greatest danger, they generally do not go to their rescue.

AN ENGROSSED FEMALE ignores the pawing of her infant to concentrate on a mango. Sharing food is not part of maternal care: The infant must learn by copying to take care of itself.

HUDDLED TOGETHER, adult females, an infant and a juvenile form a tight social unit. It is in such groupings that the infant has its first prolonged experience with other young monkeys.

Rehearsing for Adulthood

Growing up involves long hours of play, in groups of two, three or more. The young monkeys jump, wrestle, chase each other and pull each others' tails. As they become older, they grow more mischievous, teasing the adult females, jumping on them, bumping up against them, and grabbing their hair or swinging from their dangling tails. By the time Indian langurs reach their 10th month, they are spending upward of four hours a day hard at play and often travel together, rather than with their mothers, when the troop moves from one area to another. Unlike the females, the young males now begin to have contact with the older males—but almost always in the same highly stereotyped manner. Screeching, they first touch the adult, then tensely they mount them, and finally run around and embrace them.

About this time, when life would seem to be at its very best, something untoward happens—the infants begin to be rejected by their mothers as part of the two-to-five-month weaning process. No longer able to run to their mothers at every scare, no longer protected by them when threatened by adults, the weaned infants—or juveniles, as they are called—must learn to solve their own conflicts themselves. And in doing so, they become full-fledged members of the troop—and eventually grown-up monkeys.

ENGAGING IN A LITTLE MONKEY BUSINESS, A YOUNG FEMALE TAKES A SWIPE AT AN ADULT FEMALE'S TAIL—AND THEREBY GIVES AWAY HER AGE, SINCE

A STARTLED JUVENILE, its teeth bared, snarls at an intruder, taking it so much by surprise that it bounds upward. Such threats among the young are often a part of play. Adults threaten by opening their mouths and grunting or belching, by tossing their heads and biting the air, or, when they really mean it, by lunging at each other and slapping the ground.

PLAYFULNESS IS TYPICAL OF SEXUALLY IMMATURE LANGURS. AMONG THE YOUNG, GRABBING TAILS IS A FREQUENT FORM OF PHYSICAL CONTACT

AN ADULT MALE BABOON AT RIGHT WATCHES ATTENTIVELY AS A FIGHT STARTS AMONG THE JUVENILES OF A TROOP IN THE AMBOSELI RESERVE

5 Life in the Group

IN KENYA. IT WILL INTERVENE IN THE FRACAS IF THE YOUNG BABOON BEING CHASED SHOULD, IN TURN, ATTACK THE SMALL JUVENILE AT CENTER

On the side of a steep mountain on the Japanese island of Kyushu, where bushes and trees sprout thick among the boulders, live Japanese macaques of Takasakiyama. They have split up now into smaller units, but when they were intensively studied during the 1940s, they formed one single, integrated unit about 200 strong. Their discipline was surprising. In the morning, the group would set out from its sleeping sites on the upper slopes of the mountain to a feeding station established by Japanese zoologists at the base. They walked always in the same order: the young males frolicking on ahead and at the sides, the dominant males walking in the center, together with the females and infants. They fed always in a similar order of rank: the dominant monkeys first, then the others in descending gradations of status. And at rest, the dominant males, surrounded by females and infants, occupied the most attractive area in the middle of the feeding station, where no subordinate males were allowed to encroach on pain of severe chastisement.

There is no mistaking a dominant male macaque. These are superbly muscled monkeys. Their hair is sleek and carefully groomed, their walk calm, assured and majestic. They move in apparent disregard of the lesser monkeys who scatter at their approach. For to obstruct the path of a dominant male or even to venture, when unwelcome, too near to him is an act of defiance, and macaques learn young that such a challenge will draw a heavy punishment.

To be dominant means to a monkey that it gets the best of everything. It is easy to test the status of two macaques: All one has to do is toss some desirable object between them and see which one takes it. Once, for example, a tangerine was thrown midway between Jupiter and Titan, the two most dominant males of the Takasakiyama group. While Titan remained still, Jupiter, showing absolutely no sign of hurry, rose, walked calmly over and took the tangerine. Another was thrown, this time right between Titan's feet. Once more Jupiter padded over and took it while Titan stood immobile. Later, another tangerine was thrown and it rolled several feet away from Jupiter to the number five male, Monku, who was injudicious enough to stop it. With this implied claim to the tangerine, Monku's act was sheer defiance. Jupiter rushed at Monku and Monku promptly fled.

Jupiter did not press home his attack. For just as he was about to be cornered, Monku stopped, turned his hindquarters and stood passive while Jupiter calmly mounted him, as he would mount a female. Among these monkeys, mounting is the supreme assertion of dominance and presenting the hindquarters is its complementary admission of inferiority. By submitting to Jupiter's mount, Monku was admitting his lower status and seeking to stave off an attack. And Jupiter, having asserted his dominance, could afford to spare Monku from actual physical chastisement.

This kind of symbolic assertion of power is common among monkeys. It saves the dominant animals from wasting their energy and the subordinate ones from suffering unnecessary pain. Yet not to assert dominance is to risk losing it: Power not exercised is all too likely to degenerate into power lost. Suppose a dominant macaque does not want a tangerine. If he allows an inferior to take it, his charity might be construed as weakness. Symbolic assertion is the ideal solution. When Pan, the number three male of the Takasakiyama group, did not want a tangerine that was tossed between himself and Monku, the number five, he first went over and mounted Monku. His dominance made clear, he then allowed Monku to take the tangerine.

Every morning, when the dominant males reached the feeding station, the animals of lower rank were mounted by animals of higher rank to show who was master. This kind of regular status parade has never been observed among any other group. It was, no doubt, a symptom of the exaggerated competitiveness that afflicts monkeys when they must crowd in to feed in a restricted area. But among all monkeys that have been studied in the wild, a dominance hierarchy does exist, forming a framework on which all social relationships depend. Take, for example, space. One would imagine that in the forests or on the open savanna a baboon, say, could have all the space it wanted. Actually the amount of space a baboon can command directly reflects its status. A dominant animal controls the space around it; a dominant baboon occupies the best site when a group is resting, and asserts an exclusive right to more space than its inferiors. It can invade an inferior's space as a right, whereas no inferior would dare to venture into its space without first making a gesture of appeasement—such as a smacking of the lips—to show its intentions were friendly. It knocks at the door, as it were, before entering. If the dominant monkey is in an irritable mood, the others give it a wide berth. If it is feeling amiable, they come closer. One can, after all, sometimes chat with the boss.

Or take grooming, perhaps the most commonly observed form of social contact between simian primates. One monkey grooms another by picking through its hair to clean out the dirt and the parasites. Physically, grooming is simply a cleaning mechanism, and it is highly effective, as one can see by comparing lions and baboons which inhabit the same areas of the East African savanna. Although lions are cleanly animals, the backs of their necks, where they cannot reach to clean, are thick with ticks, whereas the baboons' hair is totally free of them.

But to higher primates, grooming is far more than a form of hygiene. It is the most important means to social interaction among members of a group, and it serves a variety of purposes. While it usually occurs as part of the dominance ritual, grooming seems to be an effective instrument for reducing tension of all kinds, particularly among the aggressive baboons and macaques. At other times, it serves simply as an enjoyable pastime when groups are not in search of food. Much as humans gather in conversation groups, these monkeys gather in grooming groups. The same function is served—the maintenance of friendly social relations. Being groomed is obviously an enjoyable process. The groomed animal sits or lies in an attitude of beatific contentment, like a woman having her hair combed or a man enjoying a scalp massage in a barber's chair. Most of the grooming is done by females. Equals groom each other in approximately equal amounts, while subordinates groom their social superiors much more frequently than they are groomed in turn. As one might expect, dominant males get the most grooming and give the least. There is, however, a semblance of reciprocity, which might be called "pump-priming," in a female's grooming of a male. After she has worked over him for perhaps 10 minutes, she will turn and sit, inviting him to groom her. The male obliges by grooming her for about 30 seconds, then turns indolently and is groomed by the female for another 10 minutes. The significant function of grooming in monkey society is that it cuts across hierarchical lines, establishing friendly relationships without reference to dominance status.

The existence of a hierarchy helps to assure order and discipline, and these things are important among monkeys just as they are among humans. They permit, first, the making of quick decisions. Whenever people are brought together, they will only be able to reach decisions quickly if some kind of hierarchy is established. Every jury needs its foreman; every football team a quarterback.

The same is true of monkeys. Some animal has to decide when the group shall move, which direction it shall follow, what action it shall take to avoid predators. Some form of leadership is essential if action is to be taken quickly, and the hierarchy has come into existence to avoid the total inertia or, at best, the protracted wrangling that is the inevitable consequence of total equality.

LIFE IN THE GROUP

The second purpose achieved by the hierarchy is the preservation of the peace. For total anarchy is another consequence of absolute equality among any group of primates living in close contact with each other. And if the primates are aggressive, anarchy will keep them in a continual state of turmoil. The rigidity of the hierarchy varies, therefore, with the aggressiveness of the species. Though arboreal monkeys, such as langurs, are organized into a hierarchy, it is a comparatively benevolent one. A dominant langur will assert itself over its inferiors; it will push them aside to get the best sleeping site or right of way along a trail. But langurs assert and maintain their status more by bluff than by force, and they almost never get involved in actual physical conflict. The behavior of a group of gorillas illustrates equally well how an effective hierarchy can be maintained among animals which have little tendency toward violence. Every group has a leader, and each subordinate possesses its own individual status. But though the gorillas inside a group occasionally squabble and bicker, as langurs also do, they seldom if ever settle arguments by force.

To turn from gorillas to baboons and macaques is rather like leaving a Sunday school picnic and driving into an army compound. These monkeys have acquired an aggressive temperament as a defense against predators, and aggressiveness cannot be turned on and off like a faucet. It is an integral part of the monkeys' personalities, so deeply rooted that it makes them potential aggressors in every situation. A macaque does not struggle to dominate its fellows because it consciously desires to sit at the center of the group and enjoy its pick of the females. It dominates every monkey it can because it is a fighting animal.

So urgent a drive to dominate means inevitably that any group of baboons or macaques is constantly threatened from within by the danger of disruptive conflict. They live, as they normally do, at peace only because that peace is enforced by the dominant males. In addition to defending the group against external attack, these males serve also as a police force, and whenever a squabble breaks out one of them is liable to come running over to stop it.

A dominant male does not usually have to use force. No society could survive if its rulers constantly had to deploy their maximum strength to impose order. If any government employed its full armory to keep the peace, there would be nobody left to govern, and if the dominant macaques, for example, used the full power of their canines, they would kill off the rest of the group. Instead they preserve order through a system of symbolic threats backed up by their canines, which play rather the same role as the gun in a policeman's holster.

Suppose that a dominant male is annoyed by a squabble. Its first reaction will be to stare at the offenders. The stare is long and steady, with the animal's whole attention concentrated behind it. If the stare is not enough to quell the trouble, it pulls back the skin on the top of its scalp, drawing back its ears and opening its eyes wide. The movement is a preparation for a fight. It protects the ears from possible bites and allows the animal to see with maximum clarity. A dog, of course, lays back its ears in preparation for a fight in the same way. But these monkeys have carried the process a step further. The preparation has become ritualized to serve as a threat, like a man taking off his coat when an argument gets hot. If the facial threat is still not enough to impose order, the male stands erect, with its body tensed and the fur on its mane stiffened. A baboon may grunt, take a few steps forward, slap the ground threateningly and take a few more steps. Finally, if it still feels defied it will give chase. When it has caught the offending monkey, it may simply pin its inferior to the ground to

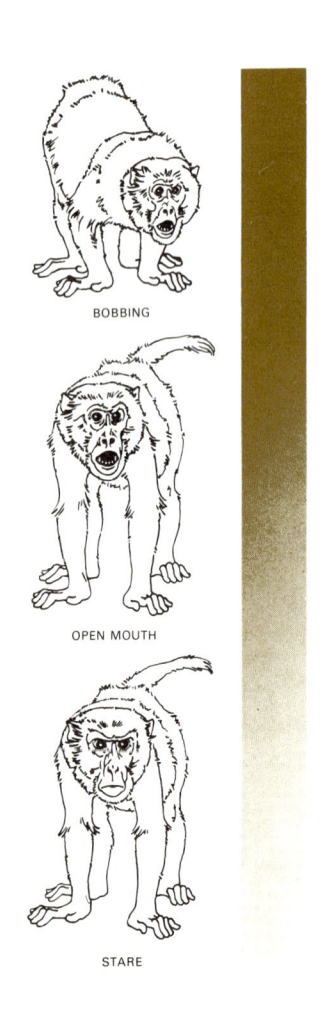

THREAT THERMOMETER

Macaques express their aggressive feelings with three basic attitudes. These are of increasing severity as the colored graph at the right of the drawings shows. First, and mildest, is the stare—a hard look serving to intimidate. If it does not, the macaque adds extra menace by opening its mouth and showing its teeth. If the target of this enmity is still unimpressed, the last and presumably most terrifying gesture reinforces the facial threats—a bobbing up and down of the head. This is the climax; from then on there can be only fighting or fleeing.

show superiority, like a wrestler who wins by pinning his opponent's shoulders. If sufficiently aroused, it will bite, but even this bite is directed to the thick skin at the neck and very rarely draws blood.

All this happens very quickly, but usually it does not all happen, especially if the threatening male is clearly dominant. The higher its status, the fewer threats it has to employ. The threatened monkeys normally either stop squabbling and assume an innocent air, or else they run. On being threatened by a definitely dominant monkey, a subordinate is likely to display submission. Confronted with the fixed stare, it will look away. Faced with a possible charge, it is likely to crouch close to the ground, its head turned away. And if it flees and is chased, it will cringe away from the threatened bite or try to avoid punishment by presenting its hindquarters, as Monku did to Jupiter.

The whole elaborate structure of dominance and submission, of threat and surrender, is surely terribly familiar. It is like a preview, a parody of status relationships between humans. The disciplinary glare of the dominant male closely resembles the stare of a schoolmaster enforcing order in class. The subordinate looking away is the weak man, trying to avoid the challenging glance of a bully in a bar; its flight and surrender crouch are those of a schoolboy begging a stronger boy not to hurt him. The dominant male's authoritative stride is like a general's; its subordinates, carefully stepping back out of its path, could be junior officers. And its decisions, because of the fear it inspires, go largely unquestioned, as do those of a corporation president delivered to subexecutives who are reluctant to disagree with him.

Since the dominant males get the best of everything, why do the subordinate ones put up with life inside the group? Why don't they leave? Why, in other words, does the group stay together in the first place? Until half a dozen or so years ago, it was generally assumed that the members of a group were bound to each other by the urge to satisfy their sexual needs. In many mammals—deer are among the most familiar examples—males and females are together only during the breeding season, forming separate societies during the rest of the year. Since it was generally believed that monkeys were active sexually the year around, it was argued that sex was a logical explanation for their staying together. Actually, as recent field studies have shown, many monkeys breed only in a specific season—for example, the rhesus and Japanese macaques—so this simple explanation has had to be abandoned: The closely knit monkey societies continue even when there is no primary sexual activity.

THUS, once again, the study of captive animals proved a misleading guide. In the controlled environment of a laboratory, a monkey's endocrine system, which governs its sex hormones, is not subject to seasonal variations, and the monkey can copulate all the year around. In the wild, its hormones are influenced much more heavily by such external factors as day length, humidity and diet, and the result is that he copulates during only a few months of the year. This is one means of ensuring that the young will be born at an auspicious time, when they are most likely to survive.

Even if the males could copulate all year around, the females cannot—or at least, they do not. Consider, as illustration, the female langur. She is not sexually receptive when she is pregnant—approximately one quarter of her adult life. Nor is she sexually receptive when she is lactating or nursing her young—another third of her adulthood, or, normally, when weaning them—another fifth. Even in the brief periods between pregnancies, she is

LIFE IN THE GROUP

sexually receptive for only five to seven days in every month, which means that, *in toto*, she is sexually active for only 1 to 3 per cent of her adult life.

Given these circumstances, sex can hardly be the principal element that holds a group together. The urge to protect and to be protected is far more significant. More eyes and ears are more likely to detect a predator, and a warning call from one animal may save several. A group aids through distraction too: The predator that swerves from one primate to another loses both. Most important of all, the group provides a secure environment in which young monkeys can grow up in relative safety until they have learned enough and are strong enough to assume their own places in society. Feeding also binds primates together. If food is abundant but uniformly dispersed in large pockets throughout an area, many primates form large aggregations. In this way they can benefit from one or two individuals' success at finding food or they can cooperatively stalk their prey. Primates also band together because they enjoy the sense of ease that comes from living among familiar faces. To monkeys and apes, as to men and women, old friends are the best friends.

Few other primate species are as social as the baboons and macaques. However put-upon it may be, a baboon or macaque tries to be loyal to its group. Observers are learning that it is quite common for baboons and macaques to change groups, but most of them probably pass their entire lives in the group into which they were born. Firm though group discipline may be, the existence of a subordinate need not be intolerable. Living together from birth, the members of a group learn how to get along. Those who cannot stand each other keep at a distance. When tensions do arise, the monkeys involved usually stay apart until tempers have cooled. Only the attempts of one male to displace another in the hierarchy precipitate really vicious fighting, and such occasions are rare. They crop up perhaps once every few months inside even a large group. But when every monkey knows its place, daily life is fairly peaceful.

For it is uncertainty that creates conflict. The hamadryas baboons in the London zoo fought with such savagery largely because they were strangers trapped and brought together from different groups, and they were too closely confined to avoid each other until differences could be settled more amicably. In the wild it is the females who do most of the bickering and squabbling. For while the male hierarchies are rigid, the position of the females is constantly shifting: Their status is less clearly defined. This is largely due to the fact that the behavior of a female is closely tied to the different phases of her reproductive cycle. As long as a female has a young infant she is so closely protected by the adult males that she is not subject to attacks from other females; during motherhood she is, in effect, outside the female dominance hierarchy. A female in estrus is quite another matter. The word estrus is derived from the Greek *oistros*, a gadfly, and implies the frenzied behavior of an animal stung by such an insect. The estrous female is far more active than normal, both attacking other females and being attacked by them more frequently. Furthermore, when she is most attractive to the adult males, at the height of her estrous period, she is often under the protection of an accompanying male and can use the status she derives from him to dominate a female normally superior to her. The result of this unstable female hierarchy, and its frequent disruptions, is the constant minor bickering characteristic of female baboons and macaques. Despite this, adult females of a group do have a basic rank and can be subdivided into dominant- and subordinate-female clusters. A few even sit with

DOMINANCE IN LANGURS

The order of dominance among male langurs is a relaxed one, with the most dominant male (here enclosed in a rectangle) at the top. In this actual field study by Phyllis Jay, Rip, shown in black, was the leader of the male social order, a position he held uncontested for months (before). Then gradually tension developed between Rip and Slate, shown in color. Slate pressured Rip with whoops and belches until finally, after about three weeks, he had taken Rip's place (after).

dominant males. But none ever quite commands the full authority of a male.

Whatever the cause, quarrels are always disruptive, and continuous disruption would endanger the group's safety. The peace therefore must be maintained, and among baboons and macaques, peace is simply another word for preservation of the status quo. Like the rulers in a human society, it is the dominant males who have the greatest vested interest in preserving it. They do not, of course, labor to do so out of conscious decision. Since the dominant males do most of the breeding, many of the animals in the group are related to them and it is therefore in their genetic self-interest to protect other group members. Nonetheless, the effect is the same as if the dominant males were members of a human aristocracy deliberately working to preserve their inherited privileges.

Aristocracy, of course, not dictatorship. One of the most intriguing aspects of baboon and Japanese macaque social life is that the dominant males form a ruling clique and act in concert to maximize their strength. Individually, a member of the clique might be defeated by some male outside it, and the status quo seriously disturbed. In self-preservation, therefore, or out of personal loyalty, the members of the Establishment back up each other. When a subordinate male of the Takasakiyama group, thinking that no dominant males were present, was injudicious enough to venture into the feeding area and bite a female, he was instantly attacked by the number three male, Pan, who happened to be sitting behind a rock. Pan, enforcing the power of the elite, was immediately backed up by two other dominant males, and together the three severely injured the rash intruder. Inside the elite itself a similar rule holds; the dominant males support the most dominant member. When the number five male, Monku, stopped the tangerine that Jupiter wanted, Jupiter gave chase and was assisted by Pan. Precisely the same kind of discipline by collaboration is practiced among baboons. One often sees two dominant males threatening an inferior: staring together, slapping the ground together and charging together.

Among birds and other mammals—even other monkeys and apes—that are organized into hierarchies, the status of each individual animal seems to depend on the efforts of that individual alone. The system of rule by clique or Establishment is peculiar to baboons and macaques, and one can easily see why it came into existence. Because the monkeys are potentially so aggressive, the peace in a large group can only be preserved by a force stronger than any one animal could command. Moreover, the existence of a dominant clique also provides a solution to the problem of succession which bedevils monkeys and apes as it does human societies. Rule by a single individual is always hazardous. When Cromwell died, the government he had established soon disintegrated. The murder of Caesar plunged Rome into anarchy. The same kind of anarchy is liable to afflict nonhuman primates which rely on individual leadership, as gorillas do. But what happens when a gorilla leader dies? Frequently the group splits up, its individual members going off to join other groups. And if the leader should suddenly be killed by hunters, the group may not be able to function in this crisis. "I have seen native hunters," wrote the hunter Fred Merfield, "having dispatched the Old Man, surround females and beat them over the head with sticks. They don't even try to get away, and it is most pitiful to see them putting their arms over their heads to ward off the blows, making no attempt at retaliation."

Because they have for so long been in much graver danger from predators, any comparable breakdown in leadership among baboons and macaques could,

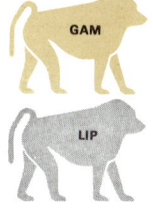

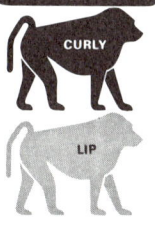

DOMINANCE IN BABOONS

In contrast to the langurs, male baboons are aggressive, their hierarchy dominated by groups or pairs best able to combine to rule. Curly and Humbert were such a ruling pair (before), aiding one another when males like Gam threatened their leadership. Then one day Humbert disappeared and Curly was left without his ally. While others floundered among themselves for dominance, Gam and Lone, a male from outside the troop, combined and emerged as the new leaders (after).

if repeated often enough, have seriously imperiled their ability to survive. The group of dominant males constitutes insurance against such breakdowns. If one dominant male falls sick or is injured or killed, the others simply carry on, incorporating other males into the ruling elite as they wish—or of necessity if the challenge of a subordinate on his way up becomes too strong to be resisted. But how does a monkey get into this clique? The question is surely a familiar one to any student of human history and the answer appears to be that entry is won by precisely the same qualities which have traditionally qualified humans for membership in ruling groups.

STRENGTH, first of all, simple brute strength. From the moment it joins its peers in a play group, the young baboon or macaque is continually fighting and jockeying for position. During its subadulthood, it forces its way steadily up the hierarchy, knocking out its rivals like a heavyweight on his way to the top. The battles can be vicious and they are decided by sheer fighting capacity. But muscles and canines are not the only elements involved in the power struggle. The status of a baboon or a macaque is affected also by the strength of its drive and the degree of its self-assurance.

Hereditary right, or at least hereditary backing, appears to be a very important element in effecting an entry into the ruling group. Every male baboon and every male macaque has a mother, and each of these mothers has her place in the female social hierarchy. The females occupying the lower rungs of the hierarchy are the ones most likely to be tense, nervous, continually threatened and sometimes attacked by their superiors. It is in this atmosphere that their offspring are raised. Almost certainly, they will take on the attitude of subjection they perceive in their mothers. They grow up afflicted with a sense of inferiority. They lack the style, the manner, the habit and the attitude of the domineering animal; and, as if these drawbacks were not enough, they also lack the entree to the dominant group.

Somewhat different is the situation of a male offspring of a dominant female, if surrounded by confident, dominant males and females. In this exclusive atmosphere, the infant is likely to acquire the same sense of self-assurance and superiority that its elders display. The family support such a young monkey enjoys continues long past childhood. Field studies have been able to establish which members of a group are related to which others. And in the study of the rhesus macaques on the island of Cayo Santiago, most of the monkeys were tattooed with numbers shortly after birth so that records could be kept of their relationships for several generations. According to a study by Don Sade, an anthropologist from the University of California, the social groupings of the Cayo Santiago macaques are governed very largely by kinship. Mothers spend most of their time with their offspring and the offspring also tend to stick together not only in their youth but long after they have reached adulthood. The result is that any subgroup of the Cayo Santiago monkeys is likely to consist of close relatives—of brothers and sisters and nephews and nieces—so that, for example, the female seen grooming the dominant male of a group often turns out to be his mother or his sister.

As masters of the groups, the dominant males usually copulate only with the most alluring females: those who are at the height of estrus. When a female baboon starts coming into estrus, she does not at first attract the dominant males, but only the subadults. As her estrus proceeds, however, the female becomes more attractive to the adult males. With baboons, for instance, the males can observe her condition the more readily because her sexual skin, distended by water retained underneath it, swells up until, at the height of estrus, she looks as if she is sitting on a cushion several inches deep. At this point, the dominant males are ready to accept her. The arrangement is advantageous because she is now ovulating and the infant she bears, sired by a dominant male, will have the best possible genetic start.

Generalizations about monkeys are as dangerous as generalizations about men and women. To much that has been said about group organization among baboons and macaques, the hamadryas baboons form an exception. No species better illustrates the rule that social behavior, like anatomy, comes into existence as an adaptation to environment. For the unique social pattern that obtains among hamadryas baboons may very well have been acquired to meet the unique conditions under which they live. All other monkeys—and apes— live in areas where there are normally adequate supplies of food and, always, plenty of trees, so that the members of any one group can easily find safe sleeping sites at a distance from other groups. The hamadryas do not. They are scattered all over northeast Africa and Arabia—for example, places like the near-desert country in the highlands of eastern Ethiopia—living in areas where both food and sleeping sites are in short supply. This situation produces conflicting pressures. The shortage of sleeping sites forces large numbers of the hamadryas to come together at night. Only in that way can they take full advantage of the few sites—such as rocks jutting out from a sheer cliff face— where predators cannot reach them. On the other hand, the scarcity of food may very likely influence the hamadryas baboons to split up into small foraging groups during the day.

Caught between these two forces, the hamadryas baboons appear to have compromised. At night as many as 750 of them will come together to sleep on the rocks. Then, when day breaks, they leave the cliffs in groups of 30 to 50, much like other baboons. But the basic hamadryas social unit is smaller still. It consists of only one male, a few females and their young. The members of these one-male units stick very close together at all times. During the day they may forage in fairly close association with other similar units or they may wander a bit on their own. But they stay always together—even at night, when surrounded by other groups, just as a family on an outing to Coney Island remains a unit though surrounded by thousands of other people.

Still, any family is liable to get split up when caught in a crowd. Facing this danger, the hamadryas baboons have acquired a highly individual form of behavior to guard against it. The males are exceedingly possessive, and when the hamadryas baboons leave their sleeping sites, each male walks in front of his own little group, constantly looking around to check that his females are following and have not linked up with another male. The younger, less confident males glance back the most often and, if a female drops back too far, they run back and discipline her with a bite on the neck. The spectacle of the hamadryas baboons leaving their sleeping sites is often enlivened by the sight of an anxious male running back and hunting for a female; then, after he has found her and inflicted his bite, by the sight of the screaming female, following close behind him. For she does not really want to escape; the need for cohesiveness has developed in her too strong an urge to follow a male. Unlike the hamadryas baboons, the dominant males of baboon groups which inhabit the savanna neither need nor make any effort to keep their females near them; nor do dominant gorillas or, so far as is known, dominant macaques. Such effort is unnecessary because the females want to stay as close to them as they can get. Whenever the adult males prepare to set off, the females immediately follow, and only rarely does a female baboon leave her group.

Some male baboons and macaques, however, do leave their group if their position in it is made intolerable by the leaders. Possibly their physical strength makes them a danger to the elite; possibly personal dislike is involved. A male that finds itself in this unhappy position will be subjected to constant pressure, set upon, harassed and threatened. The situation will be familiar to anyone who ever felt himself to be an outsider at school. In the end, the unfortunate male may be driven out by force, which is what happened to the number six male of a large baboon group in southern Zambia, who was literally expelled by the top five. The same day, it joined another group, fought and defeated its lone male, and took over its position—very much like a man who is fired by one company and promptly gets a much better job in another.

More often, a baboon or macaque that leaves its group does so because the pressures gradually become so unpleasant that it finds leaving more comfortable than staying. One such case occurred among a small baboon troop in Kenya, in which the number two male was continually harassed by the number one. Gradually it moved to the periphery of the group and then into the periphery of another. There it stayed for about a couple of weeks, gradually working in closer until, after a few indecisive fights with the males, it joined the group at about place three or four. Because baboon and macaque groups are so cohesive, a male that leaves one group may have to follow another for weeks or even months before it is finally able to enter, and some males probably never do manage to break in.

YET, for all their intense cohesiveness, baboon and macaque groups do sometimes split up. As the generations pass and the numbers grow, the group may swell to such a size that some kind of a breakup becomes inevitable. It was instability caused by excessive size that finally split the Takasakiyama group. Quite peacefully, when the group had swelled to more than 500, some of the females took their infants and left the central feeding area to join the young males at the periphery. Gradually, the two sections drifted farther apart. They left to eat at different times and spent less and less time together. Finally, instead of returning to their usual sleeping place, the seceders chose a separate area to spend the night in, and the break became complete.

The break was quite peaceful. All the dominant males, from Jupiter down, remained together, and the seceding unit was led by six young males, one of whom became the leader. But the breakup of a group can also be precipitated by internal dissension involving the dominant males. Another group—also of Japanese macaques—has been seen to break up, and in this case the split was triggered when the number three male was displaced by a rising young aggressor. Following this shift in power, severe fighting broke out in the group, and a quarter of the animals—about 50 of them—stopped coming to the feeding place. Led by the deposed and rebellious number three and by another younger male, they formed a separate group of their own. Significantly, the mutinous monkeys obeyed the rules of dominance much more rigidly than the original group had done, as often happens in human society when a revolution occurs and the rebels then emphasize discipline as a counter to the anarchy which is so likely to attend rebellion.

A RELAXED FEMALE ENCOURAGES A DOMINANT MALE TO GROOM HER, WHILE A LESS DOMINANT MALE WATCHES FROM A PROPER DISTANCE

The Aggressive Baboons

Unlike the arboreal monkeys, the savanna baboons in Africa must constantly guard against predators. To do so they live in large troops that are organized along lines of dominance and subordination. Despite the intense competition that exists between young males and those in authority, each troop, cemented by a desire to protect its females and young, honors the rule of a central hierarchy.

THE DEEP BUT FAST-HEALING WOUND ON THIS YOUNG MALE'S SNOUT BESPEAKS A FIGHT WITH AN OBVIOUSLY MORE DOMINANT MALE

THE RELAXED YAWN of an old male exposes broken, rotting teeth—a dead giveaway of its advanced age. However, it is still included in the central hierarchy, despite its worn canines.

If Looks Could Kill

The ability of one male baboon to dominate others is based upon its age, its strength and aggressiveness and the size and condition of its canine teeth. All these enable it to assert itself whenever necessary, which it does by using increasingly severe threats to maintain its authority. The most spectacular threat is shown opposite: Here a young male, shoulders hunched and mouth agape, is giving a canine threat, the effect of which it heightens by flashing its white eyelids. Accompanied often by grunting, such a threat is generally sufficient to bring a subordinate quickly to bay—but occasionally, as the wound on the face of the baboon above attests, it is not enough, and actual violence erupts.

THE FIERCE GAPE OF A MALE IN FULL PRIME DISPLAYS CANINES SEVERAL TIMES THE SIZE OF A FEMALE'S

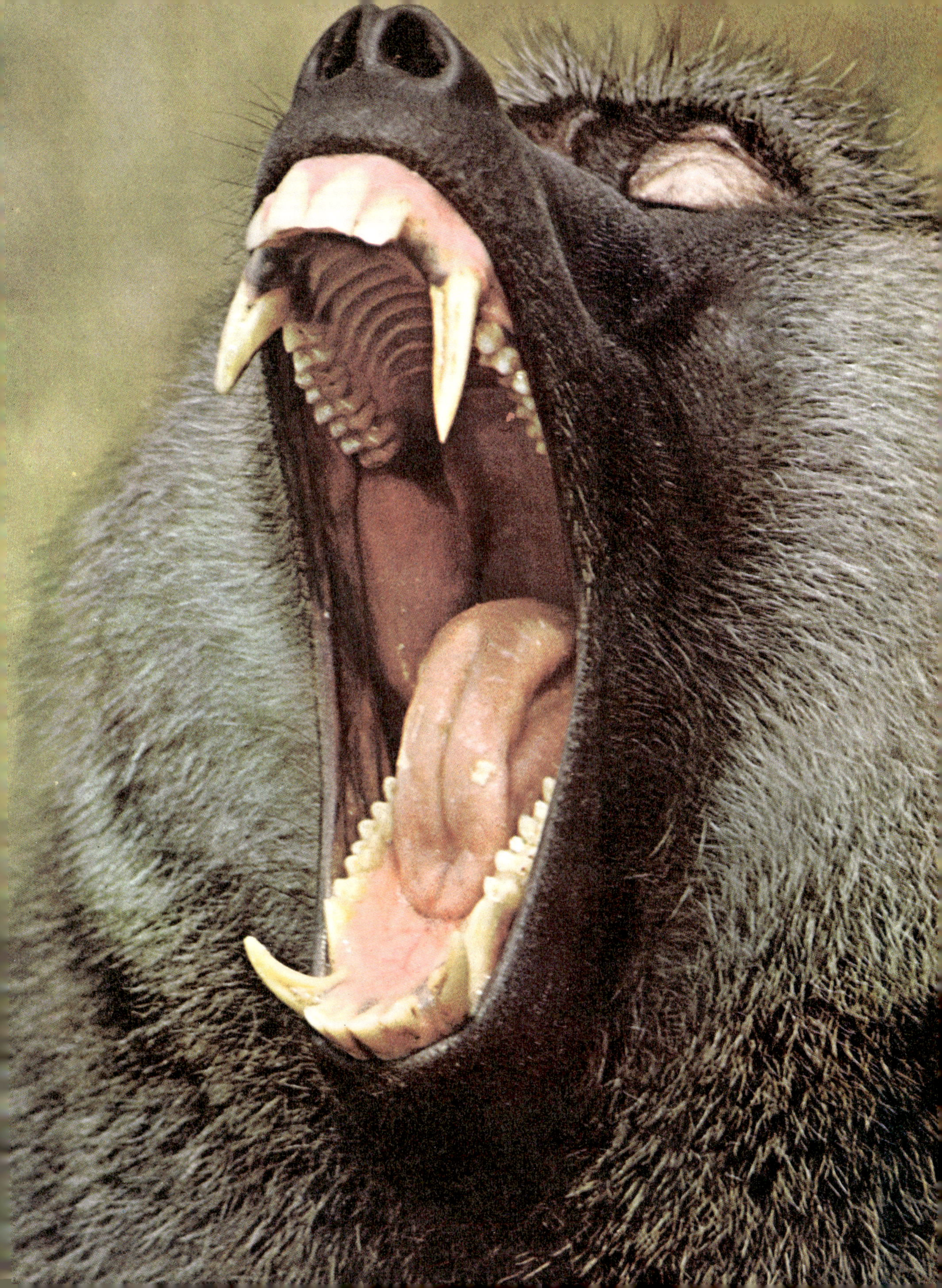

AGE FACES YOUTH in a brief dominance flareup. Although it has turned to face its younger, stronger adversary, the old baboon at right is extremely frightened—as its screams and erect tail clearly indicate—but for the moment it stands its ground.

HARASSED BY A YOUNG MALE, A FEMALE (CENTER) ATTEMPTS TO GET THE SUPPORT OF A DOMINANT MALE AGAINST HER TORMENTOR

Struggling for Room at the Top

The process by which a male baboon achieves a position of dominance in the troop is long and arduous. First the infant male must establish itself in relation to its peers. Then, as a juvenile, it begins to harass the adult females *(below)*, who are always subordinate to the adult males. Only after passing through this phase does it finally reach a point where it is old enough, strong enough and skilled enough to make its way into the circle of adult males *(left)*. But as many as half a dozen years may pass before it enters the upper level of the male hierarchy. The climb to the top involves numerous attempts to displace other more dominant males, largely through a kind of persistent baiting that sometimes leads to fights, and sometimes even to the backing down of an older and previously higher-ranking animal. Occasionally a threatened male will turn on a subordinate and vent its frustration on this scapegoat; the subordinate may then turn on a male of still lower rank, and so on down the line, in a clear-cut demonstration of who's who in male baboon society.

PUT IN HIS PLACE, the old male continues to scream in an attempt to get aid; the opponent strolls calmly away.

BACKED BY MALE STRENGTH, THE SCREECHING FEMALE TURNS WITH IMPUNITY ON THE JUVENILE AND TOGETHER THEY CHASE HIM OFF

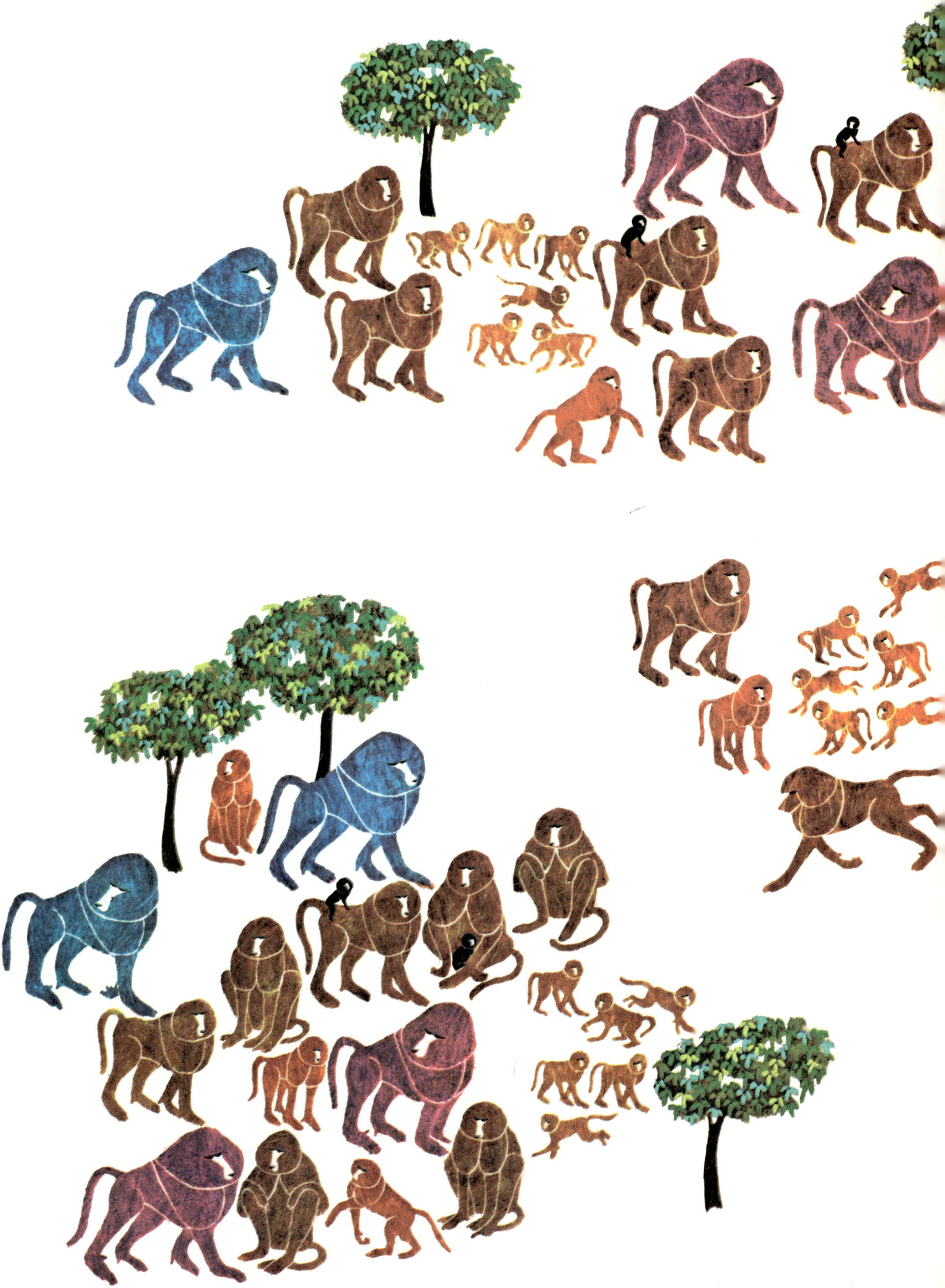

Patterns of Defense

Living out in the open as they do in predator-patrolled country, baboons must be ready at all times and in all situations to defend themselves. The diagram above shows how a troop —here reduced in numbers for simplicity's sake—would be organized for defense when moving to a feeding area or waterhole, at rest or on the offensive. The dominant males on which the burden of defense falls are colored purple, the subordinate males blue, the females brown, the weaned juveniles rust, the younger juveniles tan and the infants black. When a baboon troop is on the move *(top)*, the subordinate males take up positions at the front and rear of the group like expendable outriders. The females and infants stay in the center with the strongest males close by. At rest *(left)*, the troop tends to keep much the same order it had on the march. The dominant males, the females and the infants are still in the center, but the juveniles are now romping through the troop or playing together at the edge of it. On the offensive *(bottom)*, the dominant males emerge from the heart of the troop and take positions out in front, where they lead the other males in action against a predator while the females and young retreat.

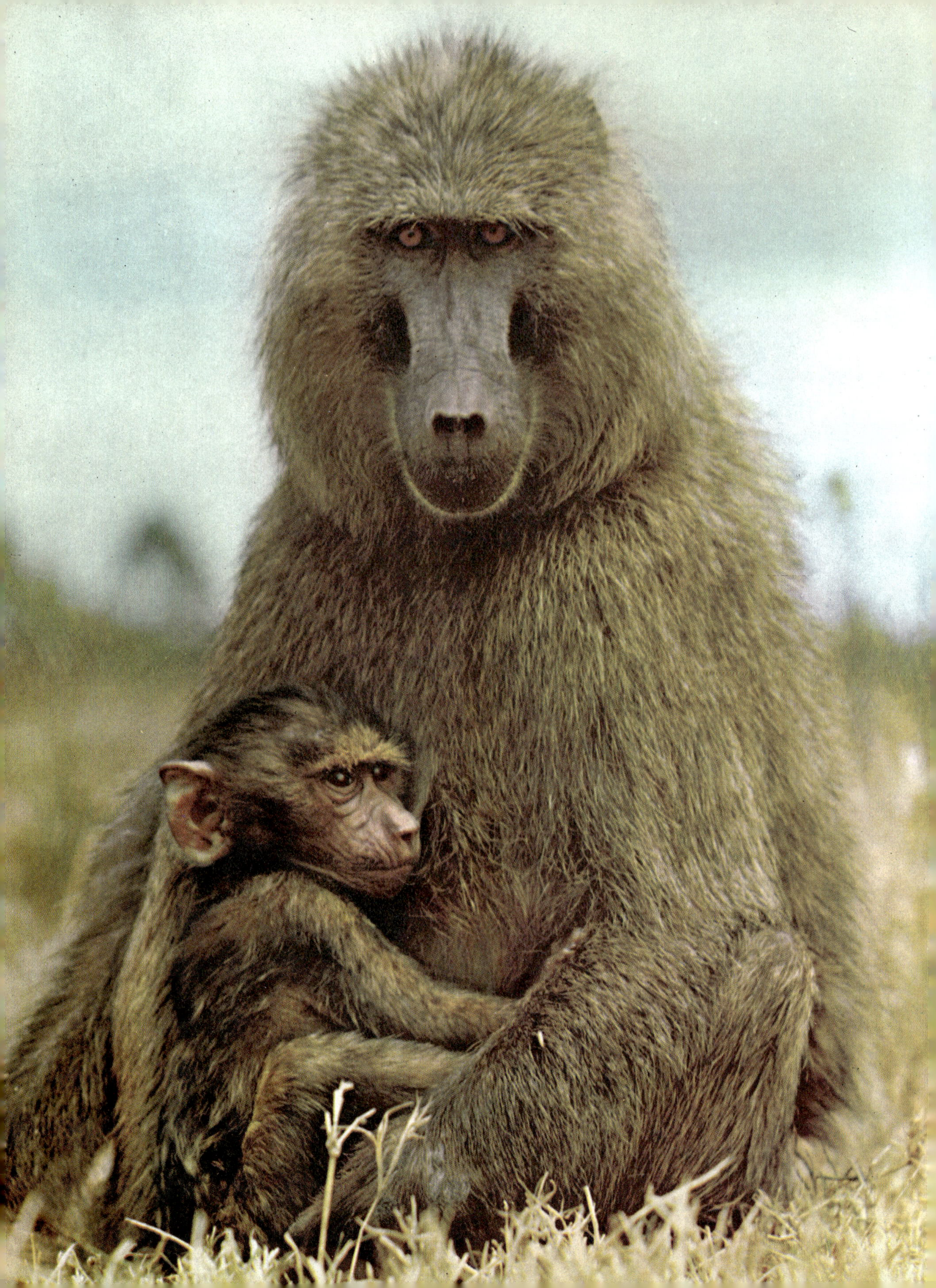

THE EARLIEST RIDING POSITION taken by an infant baboon is demonstrated here by a three-to-four-month-old that hangs upside down from its mother's belly, clinging to her hair.

A FEW WEEKS LATER, the infant abandons its berth under its mother and attempts to ride on her back. But lacking dexterity, it must lie across her and hold on with its hands and feet.

A Mother's Place

A dominance hierarchy also exists among the adult female baboons, although it is a much less rigid one. Unlike a male, a female can rise to the top quite easily—all she need do is give birth. From that moment on, she—or rather, her infant—becomes a focus of interest, the other females and even the males coming forward to look at the newborn. Mother and infant move immediately to the heart of the troop, there to gain the protection of the dominant males in the central hierarchy. With her new importance, the mother is all but immune from the threats of other troop members, and in this sheltered atmosphere, gives herself over to her infant, who will pass through many of the same stages of development as the infant langur discussed in the preceding chapter.

AT ABOUT FIVE MONTHS, the new position mastered, the infant sits astride its mother, nibbling a stem and bracing itself against her tail. When she runs, however, it lies down flat.

SUCKLING, AN INFANT BABOON PRESSES UP TO ITS MOTHER, WHO WILL NURSE IT FOR ALMOST A YEAR

AN AFFECTIONATE THREESOME—a nursing infant, a grooming female and an adult male—demonstrates the basic tranquillity of relations within a baboon troop. Because of the attraction they hold for adults, infants help bind the members together, gentling even the most aggressive males. Grooming, a social act that knows no social boundaries, has a like effect.

IRRESISTIBLY DRAWN by the sight of an infant, a female approaches the more dominant mother in a properly submissive manner, with rump lowered to denote her friendly intentions.

TUGGING AT A LEG, a young male competes with an older male for an infant—in contrast to the indifference of langur males. Such vying may get rough but never really harmful.

RADIATING POWER, a dominant male strides toward a group of subordinates and elicits an immediate response from three infants that cringe in recognition of his status. Wherever he goes in the troop, such a male has the respect of all members up to 10 feet (3 m) ahead.

THE WAYS OF DISCIPLINE employed by baboons in rearing the young are shown here in an encounter between an adult male and an obstreperous juvenile. Punishment is swift and sure *(above)* as the dominant male grabs hold of the erring youngster and gives it a bite on the neck. Such treatment of the young is not as brutal as it looks—the male's teeth fail

SITTING DOWN, and thus assuring them of his friendliness, the dominant male now is an object of great attraction to the infants. Chances are he will even engage with them in play, wrestling or letting them climb over him—or at least tolerating attempts to engage him in play.

even to break the skin. Its effect, however, is convincing: The juvenile cowers on the ground squealing *(center)*, while the male looks on and finally *(right)* walks away as the crying juvenile begins to rise. Although extremely tolerant of infants, the adult males begin to take an active role in disciplining the young when these get to be approximately two years of age.

127

ON ITS OWN, no longer the center of attention that it once was, a juvenile baboon, age two, sits in a burned-over area examining a bit of stubble. Now able to fend for itself, it must also be able to make its own way in the society of the troop—a crucial process which will determine forever its adult role.

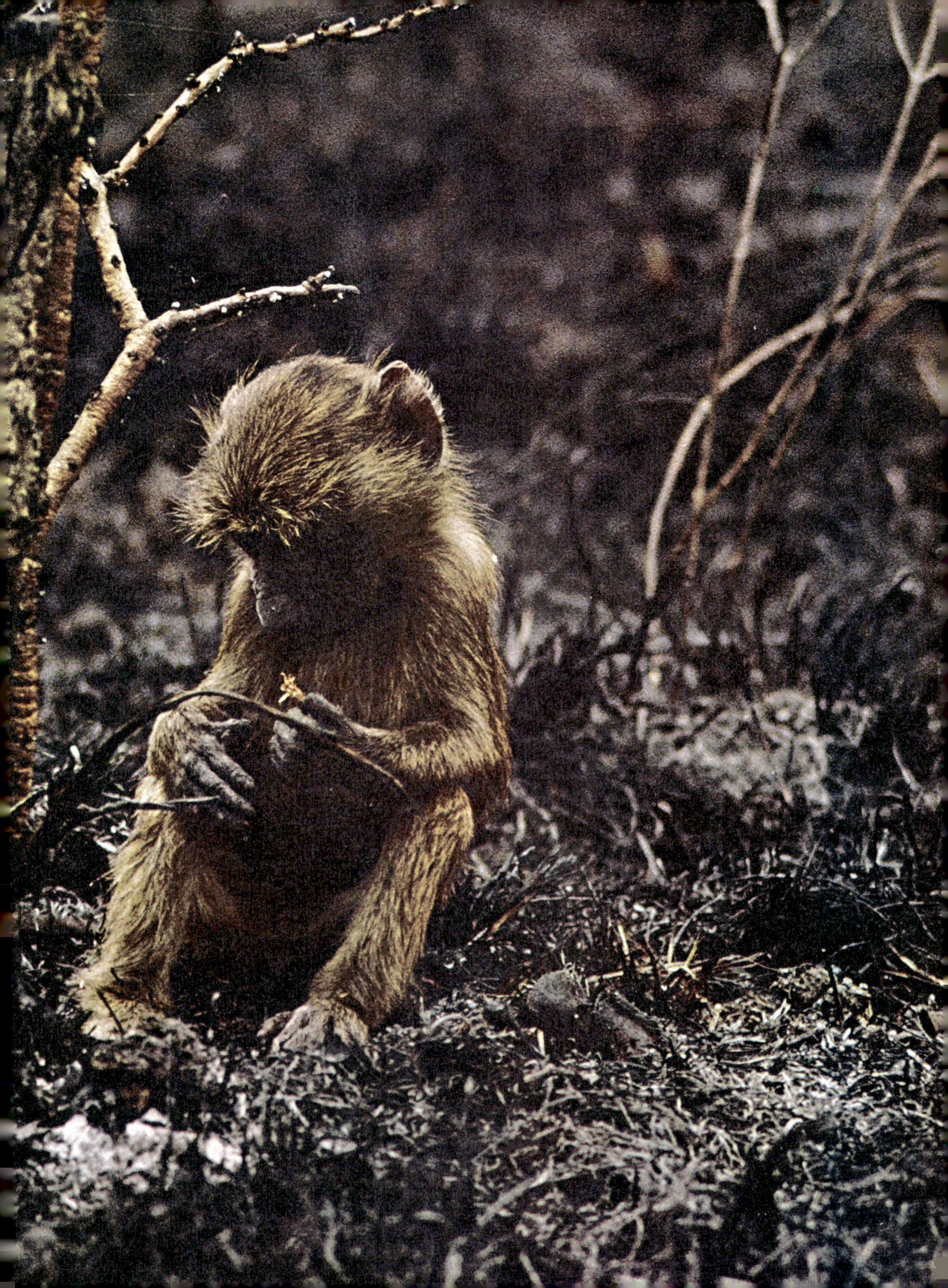

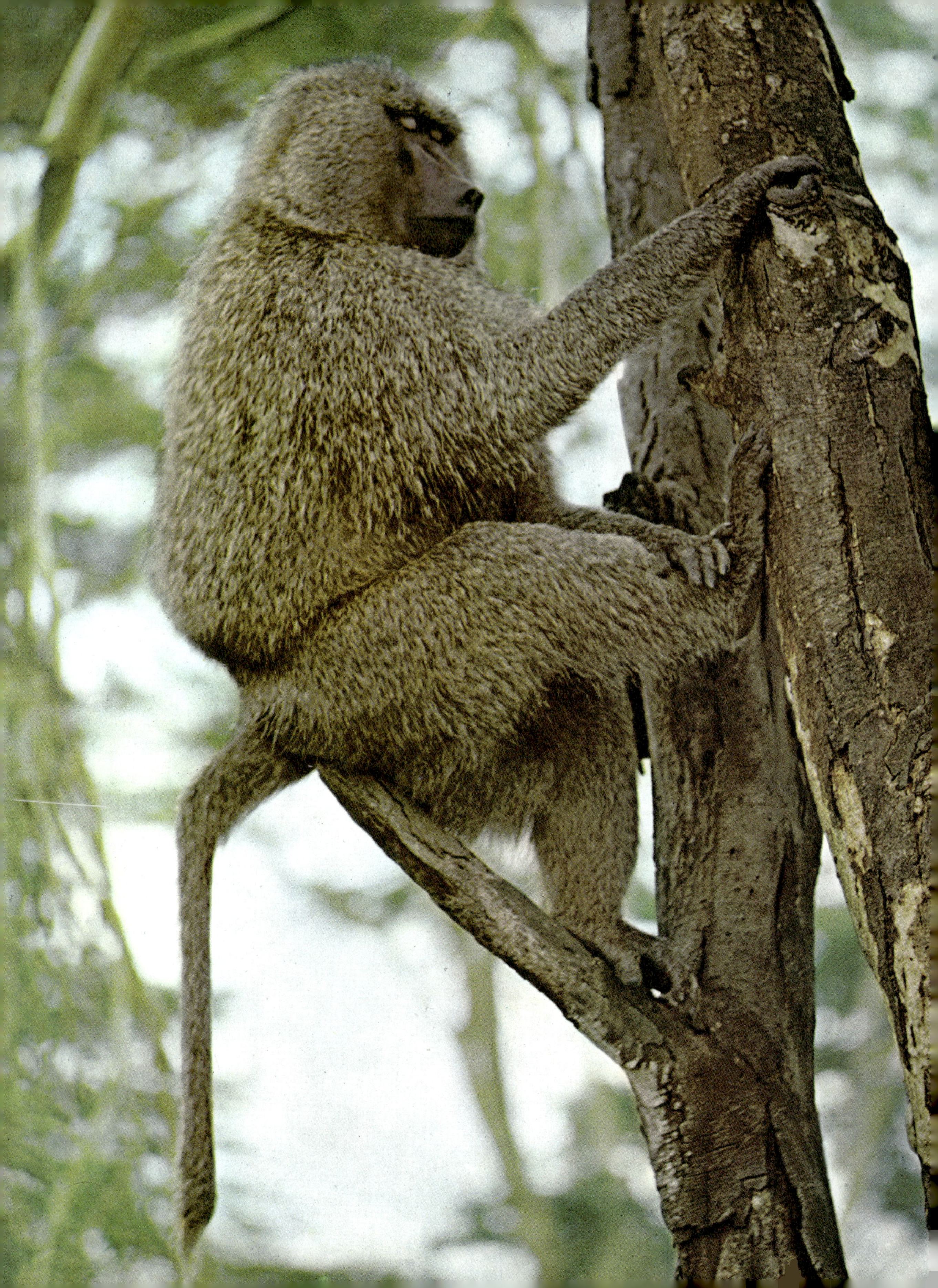

SAFE FROM PREDATORS, a male baboon assumes the posture it may keep all night. Settled on its callous sitting pads, it secures its perch by bracing a foot against a tree limb and gripping a handy tree knob.

6

The Group and the World Outside

"Man is born free," runs the famous opening chapter of Rousseau's *Social Contract*, "and everywhere he is in chains." They are, if nothing else, the chains of habit. Most of us eat at the same times every day. We sleep the same regular hours, take the same route to work, and live in one city for much, if not most of our lives. The untrammeled existence of the monkeys and the apes would seem to be different. They are free. No clock or train schedule binds them. They can eat or sleep when and where they please, stay in one place as long as they wish, wander through the forest as their whim dictates.

Such a picture could hardly be further from the truth. Compared to the average suburbanite, the life of a monkey or an ape is monotonous, repetitious and humdrum. By every imaginable yardstick, the nonhuman primates are intensely conservative. They move back and forth, round and round, constantly retreading the same well-worn trails. Most pass their entire lives amid the same small group. Some join new groups, but still do not venture beyond one area of the forest or the savanna. And they follow daily schedules just like man.

Except for one South American species, the night monkey, all monkeys and apes are diurnal and the daily routine of many species is similar. The day begins at dawn with their first meal, which continues for some time, interrupted only as the group moves, in search of food, along some familiar trail. Toward midday, they break off for a rest, very similar to the siesta enjoyed by humans who live in warm climates. The adults nap or groom each other or just laze in the shade while the energetic youngsters sport and play around them.

Eating brief snacks throughout the day, the group starts in on its second period of intensive feeding in the late afternoon, continuing to eat steadily for perhaps two hours. Then, as evening approaches, the group slowly begins to make its way back, along the ground or through the trees, to one of the regular sleeping sites, where it will pass the night. One by one, the members of the group climb out to their sleeping places. Gradually their activity dwindles away and, by the time darkness descends, all the animals are asleep.

The area covered by a primate group in the course of its normal activities—feeding, resting, sleeping—is known as that group's home range, an important concept for scientists attempting to understand primate behavior. The size of the home range varies considerably with species—and even within the same species—over long periods of time, but tends to be determined by the availability of food sources and sleeping sites secure from predators. Among the arboreal primates, of course, this home range is three-dimensional because different foods exist at different levels in the trees. Gibbons and orangutans, howlers and colobus monkeys spend almost their whole lives in the canopy of the forest. More extreme yet in its vertical confinement is the timid olive colobus. Normally it stays within 20 feet (6 m) of the ground but almost never actually descends to it and climbs higher than 20 feet only to sleep or to avoid predators. Primates with a more catholic diet range farther up and down the trees, and they also come to the ground more frequently. Horizontally as well as vertically, the more arboreal the primate the smaller its range. Gibbons, which have a home range of 40 to 100 acres (16 to 40 ha), were once thought to occupy one of the smallest domains of any of the larger arboreal primates, but it is now known that such species as the South American howlers and titis and Africa's black and white colobus have ranges smaller than that of the gibbon. The common Indian langur, which spends much of its time on the ground, has a home range of several square miles. The greatest wanderers among primates are the most terrestrial types—the gorillas, baboons and macaques. Baboons usually walk three to five miles (4.8 to 8 km) daily. During the course of a year they will travel over an area of from 10 to 15 square miles (26 to 39 km^2), constantly crossing and recrossing their tracks as they make their daily journey between feeding areas, water holes and sleeping sites.

What governs the limits of a group's range? Such local factors as food supply, topography, density of population and predators exert considerable influence. Another important factor is simply the tradition of long habit. As they grow up, young monkeys and apes observe that their group never wanders beyond certain boundaries, set by a stream perhaps, by a ridge of hills or by no particular landmark at all. Beyond these boundaries lies the unknown, threatening in its mystery. Reluctant to venture there, and conditioned by their early confinement, adult monkeys and apes continue to stay within the range they have come to know.

Generation after generation the same tradition is passed down, and this tradition is reinforced by the sense of security that comes from living amidst familiar surroundings. Like men and women who feel most relaxed in their

---

GIBBON
1/10 sq. mi. range for group of 4

HOWLER MONKEY
1/2 sq. mi. range for group of 17

NORTH INDIAN LANGUR
3 sq. mi. maximum range for group of 25

MOUNTAIN GORILLA
10-15 sq. mi. range for group of 17

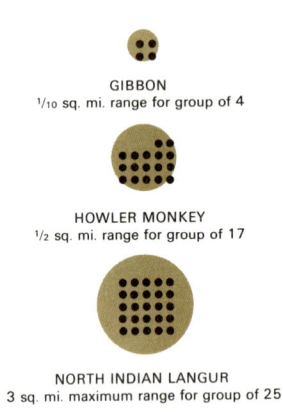

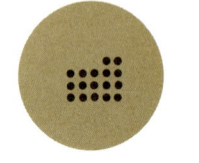

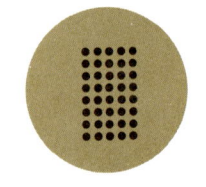

BABOON
15 sq. mi. range for group of 40

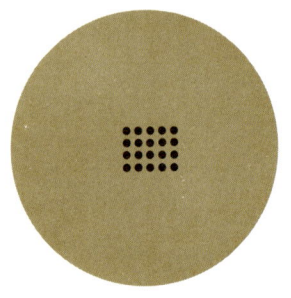

AFRICAN BUSHMAN
440 sq. mi. range for band of 20

HOME RANGES

Tree-living primates tend to have smaller groups and roam less widely than those on the ground. The circles above stand for ranges; the dots indicate individuals in each group. Gibbons and howler monkeys find enough food within small treetop ranges. Langurs, often feeding on the ground, and the more terrestrial gorillas exploit wider areas. Baboons on the savanna roam farther—but still not as far as African bushmen, representing Homo sapiens, who can travel and hunt over 400 square miles (1,000 km^2).

hometowns a group of primates feels safest and most at ease in the heart of its home range. Within the home ranges of many primates there actually seems to be a region, known as the core area, that is used intensively and perhaps exclusively by the group. There, near the heart of its range, the group is intimately familiar with the best feeding areas or trees, the safest sleeping sites, the most dependable sources of water. Because the animals use these sites so regularly it is often possible for field workers to pinpoint the core area rather easily. Always the animals appear most comfortable when operating within the secure confines of this region. As the group moves away from the core area toward the limits of its range, its members become progressively more tense, and beyond those limits they very rarely or never venture. Even prosimians will resist any effort to force them over boundaries because their dread of the unknown land ahead outweighs their fear of any other danger. The same is true of baboons, as the English psychologist K. R. L. Hall discovered when he and a co-worker tried to drive a group of baboons out of its range, only to find that when the animals reached the boundary they turned and ran back—right past the two startled people who were driving them.

While periodic overlapping of home ranges is common among primates within the same species and is of necessity more or less tolerated by the groups, there is little overlap of core areas. Almost all primate groups tend to defend their core areas from intrusion by members of the same species, a characteristic known as territoriality. And even home range boundaries are sometimes jealously guarded. This appears to be particularly true where population densities are high, food is scarce or restricted to well-defined areas and home ranges are small. Gibbons and the South American titis are noted for their territorial behavior, and many other species seem to exhibit at least some degree of territoriality, although this may be manifested more by hoots and calls and aggressive displays than by actual fighting. Violent fighting in defense of territory is extremely rare. Perhaps the same fears and habits that keep a group within familiar territory inhibit any calculated invasion of a neighbor's area.

Far more common than invasion or fighting are visual and vocal displays, known as demonstrations, which regularly occur among many species where regular contact with neighbors takes place. William A. Mason, who studied a community of titis monkeys in Colombia, noted 20 such demonstrations or border confrontations among three titis groups in a 12-day period. There is very little overlap of home ranges among the titis monkeys that Mason observed, but where these small overlap areas occurred, the groups met frequently and engaged in elaborate and extended displays. Calling, rushing and chasing figured prominently in these face-offs. The confrontations usually began when two of the groups approached each other and stopped a few yards apart. Members of the two groups sat facing each other and went through a variety of calls and showed signs of extreme agitation—raising of hackles, arching of the back, stiffening or bowing of the arms, and lashing of the tail. Sometimes individuals in one group would rush the monkeys opposite them, and a long and vigorous chase followed. But Mason observed only infrequent fighting and no severe injuries. The whole encounter seemed designed not to inflict injury but rather to clearly define home-range boundaries and to maintain specific areas for groups inhabiting them.

That there should be definite limits to range among the groups of even the same species is no accident. It is an adaptation for survival. Since they eat the

HIGH AND LOW LIFE AMONG THE MONKEYS

Although monkeys are often thought of as ranging widely from the tops to the bottoms of trees, many of them actually spend most of their time at specific levels in the canopy, each seeking out its own level according to food preference. This drawing illustrates in simplified form the layering of different species of colobus and guenons (shown in various colors). Some species of monkeys have become so accustomed to their particular levels that they will not shift to other sections of the canopy even for the types of food they prefer to eat.

COLOBUS

GUENON

same food, different groups of the same species can better spend their time and energy seeking food within their range than getting involved in suicidal fights by foraging over a wider area in competition with other groups. Inherited tradition and habit help to keep groups apart, and a variety of calls, hoots, hollers and other vocal signals—arboreal primates, unable to see through dense foliage, have little use for visual signals—prevent them from blundering into each other. For example, as soon as they wake up in the morning, adult males of the typical howler group set up a steady roar that lasts up to half an hour. The roar is repeated whenever the howling monkeys, which actually have a sort of mobile home range, move from one feeding station to another. When two howler groups come into contact, the males will roar at each other until one group retreats. Recent field observations of groups of howlers in the Panama Canal Zone confirms the effectiveness of these vocal signals to control and direct ranging activity and to minimize intergroup contact.

Langurs and gibbons use whoops to let other groups know where they are, and titis monkeys use both dawn calls and other vocal interactions to mark their range. The very arboreal spider monkeys of South America give warning calls that sound like the bark of a terrier. And, in Africa, the dominant males of the free-ranging colobus indulge in choruses to let every creature within earshot know they are on the job.

THE care a group takes to warn other groups of its presence is yet another manifestation of tradition. Only the familiar is safe: Strangers are suspect and their mere presence is cause for alarm. Still, not all monkeys and apes are equally apprehensive of strangers. For suspicion is always defensive, a reaction to danger experienced or anticipated and, as we have seen, the species that are most fearful are also the most aggressive. As one might expect, gorillas and chimpanzees, which have little to fear from predators, are the least perturbed by unfamiliar members of their own species. A resident chimpanzee population will accept stray individuals. Two gorilla groups will often come together quite peacefully and, provided the leaders are not unusually suspicious individuals, the members of different groups may intermingle freely.

Howlers and langurs, on the other hand, though not in much danger from predators, do not feel as secure as gorillas. So if, as sometimes happens, a male howler or langur leaves its group, it may find it extremely difficult to join another. Suspicion of strangers and its complement, aggression, reaches its peak in baboons and macaques, especially in the rhesus macaque, probably the most aggressive of all nonhuman primates. The difference in attitude between the more and the less suspicious species was demonstrated very neatly a few years ago when a male and a female macaque joined a group of langurs. The male bore on his face the traces of a healed scar, which suggests that he had been wounded in a fight and had either been driven from his group or had voluntarily decided to leave it. Presumably, being a monkey and therefore highly sociable, he preferred to convalesce among monkeys of a different species rather than be left entirely alone. Why the female accompanied him to join the langurs is a mystery. Whatever their reasons, the two macaques behaved according to form. Like two refugee soldiers billeting themselves on a village of timid men and women, they established, though hopelessly outnumbered, complete dominance over the langurs.

But this was not all. Though they were living among monkeys of a completely different species, the refugee macaques retained all their suspicion of strangers.

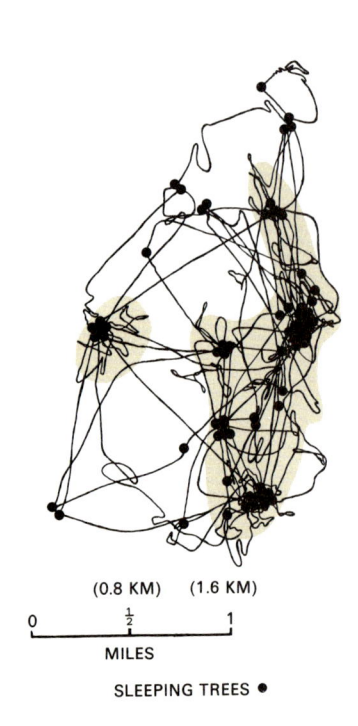

THE CORES OF THE RANGE

A group of primates not only limits itself generally to a home range: It spends most of its time in an even more closely defined area within this range. This map by Phyllis Jay shows the many routes taken by a troop of langurs over the whole of their home range in northern India, during an 80-day period. Dots indicate the trees in which the langurs sleep; where the dots are thickest are the so-called core areas (colored), the most heavily used parts of the range. Besides having plentiful sleeping trees, these core areas provide the langurs with rich supplies of drinking water and vegetation.

At one point, a lone male langur appeared on the scene and started to wander around the periphery of the group, hoping to break in. Acting like a self-appointed sentry, the male rhesus would draw the attention of his male hosts to the presence of the outsider. Once alerted, the male langurs then joined in repelling the stranger and eventually he wandered away. It is hard not to feel sorry for him, for had it not been for the presence of the rhesus male, he might well have succeeded in joining the group.

THE apprehension and fear that an unfamiliar member of the species can inspire in macaques was illustrated even more dramatically by another incident that took place one summer at the University of California. Above the Berkeley campus, in Strawberry Canyon, there is an animal research center where a number of monkeys are kept together in groups, each inside its own large cage. At the time of the incident about a dozen crab-eating macaques were among them. The species, compared to most other macaques, is quite mild and unaggressive. One afternoon a group of people, including Sherwood Washburn, the director of the primate section of the center, was standing in a small, cell-like room, which is separated from the macaques by a wire net. It was a hot, lazy summer day. The macaques were basking somnolently in their cage, and a visitor to the center was describing an experiment in which an anesthetized chimpanzee had been shown to a group of nine adult chimpanzees in a cage. They had reacted with great violence to the sight—screaming, spitting and trying to attack the anesthetized animal. This reaction, the visitor suggested, showed that the chimpanzees obviously shared man's fear of death.

"But how do you know," Washburn asked, "that they wouldn't have reacted just as violently to the sight of a live chimpanzee if it were a stranger?"

The visitor replied that this seemed to him highly unlikely.

"Let's try it," said Washburn. "Let's go fetch Isabelle."

Isabelle is another crab-eating macaque, about two years old, who has never belonged to the group, and is kept in a cage by herself at the top of a hill that leads up from the monkeys' cages. Holding her carefully, because Isabelle is nervous and frequently given to biting, Washburn brought her down into the room. As he came in, two of the other macaques were standing near the netting. At the sight of them, Isabelle let out a small squeak of alarm. The effect was electric. Within a few seconds, all the other crab-eaters were clinging to the netting, a solid mass of alert, frightened monkeys, all gazing spellbound at the hapless Isabelle.

There was a very brief silence and then Isabelle gave another call, louder this time, half a squeak, half a cry. The other macaques, normally quite placid, responded with the utmost vehemence. They shook the netting, they threatened furiously, they screamed. They were, of course, threatening Isabelle in a language she could understand and, in her terror, her heart began to beat so rapidly that Washburn decided to take her away.

But the incident was far from over. As soon as Washburn had gone, the macaques left the netting. Half a dozen of them raced up the sides of the cage and clung to a beam that stretches across the roof. The others also took refuge in some distant corner—all except the leader, a four-year-old male generally known as Fats because he was a compulsive eater and grossly corpulent. Normally Fats was lethargic. But now he was transformed into a dynamo of energy. First he scuttled across the floor to an eyehole from which he could see outside the cage and look up the hill to where Washburn was walking. Then he

TELLING MALE FROM FEMALE

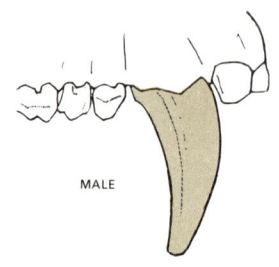

Because of obvious differences in size, male and female baboons can be told apart at a glance. In addition to being nearly twice as heavy as its mate and having a bushier head, the male has much larger canine teeth (color). Among the ground-dwelling baboons, large size and large teeth are essential male attributes since the males protect the entire troop.

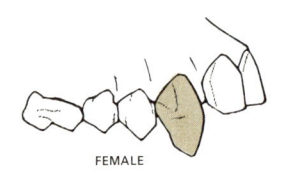

tore back, raced up one side of the cage and onto the beam, and swung himself out and past the other monkeys until he reached an eyehole in the wall that gave him an even better view up the hill.

At this point, the visitor noticed that all the macaques, including Fats, were in the process of defecating. As zoologists know, this is a sure sign of fear. A gorilla in a zoo was once cured of constipation by being shown the head of a turtle that he mistook for a snake. Yet the sight of Fats, usually so self-assured but now so frightened, was curiously uncanny; the sensation he evoked was precisely what one feels when a grown man bursts into tears.

A few minutes later, Washburn came back. "You see," he said, "they don't like strangers. Even live ones." It was a comment that nearly disposed of the visitor's contention about the chimpanzees.

The macaques involved were, of course, captive animals that were reacting in a thoroughly unnatural situation. In their natural state in areas where there is no overcrowding and food is plentiful, monkeys do not display this kind of intensely aggressive defensiveness. In the wild, members of even the most aggressive species reach a mutual understanding that takes account of their neighbors' need to survive. "You keep out of our hair," is the sense of it, "and we'll keep out of yours." This live-and-let-live arrangement is essential if physical combat is to be avoided. For although neighboring groups normally avoid each other's central feeding places, they do not necessarily keep apart altogether. Like two families who each possess their own living quarters but who share the same kitchen, two or more groups of baboons will often come together to feed out of the same fruiting tree or to drink from the same water hole. They share this part of their range in common; obviously the arrangement can work only if the groups are mutually tolerant.

Even when drinking from the same water hole, the two groups do not noticeably intermingle. Normally the smaller one will move away when the larger and more powerful group arrives, but from years of sharing the same drinking water the members of different groups undoubtedly know each other by sight. More likely, the different groups are the result of peaceful splits in what was once a single group, or contain members that switched loyalty from one group to another. Continued contact refreshes this familiarity and a limited amount of camaraderie may be maintained between the groups. One young baboon, for example, often used to go off and play with the juveniles of another group encountered at a water hole, much as a boy might visit the house of a neighbor. And this kind of early friendship, no doubt, can make it comparatively easy for the baboon to shift groups later, if for some reason its situation in its own group should become unpleasant.

The pressures of predation have led baboons to develop a mutual assistance program with animals of different species altogether—principally, in savanna and forest alike, with ungulates, who share with them a common fear of carnivores. Together, baboons and their hoofed neighbors derive mutual benefit from an efficient, complementary warning system. As baboons have a keen sense of vision and ungulates possess a keen sense of smell, they are, in combination, almost immune to surprise, and a single warning bark will alert all of them to danger. A group of baboons was once seen in Nairobi Park, feeding on the side of a hill that was separated by an open space from the dense bushes around a water hole. Two lions came into view, the baboon males gave warning barks, and, within a few seconds, a mass of giraffes, impalas and waterbucks, previously hidden in the bushes, had streamed out into the open, where they stood, nervously testing the air, trying to identify the danger.

The savanna baboons' own defensive system is an elaborate one, and it is yet another example of how selection for survival can lead monkeys to develop patterns of behavior which serve a variety of purposes. We have seen how, when they are at rest, baboons take up positions that reflect their personal relationships. The dominant males sit at the center of the group, near the females and the infants, while the younger and less dominant males stay out on the periphery. When the group is moving, this spacing pattern is maintained; it becomes, as it were, mobile. The dominant males, the females and the infants stay in the middle of the marching column, while the other males either go on ahead in the manner of an advance guard or follow behind.

In this situation, the positioning of the baboons serves as an instrument of group survival. At the front and the rear the young, powerful males are most susceptible to sudden attack; they are also the most expendable members of the group. The females and infants are escorted by the older, dominant males who can defend them; if predators do approach, the females and young may slow down or retreat while the adult males form a defensive screen.

A dominant male will also drop back to help a female or an infant in distress, as one was seen to do for a female burdened with a newborn infant which could not cling properly. Compelled to use one arm to hold the infant, she lagged behind the group. Whenever she stopped, her male escort also stopped; when she moved, he moved. He never left her for a moment unprotected. Just how protective a male baboon can be to an infant was illustrated even more dramatically on another occasion when a mother, after carrying a dead infant for several days, finally abandoned it. Immediately a male appeared at her side and barked, and the mother wearily took up again her useless and pitiful burden.

Because effective defense is essential to their survival baboons learn how to cope with danger with amazing rapidity, and they forget only very slowly what they have learned. Furthermore, it would appear that the frightening experiences of some can be passed along somehow to become part of the experience, the tradition, of the entire group. This ability to pool knowledge is, of course, one of the basic advantages of group living, for it means that individual animals do not have to make their own mistakes in order to learn caution. The young especially can draw the appropriate conclusions from the mistakes or the bad luck of others, and a baboon who is killed does not, one might say, necessarily die in vain. For the mode of its death may have the effect of improving the chances that its companions will survive.

If there is one generalization that holds true for all the monkeys and apes so far studied, it is that they are full of surprises. Observers in the wild are constantly discovering that our relatives exhibit a surprising degree of variation, just as we do. The observer who goes out to conduct the first study of a species is always liable to return with a sheaf of notes that will astonish his colleagues. Consider, for example, the patas monkey, which for years had kept primatologists baffled. Though adapted to terrestrial life, it is neither tough nor equipped to fight off predators, as baboons and macaques are. Instead, it is a slender, long-legged monkey with a considerable turn of speed, which led primatologists to assume that it managed to avoid predators by outrunning them. Then, in the summer of 1963, K.R.L. Hall carried out a study of patas monkeys living in Kabarega National Park in Uganda. One day a group of patas that he had been following

Male and female gibbons are far more difficult to tell apart than male and female baboons. The male gibbon is only slightly bigger than the female, with only slightly bigger canines (color). But gibbons, unlike the ground-dwelling baboons, live in trees and thus have less need to defend themselves; when a predator strikes, it is every gibbon for itself.

unaccountably disappeared. Though he searched far and wide over the savanna, he failed to find them—until he returned to the place where he had last seen them. And there they were: Instead of fleeing they had simply crouched down out of sight in the long grass. Nevertheless, under other circumstances—as when a group of baboons is approaching—patas run away very fast and far.

The habits of the patas, as Hall has described them, indicate that their adaptation to life on the ground is quite different from that of other ground-living monkeys. Silence, caution and withdrawal are their protection, rather than the long canines and tough fighting qualities of the male baboons and macaques. Instead of remaining always close to each other, as the members of a baboon or macaque group do, the patas monkeys stay far apart at night, so that if one monkey falls victim to a predator, the others will have a good chance to escape. Yet, although their behavior seems to be unique among ground-living monkeys, the patas' timidity and caution toward man is typical of many other nonhuman primates. Only those that are habituated to human beings will remain calm when a man or woman approaches. The others will immediately seek refuge in some fashion, commonly by beating a hurried retreat.

Even the powerful gorilla is afraid of man. Although a male may pause and beat his chest in brief threat when a man approaches, it will very quickly fade back after the rest of its group into the concealment of the forest. The gorillas' nervousness, of course, makes them hard to follow, as George Schaller and Dian Fossey have learned. Undoubtedly their success was largely due to the remarkable patience and caution they displayed. Until the gorillas were thoroughly used to Schaller, for example, he never looked gorillas directly in the eye. Nor did he point a pair of field glasses or a camera at them in case they might have interpreted the staring eye of the lens as a threat.

An individual gorilla could still be exceedingly nervous, as Schaller discovered, even when surrounded by other gorillas who had lost their fear. Once, a strange female joined a group that he had been following for several weeks. The other gorillas were no longer at all scared but whenever the female saw Schaller, she immediately screamed and dashed away. With some amusement, he noticed that the other gorillas appeared baffled by the violence of her reaction, since they had presumably forgotten that he had ever disturbed them. And the female, no doubt, must have been equally mystified by her companions' strange imperviousness to this intruder, a man—the gorillas' one really dangerous enemy.

As the other nonhuman primates share the gorilla's nervousness, any man or woman who wants to get close to them must be careful, as Schaller was, not to perform any action that might appear aggressive. Still, even the best students can slip up occasionally, as Phyllis Jay once did, thereby provoking one of the most curious interactions ever to take place between a monkey and a human being. She had been scrupulously careful not to do anything that might be construed as a threat, until one afternoon, when sitting in the middle of a group of langurs, she turned to get a notebook from her bag and accidentally hit a young female who was sitting close beside her. The langur immediately ran off. Next time the two met, the female turned and presented her hindquarters as if she expected to be mounted. By hitting her, Jay had achieved dominance.

One cannot, of course, read the mind of a monkey. Still, the mere fact that the langur reacted very much as she would have done to another monkey certainly suggests the possibility that she sensed the close ties of kinship that connect monkeys to man.

BRIEFLY AWAY FROM THEIR MOTHERS TWO YOUNG CHIMPS SHARE A RELAXING MOMENT IN A TREE—ONE IDLY CHEWING A STICK

The Convivial Chimpanzees

Unlike baboons, chimpanzees travel in small bands or alone. Yet each one knows every chimp within its permanent home range—an area of 10 to 30 square miles (26 to 78 km^2). This is because chimpanzees are constantly socializing. They congregate in feeding areas, leave one band and join another. Though often separated chimpanzees form a quite cohesive and organized community.

The Signs of Class

Whenever chimpanzees come together they use expressive gestures, looks and sounds to establish their relative social status. For example, a male who wants to win the respect of other chimps may let out a loud "waa" bark, then glare and with his hair standing on end charge back and forth swinging and dragging tree branches. On the other hand, a chimpanzee that feels inferior to another chimp will bow, present his rump or beg for reassurance from his superior by whimpering and screaming. Social ranking helps maintain order in chimpanzee society. But since rank can change with each new situation, chimpanzees are not trapped in the sort of rigid hierarchy that produces social tension and conflict.

A SUBMISSIVE FEMALE CHIMPANZEE bends away and "pant-grunts" as a male charges by. In the background another male, anxious to avoid a confrontation, retreats from the scene.

CHARACTERISTICALLY SEEKING CONTACT IN FEAR OR EXCITEMENT AN ADULT MALE CLASPS HIS OLDER BROTHER'S HAND TO HIS FACE

AN OLD CHIMPANZEE advances to greet a distressed young adult male and to comfort him with a kiss. A worried youngster clings to the old male.

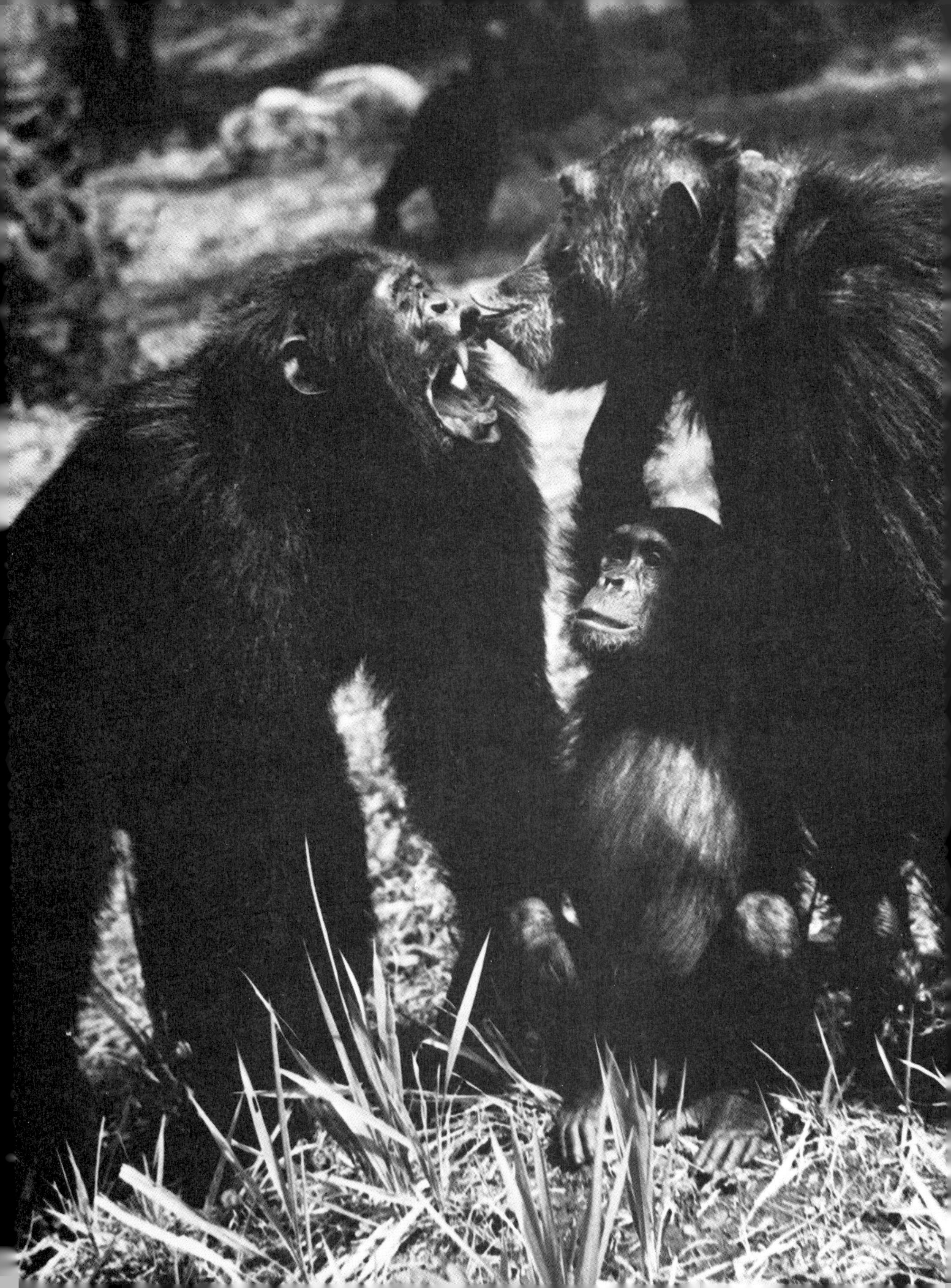

FIVE EXUBERANT MALES greet each other with screams, "pant-hoots" and embraces. When large groups of chimpanzees meet they make an enormous commotion: They bark loudly, grunt, bob, crouch, bow, groom each other, embrace, swagger and

142

stamp the ground. Since chimpanzees are separated so often they have a special need to greet one another each time they meet, for greeting behavior—comprising as it does signs of submission, aggression and reassurance—redefines their social relationships.

IN SHEER CONTENTMENT AN ELDERLY MALE CHIMP YAWNS DROWSILY AND LAZES ON A BED OF GRASS DURING A SIESTA

The Joys of Easy Living

Some of a chimpanzee's most agreeable social interactions take place during the midday siesta which they take each day. For the first hour or more chimpanzees go to sleep, stretched out on the ground or curled up in nests which they build in trees. During the remainder of their rest period—while the infants are at play—the adults relax at their favorite pastime, grooming. During grooming sessions mothers are reunited with their grown children, males pamper females who are in estrus, good friends enjoy each others' company and new bonds are forged between casual acquaintances. In chimpanzee society, grooming is simply another pleasurable way of establishing and strengthening social bonds.

A CHAIN of adult male chimpanzees forms during a grooming session. Males not only band together for grooming but for other activities such as traveling, feeding and hunting.

PREPARING FOR A NAP AN ADULT MALE REACHES FOR A PALM FROND THAT IT WILL USE AS A CROSSPIECE IN THE NEST IT IS BUILDING

AFTER THE HUNT MALE CHIMPANZEES SHARE THE FLESH OF A COLOBUS MONKEY. THEY EAT EVEN THE HAIR, EYEBALLS AND TEETH

IN QUEST OF FOOD a chimp pokes a grass stem into a termite hill. When he withdraws the stem, coated with termites, he picks off the insects with his lips and teeth. Chimpanzees usually feed on termites at the start of the rainy season, when the insects, preparing to emigrate, dig passages close to the surface of their hills.

A Collaborative Search for Food

Chimpanzees spend five to six hours a day feeding and foraging. For the most part they live on a fruit diet supplemented with choice leaves, blossoms, seeds, stems and bark. But they also look for insects and eggs as well as hunt other mammals, including monkeys, for meat.

The search for food is often a cooperative venture. When a chimpanzee discovers an inviting fruit tree he gives loud "food barks" before he climbs, and other chimps within earshot invariably hurry to join in. And when a young baboon or monkey is in the vicinity three or four male chimps will join forces to surround and kill the prey. Other chimpanzees in the area stand to profit from the hunters' success. Attracted by the hunters' cries they gather round and beg for a piece of meat, reaching out to touch the lips and hands of the hunters or holding out their hands, palms upward, while whimpering softly. The hunters, moved by these pleas, always share their catch with several chimps in the crowd. In fact, often as many as 10 to 15 chimps receive some meat after a kill.

When food is abundant in an area large numbers of chimpanzees assemble there. But when the food is gone chimps generally scatter, going off alone or in parties of two to five in search of the next meal.

CHIMPS CLAMBER UP A FIG TREE FOR SUCCULENT SHOOTS

A BEGGING ADOLESCENT peers intently at the fruit her brother is holding, before glancing once more at his face to see if he shows signs of willingness to share. When fruit is scarce—for instance, in early May in the African forest where chimps sometimes roam—chimpanzees may beg for it as vigorously as they beg for a chunk of meat.

TWO INFANTS with "play-face grins" wrestle in a tree for fun. Through play a young chimpanzee grows strong and gains an understanding of its environment and how to survive in it.

An Enduring Bond

While other chimpanzees band together for a few days or hours, a mother and her child stay together for several years. Dependent on her for food, protection and transportation, an infant constantly clings to its mother. By the age of four the child boldly ventures away to play boisterously with other young chimps: chasing, sparring and swinging from tree to tree. But even in its newfound independence it often scampers back to its mother to sit in her lap. At the age of 10 a chimp may cease to move about with its mother. But in its adult years it will return often to see her, for the mother-offspring bond is the strongest of all in the chimpanzees' world.

A GRAND OLD MATRIARCH lies at ease among three of her five children. Her daughter meticulously grooms the newest baby, while the young son watches with fascination.

148

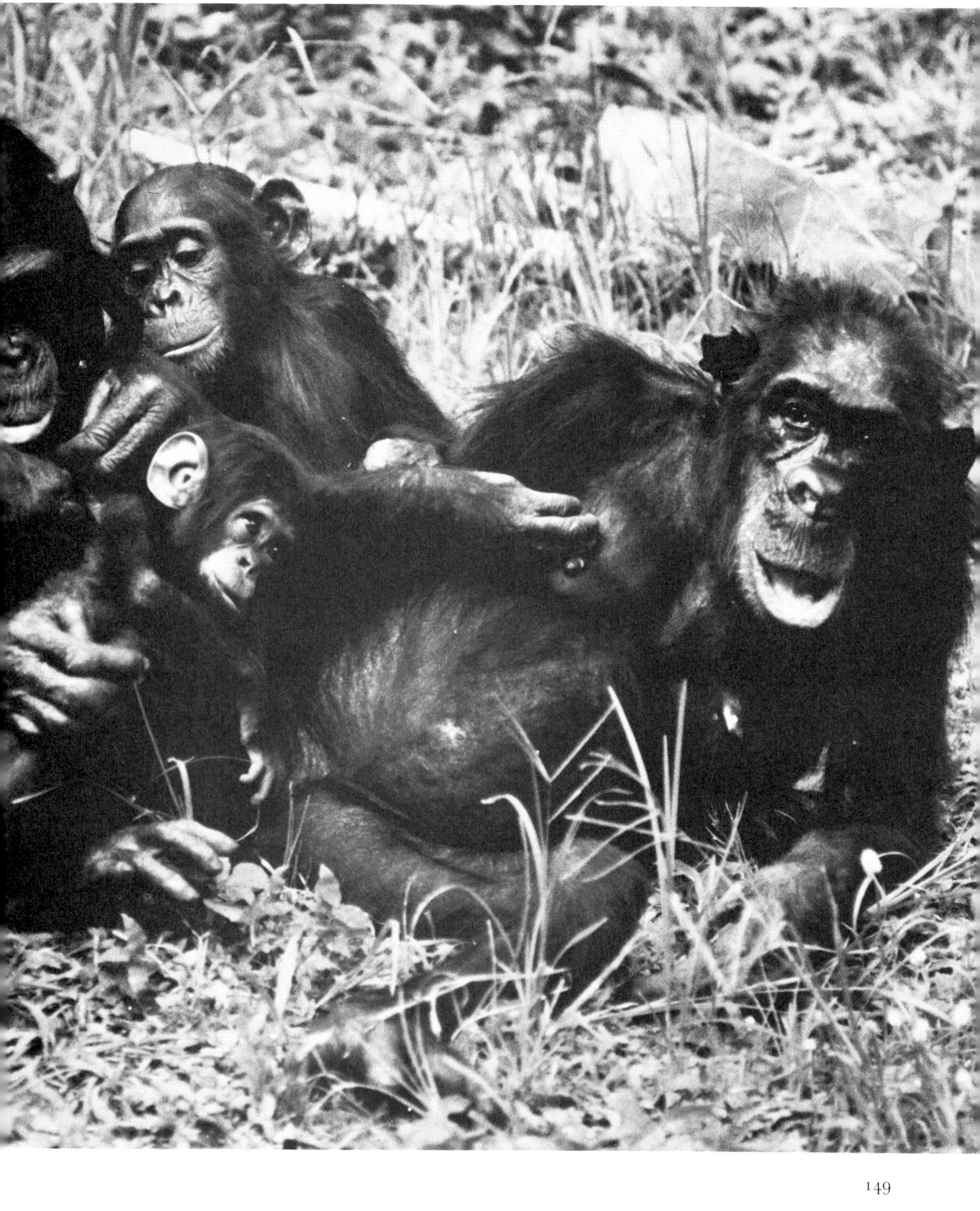

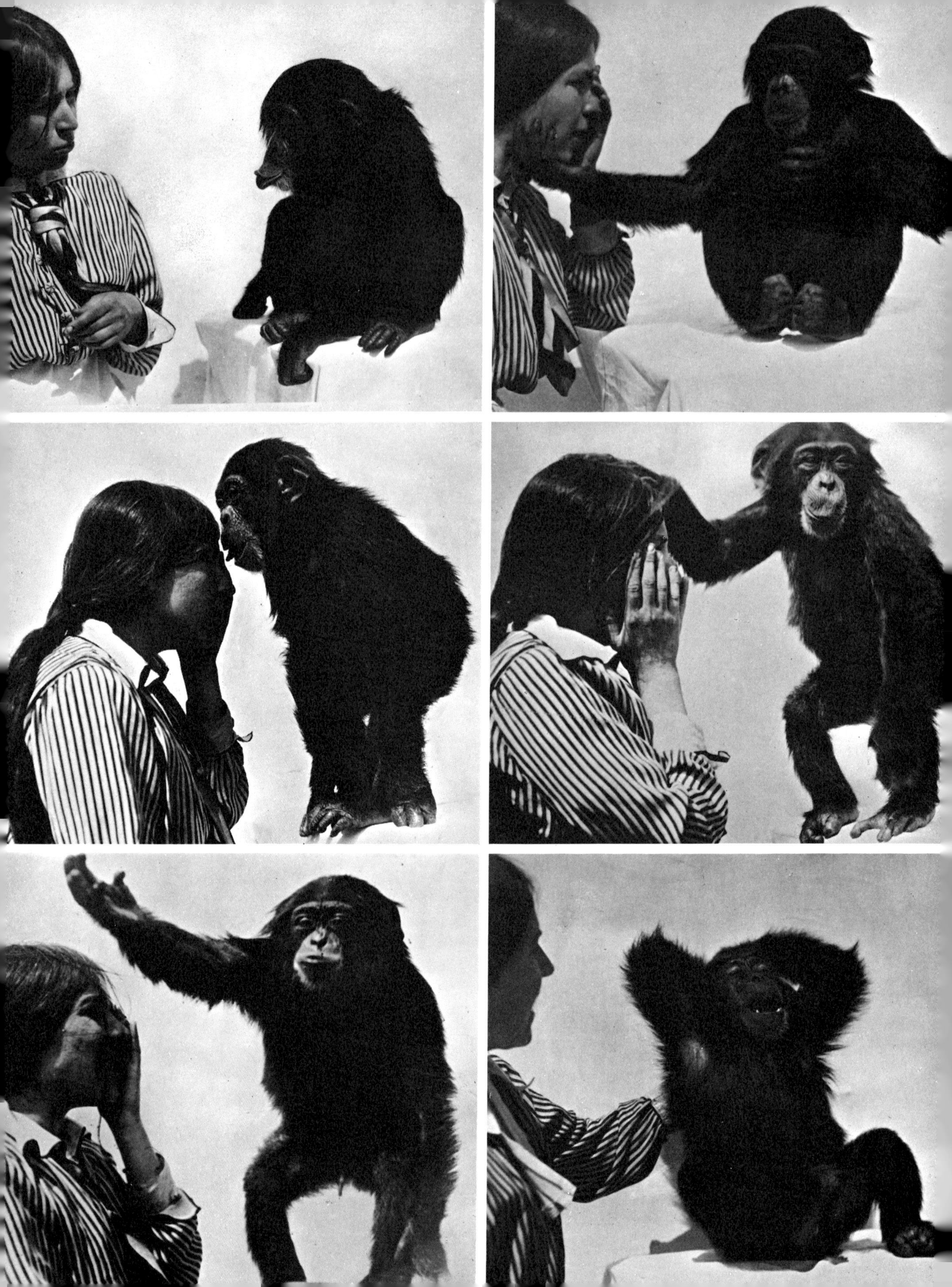

A GIFTED EXTROVERT, this chimpanzee displays a wide range of facial expressions and postures in response to visual suggestions by Moscow psychologist N. Kohts. Quick to learn, chimps can understand complex communications.

7

Clues to Human Behavior

It is hardly necessary to point out that man occupies a unique position among the primates. He alone lives entirely on the ground, needing no contact with the trees to feed in, to sleep in or to take refuge from his enemies. He alone relies on weapons for defense, can use complex tools and develop an elaborate culture. He alone systematically contemplates the past and broods over the future, speculates and plans and talks, and thinks in abstractions: perceives himself as an individual possessed of a sense of good and evil, right and wrong, progress and decline.

As man does differ so widely from all the other primates, any evolutionist who is concerned with tracing the long and complex story of human development might be inclined to echo Alexander Pope's famous line: "The proper study of mankind is man." Surely one could expect to learn little from monkeys or apes about man's separate and individual evolutionary history. Yet, curiously enough, this is not the case. Just as the preliminary drawings of an artist can help an art lover discern the genesis of the finished oil, so have the field studies of monkeys and apes in the last few decades helped anthropologists to a clearer understanding of some of the most significant aspects of man's history. Consider, for example, one of the most decisive steps in human evolution: the descent of man's apelike ancestors out of the trees. Why did they come down to the ground? What was the reward so great that it lured them out of their arboreal refuge? Until very recently, no one had a satisfactory answer. Now, however, we can understand what may well have happened by projecting from the monkeys which remain today in the environment that man's ape ancestors must have occupied several million years ago.

One may begin this comparative study with the vervet, one of the most numerous nonhuman primates in Africa. Although vervets are still tree-dwelling monkeys, they also spend a good deal of time on the ground, and one can, with some confidence, describe the process by which they gradually, stage by stage, made their descent from the trees. As tree dwellers, vervets fed—and still do—on fruits and seeds and leaves: all objects which often fall to the ground. At some point, vervets must have begun to go down after them. Then, once on the ground, they proceeded to move farther and farther away from the bases of the trees, moving out into the open to eat the grasses and insects they found there, until they finally reached their present stage of moving freely between one patch of trees and another.

The fact that they feed not only in trees but also under trees and between trees is certainly a principal factor in the vervets' evolutionary success. Still, they remain at least 50 per cent arboreal. To trace the next stage in the evolutionary progress of man's ancestors, it is therefore necessary to move on to the monkeys, notably the baboons and macaques, which have adapted far more thoroughly to terrestrial life.

Why these monkeys should have taken this further step it is impossible to say. Monkey fossils are rare and there are no records of baboons or macaques in the transitional stages to offer us any clues. Probably the best explanation is that they were equipped with digestive systems which enabled them to handle an exceedingly varied diet. In East Africa, for example, baboons have been known to feed off at least 200 different kinds of plants. The ability to digest so many ground plants was no doubt acquired after they descended from the trees, but the potential must have been there while they were still arboreal monkeys. Given that potential, they presumably found by experience that the greater variety of edible material that was to be found on the forest floor more than balanced the risks of settling there.

Baboons and macaques—and also gorillas—survive on the ground because the males possess the long canines and other fighting characteristics that enable them to fight off predators. When man's ape ancestors came down from the trees, they probably developed the same type of defensive equipment. But over the years their behavior gradually altered. Instead of using their teeth to defend themselves against predators, they began to fight with weapons, and, like the shift to terrestrial living, this shift too is anticipated by the behavior of certain nonhuman primates.

We are so used to the idea of weapons that we take them completely for granted. Actually, the use of weapons was not only a revolutionary step forward in the history of man, but it also takes quite a lot of explaining. For example, if an animal's normal method of defense is to flee from a predator, it flees. If its normal method of defense is to fight with its teeth, it fights with its teeth. It does not suddenly adopt a totally new course of action, such as picking up a stick or a rock and throwing it. The idea would simply not occur to it and,

THE DOG-HEADED MAN

Early attempts by natural historians to draw primates are full of comical mistakes, more often than not introduced by the too-lively imagination of the artist. A good example is the cynocephalus, the so-called dog-headed man, taken from a natural history book printed in 1642. Long thought to be an attempt to reproduce a baboon, this creature is now suspected to have been based on early accounts of a rare Madagascar lemur, the indri. This animal often stands erect, has a long furry coat, a muzzle and very large hands. Furthermore, its tail is so short that it is often not visible.

even if it did, the animal would have no reason to suppose that it would work.

Still, man's ancestors did shift from using their teeth to using weapons, and the most convincing explanation of how the shift may have taken place is one that has been suggested by the English psychologist K.R.L. Hall. As he has pointed out, orangs and various other monkeys and apes often throw down branches at other animals as an expression of hostility. Significantly, chimpanzees, the nonhuman primates which are in so many ways the closest to man, also throw rocks. Jane Goodall has described how she once saw a chimpanzee throwing rocks toward a photographer whose presence was keeping it from approaching a box of bananas. On other occasions, she watched chimpanzees hurling rocks, both underarm and overarm, at baboons that were competing with them for food.

Man's apelike ancestors, no doubt, also threw branches and rocks at their enemies and, very often, the weapons they hurled must have landed on their targets and sent potential aggressors into rapid retreat. Gradually the idea must have penetrated that throwing rocks at a predator could scare it away and that it was much safer than getting into a tooth and claw fight. One favorable experience must have followed another until finally, benefiting from what they had learned, men came to use weapons regularly first to defend themselves, then later to attack animals.

WEAPONS, of course, are simply a form of tool. For many years it has been fashionable for anthropologists to maintain that the use of tools is an essential constituent of human behavior: that animals can only be considered human if they do make use of tools. There is much truth in this contention. To shift from reliance on one's own hands and teeth to reliance on some external instrument is a great step forward and, as we shall see in the next chapter, the use of tools was an essential step in the evolution of man.

Yet this step forward, too—as many observers have discovered—is anticipated in chimpanzees. They will strip leaves from a twig and use them to clean their bodies, to wipe off mud or to remove honey that has been smeared over bananas. They also chew leaves briefly to crumple them, and then dip them into water when they are thirsty and want to drink. Checking this behavior, Jane Goodall found that she could draw seven or eight times as much water out of a glass by dipping crumpled leaves into it than she could by just dipping in the fingers of one hand.

The chimpanzees she observed also use tools in a more complex way by picking up twigs, grass stalks or vines, and pushing them into termite holes to draw out the insects. These tools are sometimes carefully selected. Chimpanzees may examine and reject several tangles of vines before picking one, and have been known to carry a stalk a hundred feet (30 m) to a termite hole. One male has been seen carrying a stalk in its mouth for half a mile (0.8 km) while it examined six termite holes, none of them ready for probing. The tools, once they are selected, may be prepared with considerable care, the chimpanzees often stripping the leaves from the stem with their hands or their lips. Occasionally, if a piece of grass is too wide to go into a termite hole, a chimpanzee will make it fit by pulling long strips from it.

Once the tool is prepared and the termite hole located, the chimpanzee scrapes away the thin layer of soil which seals it up. Then it pokes the vine or stalk inside, leaves it in the hole for a short time, then withdraws it, covered with termites, which the chimpanzee then picks off with its lips and teeth.

This kind of planning ahead is of peculiar interest because the ability to visualize a situation before it exists is often cited as a principal factor distinguishing man from all other animals. At first glance, the behavior of the chimpanzees appears to refute this assumption. But is a tool-using chimpanzee really thinking ahead, imagining a situation that does not yet exist? Not perhaps in the way a man does when he fashions a bow for the hunt. The man is preparing to kill an animal he has not yet seen, while the chimpanzee seems simply to be reacting to the stimulus of the termite nests, just as a Galápagos woodpecker-finch reacts to the presence of insects by probing for them with a cactus spine or a twig held in its beak, or as a sea otter reacts to mollusks by breaking their shells open with a stone.

To early man, tools were particularly useful because they enabled him, in time, to widen the sources of his food supply—to kill not only small but increasingly larger animals. In short, tools made it possible for man to become an accomplished predator—and for a long time this was thought to be one of the qualities that distinguished early man from the nonhuman primates, since these, except for the eating of insects, were generally assumed to be vegetarians.

But is the distinction quite that absolute between man, the hunter of animals and eater of meat, and all the other primates? We know now, on the basis of a great deal of information gathered during the past decades, that it is not. Observations in the wild have shown that baboons, chimpanzees, vervets, macaques and, among the New World monkeys, capuchins and woolly monkeys all occasionally prey on smaller and weaker animals for food. The behavior of baboons as meat eaters is particularly interesting because it appears to vary with the experience of the group involved. All baboons so far observed will eat eggs, fledgling birds or small animals that they happen to stumble across in the grass. Beyond that, however, the behavior of different groups seems to vary. Some will mingle quite peacefully with guinea fowl; others will kill and eat them. Some baboons will deliberately chase, kill and eat hares, young gazelles or even vervet monkeys. One baboon, indeed, was seen to chase a young hare for 70 yards (64 m) before catching it. And yet others may actually grip an edible animal in their mouths, only to release it, as a female baboon was once seen to do. She caught a vervet, held it in her jaws and then, apparently bewildered by the situation, let the smaller monkey go free.

Why all the variations? The answer seems to lie in group tradition. Possibly, among one group, a tradition of meat eating will arise by accident. A baboon will find a hare or a vervet, will kill it and eat it. The same thing will happen again and again, until many group members are chasing animals for food. Predation will become part of the group's general behavior, and an animal changing to a neighboring group will carry the new habit, passing it down to later generations. Among other groups of baboons, however, living in different areas, such a tradition for various reasons may not develop. Possibly the original fortuitous catches did not occur in sufficient numbers for a new tradition to become established; or possibly the nonpredator baboons lived in areas where there was enough vegetable food available to satisfy their needs, so that they never acquired the drive to catch and eat animals.

Chimpanzees, too, are predators with a seemingly ambiguous attitude toward animals that are their prey. Certainly they have demonstrated variable behavior on many occasions toward—of all possible victims—their neighbors, the baboons. During his study of a chimpanzee group in Gombe National Park in western Tanzania, primatologist Geza Teleki once saw an adult male baboon sit close to three adult male chimpanzees while the latter divided up a bushbuck they had caught. Nearby other baboons and chimpanzees searched together for pieces of meat. On another occasion, however, he observed a chimpanzee rush suddenly into the middle of a baboon troop and capture a young member (despite the vigorous efforts of numerous male baboons to prevent the seizure).

The predatory action of chimpanzees against baboons is difficult to explain, considering the fact that the two groups at Gombe are so accustomed to each other's presence. As ground dwellers, they use the same trails and eating areas; and each understands many of the communicative signals of the other. Furthermore, the baboons and chimpanzees at Gombe exhibit frequent social interactions. For example, Teleki reported that he saw the young of both groups mingle and play together almost daily.

Contradictory as their behavior appears, chimpanzees have clearly shown that as predators they do in fact hunt their prey. They have been known to select a victim prior to pursuing it; and even more interesting from the point of comparison with human practices, they often hunt cooperatively. Both Teleki and Jane Goodall, who initially established the field study at Gombe, observed unquestionable teamwork in the seizure of a prey animal.

"The prey," as Goodall has described one such incident, "a red colobus monkey, was sitting in a tree when an adolescent male chimpanzee climbed a neighboring tree and remained very still as the monkey looked toward it. A second adolescent male chimpanzee then climbed the tree in which the colobus was sitting, ran quickly along the branch, leapt at the colobus, and caught it with its hands, presumably breaking its neck, as it did not struggle or call out." As soon as the colobus had been killed, other chimpanzees jumped up into the tree to share in the spoils. Teleki, during his period of field study at Gombe, observed two or more chimpanzees hunting together. On one occasion, he watched no fewer than five of them close in on three baboons. This killing and the reactions of the other chimpanzees bear all the marks of deliberate—and coordinated—hunting.

In another way, also, the behavior of chimpanzees appears to anticipate the evolution of human attitudes toward meat and hunting. Chimpanzees spend far more time eating their prey than they do in chasing and catching it. In fact, Teleki estimates that, among Gombe chimpanzees, over 90 per cent of the time spent on a predatory excursion is devoted to the feast after the kill. When adult male chimpanzees are in possession of some meat, the other members of the group will sit around, holding out their hands as if begging for a share. This kind of begging and sharing has also been observed in several other primate species. Inevitably, one is reminded of the situation that came about as men became increasingly skillful hunters and the females and young in the group depended on the adult males to share the meat they had caught.

THE comparison with man must not be pushed too far. Essentially, chimpanzees are vegetarians, and meat forms a very minor part of their diet, as it does with baboons. Nonetheless, one may speculate that the predatory behavior of chimpanzees and baboons does offer a clue to the origins of organized hunting, the practice that, as will be seen in the following chapter, played an absolutely central role in the history of human development.

In yet another and quite unrelated form of activity generally considered unique to humans, some monkeys and apes do definitely anticipate human behavior. Only with difficulty can one imagine a monkey or an ape playing the role of artist.

Yet it is undeniable that some of them do paint. Capuchin monkeys, orangs and at least one gorilla have been coaxed into trying their hand with the brush, and chimpanzees, as is often the case, have proven particularly cooperative.

The results have been intriguing, even startling, for apparently chimpanzees paint very much as a human child does. This, at least, is the contention advanced by an English zoologist, Desmond Morris, who observed the work of a young male chimpanzee, Congo, for more than two years, and has described his findings in a fascinating book, *The Biology of Art*. Congo began to paint at the age of one and a half, using at first a primitive, clutching grip, and then progressing to a more delicate one with the brush held between his thumb and forefinger. Shortly before he lost interest in painting, Congo was drawing circles and making marks inside them, which is the stage a human child normally passes through just before he begins to draw faces. But the really significant point of Morris' study was his demonstration that a chimpanzee does not paint at random.

THE chimpanzees' attitude toward painting also encourages some intriguing, albeit tenuous, comparisons of their emotional makeups with those of human children. Individual chimpanzees vary, of course, just as humans do. Still, a few generalizations can be offered. When young, although playful, energetic and appreciative of favors, they can also show many of the qualities of a fractious and unpleasant child, especially in temper tantrums.

The brain of a human child is, of course, very different from that of a young ape or monkey. A human child possesses a vastly more complex brain which greatly increases its capacity to learn, to acquire knowledge and develop skills. Yet the study of nonhuman primates can also offer some valuable insights into the operations of the human intelligence—for example, into the way human beings learn, and learn how to learn.

How does a child learn to solve algebraical equations? Or to use language correctly? Or, to pose the same issue in social terms, how does a good salesman learn to perceive, as if by instinct, the right approach to use on a potential customer? For several hundred years it was widely believed that while some knowledge is acquired through the process of trial and error, the great mass is accumulated through a succession of sudden flashes of insight. Actually, these assumptions were mere armchair theorizing, for there was no way to put them to the test. One cannot keep a human being in a laboratory in order to trace the development of his learning processes. But, as Harry Harlow of the University of Wisconsin has demonstrated, one can do exactly that with monkeys. Very skillfully Harlow explored a new method of testing primate psychology. Instead of basing his tests on his monkeys' ability to manipulate objects—i.e., to solve single problems—he based them on the monkeys' ability to discriminate between objects of varying shapes and colors in a variety of situations. This ability, which in primates is not innate but must be learned, is absolutely vital to a monkey: It is only through its powers of discrimination that it can pick out food from the surrounding mass of inedible objects. One can therefore assume that the way a monkey learns to discriminate fairly reflects the general pattern of his learning processes.

Harlow began his experiments by putting two objects of different shapes, colors and sizes in front of his monkeys, with a food reward concealed under one of them. After a series of trials and mistakes, the monkeys learned to pick out the right object every time. Then Harlow moved on to confront them with three objects, one of which was different from the others. Once again, after a series of trials and mistakes, the monkeys learned always or nearly always to pick out the object that was unlike the others. Gradually, progressing from one stage of complexity to the next, Harlow kept making his problems more difficult until finally his monkeys were performing, practically without a mistake, feats that required considerable powers of thought. Confronted with three objects on an orange-colored tray, they would regularly pick out the one that was different in shape from the others. Confronted with the same objects on a cream-colored tray, they picked out the one that was unique in color.

The monkeys were able to progress because, at each new stage of complexity, they mastered some new principle of selection. Once it was mastered, they were then able to apply it to every similar problem and also to remember it for a year or more. Item by item the monkeys built up a store of knowledge, just as a child does when it learns how to conjugate different tenses of verbs or understand progressively more difficult geometrical theorems.

In Harlow's phrase the monkeys acquired "learning sets," each one an organized set of habits that enabled them to solve any problem of a particular type. As the sets accumulated, the monkeys' patterns of thinking grew steadily more complex. Projecting from monkeys to humans Harlow concluded that people learn in the same way. From early childhood on they are continually attempting to solve problems, making mistakes, and drawing the appropriate conclusions as to what will work and what will not. This means that all our knowledge is founded on immensely complicated assemblages of learning sets. The diver going off a high board, the poker player betting on a pair, the would-be lover holding off his advances to provoke a girl's curiosity . . . all of them are acting, whether they are aware of it or not, on the basis of an enormously complex mass of habits and patterns of behavior that have been tested in the past and found to be effective. "Experience never teaches," is the frequently heard cry of the despairing skeptic. But if Harlow is correct, and the concept of learning through sudden flashes of innate insight is false, then experience, however often neglected, proves after all to be the only teacher we possess.

THE study of nonhuman primates can also yield some extremely useful insight into another aspect of human behavior—into the causes of human neuroses. The reader will perhaps remember a reference made earlier in this book to Harlow's discovery that some of his infant monkeys displayed types of neurotic behavior that were strikingly similar to those observed in humans. In fact the patterns of neuroses a monkey can suffer read rather like a list of entries in a psychiatrist's notebook: inability to live a normal social life, aberrant sexual activity, incompetent—even abusive—maternal conduct, the juvenile-delinquent syndrome. These and other forms of abnormal behavior have been observed in monkeys, and all of them are the consequence of either inadequate mothering or isolation from other infants.

But how long must a monkey be kept in isolation before its neuroses become so deeply implanted that they can never be eradicated? The answer is both relevant to the human condition and, potentially, of considerable value to people engaged in trying to salvage children from the consequences of infancy without affection. Through another series of classic experiments, Harlow was able to pinpoint the period with considerable accuracy. He found that if an infant macaque is kept in isolation for some 60 to 90 days after its birth and is then allowed to mix with other monkeys, its neurotic tendencies can be corrected and it will grow up quite normal. But every added week beyond that

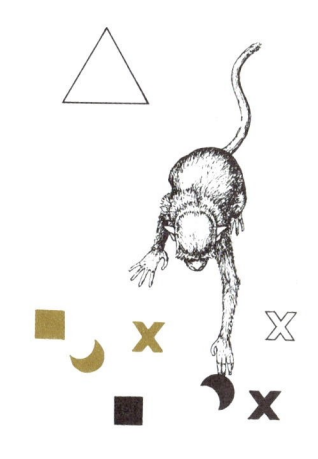

THE THINKING RHESUS

Can a monkey think? Certainly, as these experiments with a rhesus by Benjamin Weinstein demonstrate. First he conditioned the monkey to react to color by teaching it to push forward black objects when shown a black triangle, and brown objects when shown a brown circle. Then Weinstein went on to the more difficult step of presenting an uncolored triangle and circle (drawings above and below). The monkey was still able to select the appropriate colors, proving it had mastered the sophisticated mental step of linking up a shape with a color.

time reduces the chance that the monkey can ever recover from the baleful effects of its early deprivation.

A rhesus monkey, it should be remembered, is more advanced at birth than a human infant, and it matures four times as rapidly. The critical period in the development of humans, therefore, occurs later, but since laboratory experiments cannot be performed on human infants, the exactly comparable ages are not known. Probably the first 12 months of human life correspond roughly to the first week or two in the life of a monkey; for both this is the time when the most important factor is simple survival with the help of adequate food, warmth and care. But from then on, for the next two or three years, it is likely that man, with his larger brain and learning capacity, is more susceptible to his environment than the monkey. If a child is deprived during this time of affection, companionship and opportunities to learn the things it needs to know for successful living, the effects on both its temperament and intelligence may be almost permanent. Such, in any event, is the suggestion derived from experiments like Harlow's; but the results of any such work would have to be checked on humans themselves if we are to be sure.

EXPERIMENTING in his laboratory with rhesus monkeys, Harlow also came to a number of tentative conclusions about motherhood which may bear on human behavior. Why are some mothers attentive and loving, others indifferent or even brutal? Is it a question of genetic makeup? No doubt, up to a point. As Phyllis Jay has observed, some monkey females are better mothers than others. Monkeys, like humans, are not all born with equal talents. Still, monkey mothers so far observed in the wild have been generally attentive to their offspring at least during the first weeks of their lives. One might be tempted to credit this to the natural instinct of motherhood, but to do so would be only a half-truth, because the popular concept of instinct is far from accurate. Actually monkeys—and men and women—are born possessed only of emotional "tendencies," and those tendencies will flower into action only if their possessor enjoys the appropriate experiences.

If she is to grow up to be a good mother, a female monkey must, among other normal experiences, herself receive proper maternal care—or so Harlow concluded from a study of four monkey females which had been raised in isolation without real mothers. When they in their turn became mothers, they displayed none of the attentiveness that a monkey female in the wild lavishes on her offspring. They were reluctant to feed their infants. They seemed not to care when the infants were taken from them by keepers, and some treated their infants with positive cruelty. If one can, in fact, legitimately project from monkeys to humans, then the conclusion is obvious: Human females must enjoy the attentions of a loving mother if they are to give their own children the love and attention that every child needs.

And what happens to the offspring, both male and female, of such unloving mothers? Very much the same as what happens to human children who are raised without affection. The infants of Harlow's "motherless mothers" turned out to be aggressive in temper and precocious in their sexual behavior, two characteristics that have been found to be among the most common marks of the disturbed child. Farfetched as it may seem, when one considers how vast a gap separates the nonhuman primates from human beings, monkeys bear in themselves many of the emotional qualities, both normal and abnormal, of that unique creature—man.

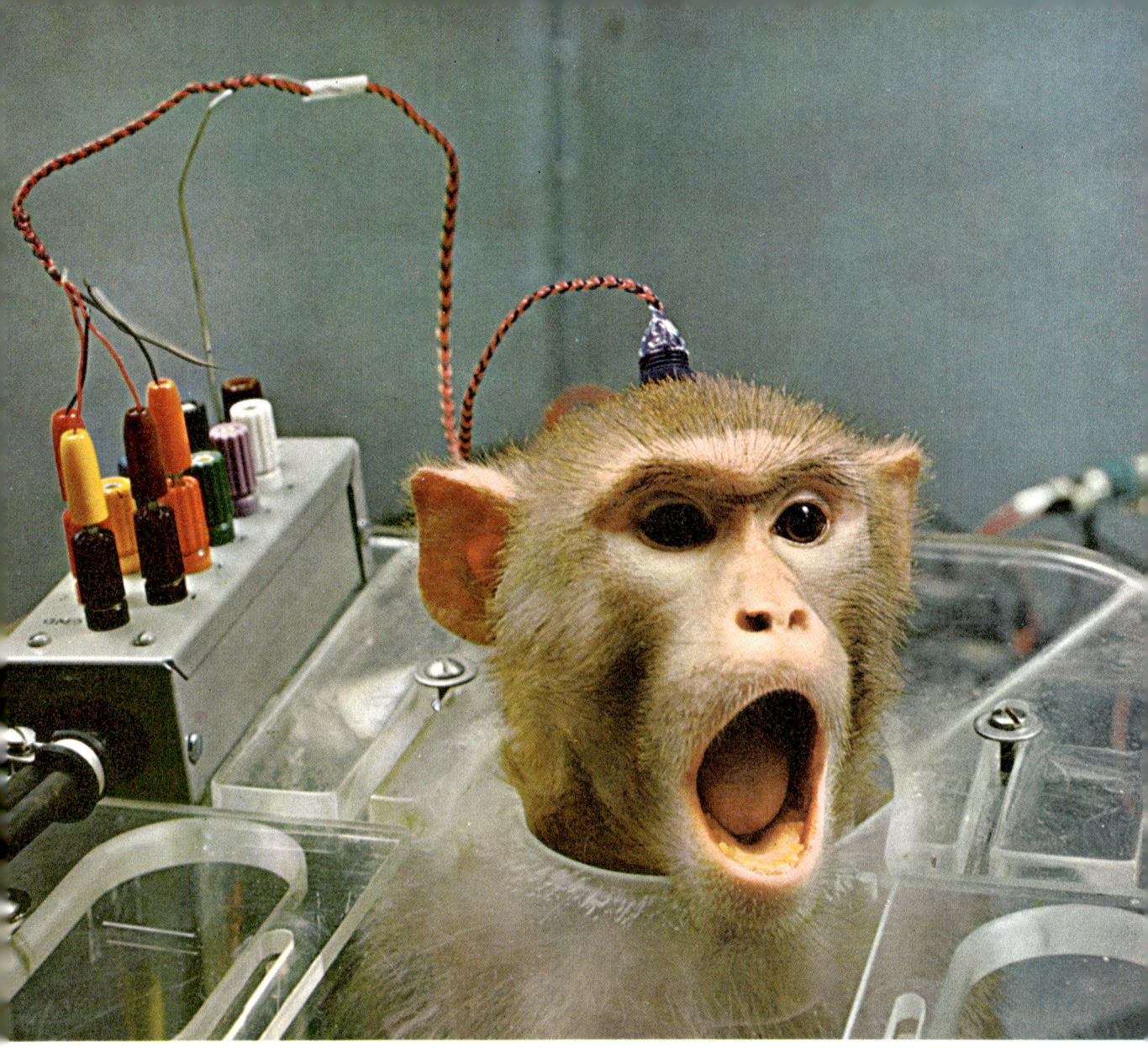

OBLIVIOUS TO ELECTRODES MEASURING ITS BRAIN ACTIVITY, THIS RHESUS MONKEY REACTS TO THE PHOTOGRAPHER WITH A TYPICAL THREAT

Science and the Primate

Because of their similarities to man, primates are invaluable substitutes in scientific research, both in the laboratory and in their native habitats. Without them many medical discoveries would never have been made, and the first astronauts would have faced far greater risks. Potentially even more important for man are the present studies of primates' behavior and intellectual capacities.

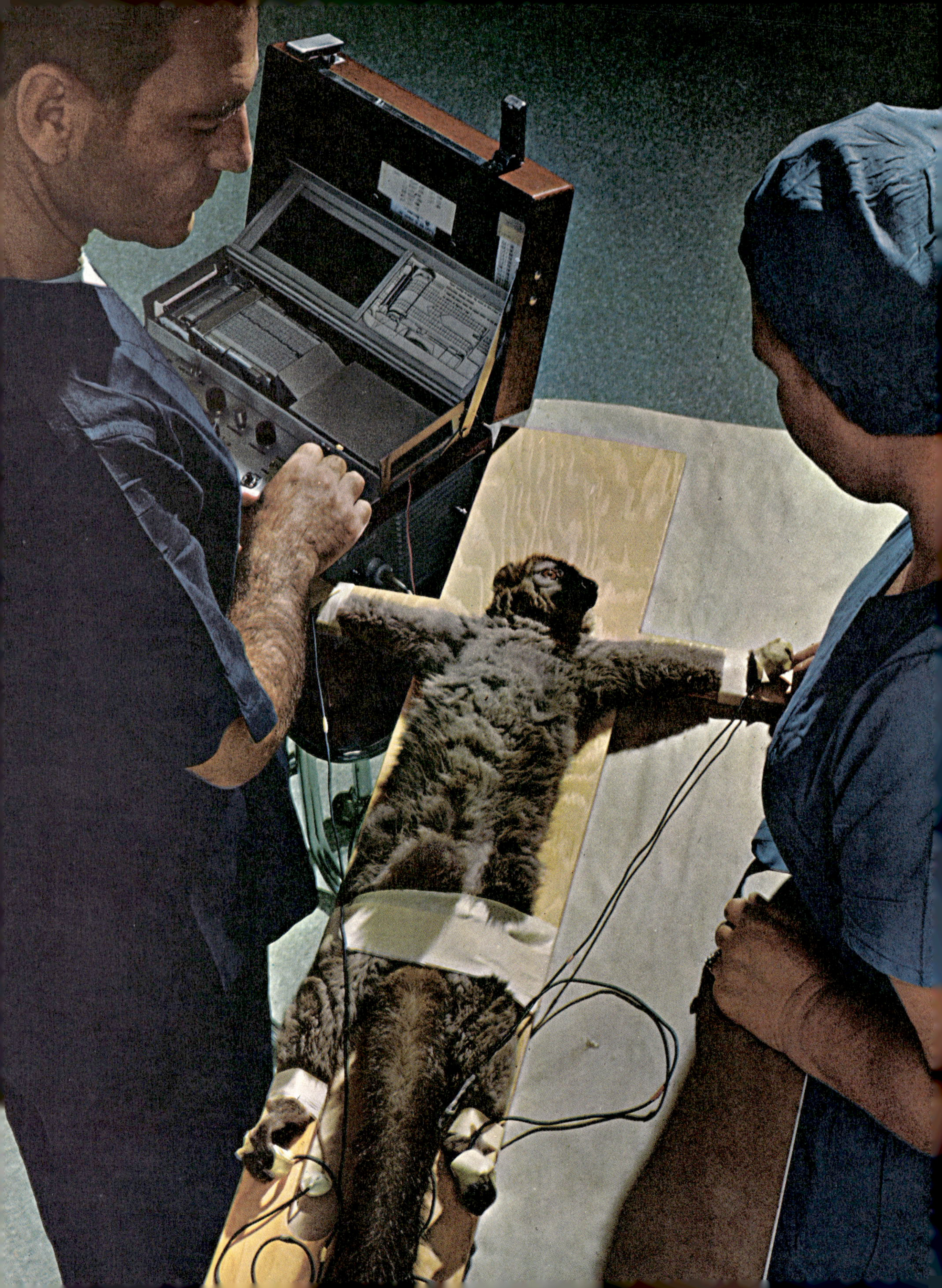

A New Age of Research

Research on nonhuman primates is responsible for some of the most important advances in modern medical history. Comparative studies with rhesus monkeys, for example, resulted in the discovery of the Rh—for rhesus—factor in human red blood cells. This gave rise to a new technique of blood transfusion that, by matching the Rh factor in the blood of donor and recipient, has saved many human lives. There are 16 nonhuman primate species living at the Oregon Regional Primate Research Center shown on this page. More than half the 2,300 animals being studied by scientists are rhesus monkeys.

There are seven primate research centers in the United States. Each of them gives its animals the best possible care not only for humane reasons, but also because only healthy animals make reliable research subjects. Because of increasing difficulties in importing these animals, several of the primate centers have established breeding colonies that have become a major source of research animals.

THE CELEBES APE, actually a monkey, is bred at the center for a specific purpose. Because it is prone to a disease that is similar to human diabetes, it may provide clues for a cure.

AN ELECTROCARDIOGRAM is performed on a lemur to help set norms for testing body functions. The Oregon center has one of the largest colonies of prosimians in the world.

OUTDOOR CAGES provide abundant fresh air for the primates at Beaverton, Oregon. This is one of six structures being used as exercise and holding areas for rhesus monkeys.

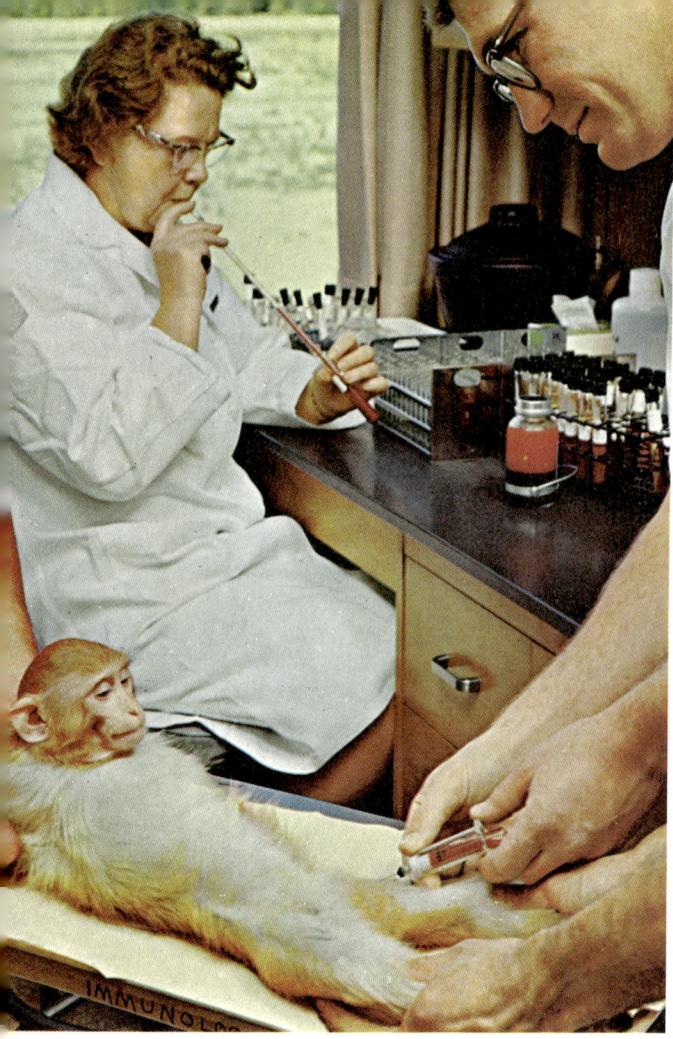

GIVING BLOOD, a monkey watches as a sample is drawn from its leg. The blood is prepared for testing by a scientist who uses it to study antibody production of the immune system.

The Primate's Role in Medicine

The medical research conducted on nonhuman primates at the Oregon center is aimed at gaining basic knowledge for the conquest of some of man's most serious diseases and disorders. The many areas being investigated include atherosclerosis and heart disease, allergies, organ-transplant rejection, cancer and skin disorders. Illness is not the only area of interest; a major study of nonhuman primate reproduction is being conducted to seek solutions to other medical and social problems of our time: contraception, infertility, premature birth and birth defects. The life history of each animal is documented from its arrival at the center and, whenever possible, from the day of conception. Such data are compiled daily by computer.

IN SURGERY a fully anesthetized rhesus monkey undergoes a cardiac catheterization—a delicate operation in which a thin tube is threaded through its femoral vein into its heart. The tongue depressor keeps the monkey from choking, and the tube in its mouth prevents mucus from collecting in its throat. A wide variety of surgical procedures is performed by the staff at the Oregon center. An excellent X-ray facility and regular dental and medical examinations of all the animals insure the conservation of a valuable living resource.

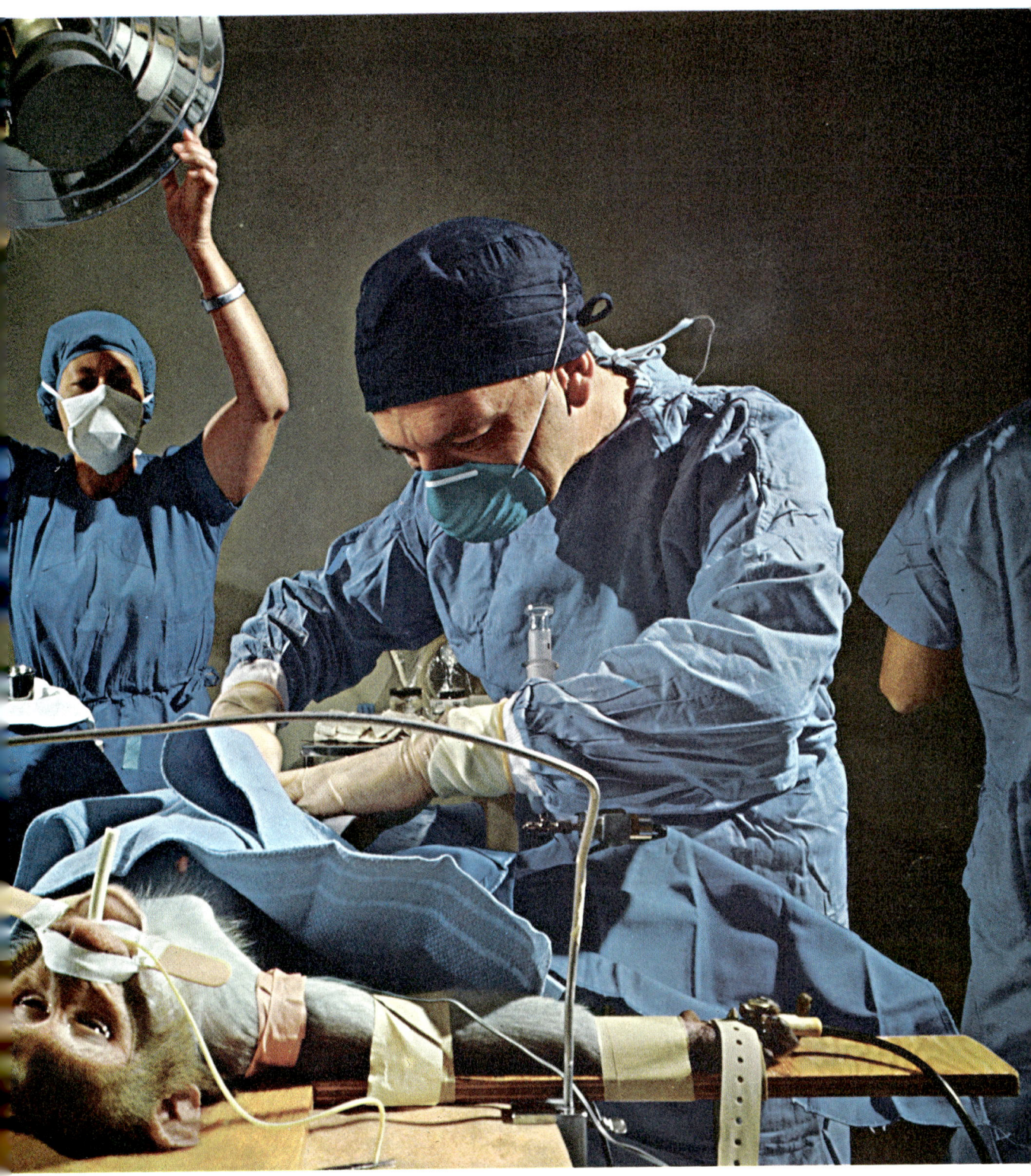

163

A VICTIM OF POLIO, this baby gorilla is improving after extensive physiotherapy. The disease was not induced; as with tuberculosis and hepatitis, apes are as susceptible to it as man.

A Laboratory for Behavior

Although it engages in medical research, the Yerkes Regional Primate Center in Atlanta, Georgia, directs much of its program to behavioral studies. Chimpanzees, orangutans and gorillas here are undergoing tests to explore their intellectual processes, personality traits and social behavior. Pigtail macaques and other monkeys are being studied to determine the most important factors for establishing various kinds of social hierarchies, and extensive experiments are being conducted into the nature of alcoholism and drug addiction.

The Yerkes center opened in 1930 in Orange Park, Florida, with a total primate population of 25 chimpanzees. In 1977 it had the largest collection of apes in the United States: 110 chimpanzees, 36 orangutans and 18 gorillas, as well as nearly 2,000 monkeys of various species. Although psychobiology is still a major part of the center's program, there is a growing volume of physiological research, including studies on the effects of stress on the nervous system. Scientists at the center are also vitally interested in primate breeding: A self-perpetuating colony has become an urgent necessity, since many species of primates living in the wild are endangered.

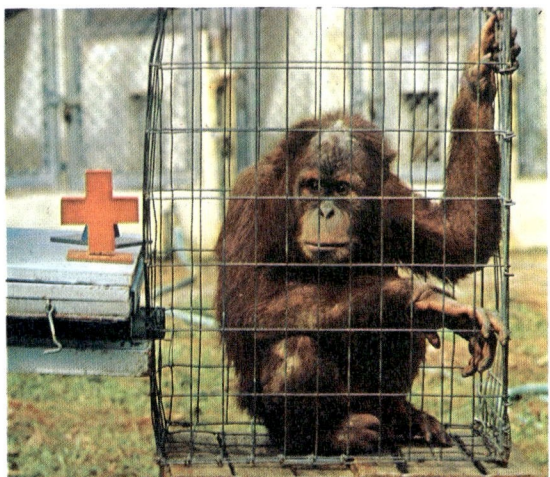

A HUNGRY ORANG picks the red cross and earns a piece of fruit in a test for shape and color discrimination. Having eaten *(bottom)*, however, a subject often becomes satiated and quits.

A BIBULOUS CHIMP savors its daily ration of alcohol and orange juice. After six months it showed no signs of alcoholism, and could guzzle a fifth (0.76 l) before it was visibly inebriated.

INFANTS PLAY in a room designed for study of infant relationships. With the toys and gymnastic equipment are two artificial mothers that give solace when an infant becomes anxious.

Studies in Monkey Love

What is the nature of primate affection? Are the emotions that a monkey or ape experiences comparable to that peculiarly human emotion called love? To answer these questions, Dr. Harry Harlow of the Wisconsin Regional Primate Center launched a full-scale study of infant rhesus monkeys and the factors that influence their behavior toward each other. After a decade of tests and observations Harlow arrived at the conclusion that primates experience affection in five distinct ways, each classified

TERROR ENTERS in the form of a drum-beating teddy bear. This was a test to determine whether a terrified infant would seek security in an inanimate mother.

THE INFANT FLEES from the advancing drummer, seeking its cloth mother. The wire mother to the right was rejected by virtually every one of the frightened infants.

166

as a separate and distinct "affectional system." These systems include the love expressed by an infant toward its mother, the affection that an adult male feels for infants, the camaraderie that exists between a juvenile and its contemporaries, the affection of a mother for her own offspring, and the sexual attraction between adults or juveniles of opposite sexes. Of all the different kinds of love, the most basic is the first—an infant's complete dependence upon its mother. Harlow has amply demonstrated the power of these kinds of affection with a number of different experiments, notably those involving infants' relationships to wire or terry cloth mothers. In a study of an infant's response to fright *(below)*, Harlow started with the general observation that young primates of any species, including human beings, usually seek the protection of their mothers during times of danger or stress. This series of experiments proved that brief contact with a cloth mother served admirably as an antidote to fear.

REASSURED by the soft warmth of its cloth mother, the infant peers at the fearsome intruder. Several of the infants regained enough confidence to leave the mother and go to investigate.

167

IN SOUTHERN INDIA, anthropologist Phyllis Jay confers with a team of Japanese scientists. They spent years pioneering in studies of macaques and langurs in their native environment.

IN EAST AFRICA, Irven DeVore, co-author of this book, took some 45,000 feet (13,700 m) of color film to record in detail the intricate structure and interrelationships of a baboon society.

IN BORNEO, Biruté Galdikas holds a young orang confiscated from an illegal owner. In addition to the rehabilitation program, she has been making a study of wild orangs.

IN THE CARIBBEAN, a rhesus macaque adopts a threat posture in a monkey colony near Puerto Rico. The "72" tattoo identifies it for records.

Revelations in the Field

Not until 1931, when C. R. Carpenter journeyed to Panama to study howler monkeys, had a scientist actually gone out into the field to observe primates systematically in their own environments. He published some revolutionary findings on monkey behavior which pointed up the fallacy of studying captive species; despite this, no further extensive field research was undertaken until after World War II. Then, with the establishment of the Primate Research Group in Japan where monkeys began to be meticulously studied under natural conditions, an entirely new concept of primate research unfolded. Today, scores of specialized experts from several countries are teaming up to study primate behavior in the wild. Such interdisciplinary field research has already produced more fully rounded pictures than man has ever had before of his primate cousins.

IN CENTRAL AFRICA, Dian Fossey walks through the forest near her isolated field station with two young mountain gorillas. She has studied this endangered species in their native habitat since 1967.

168

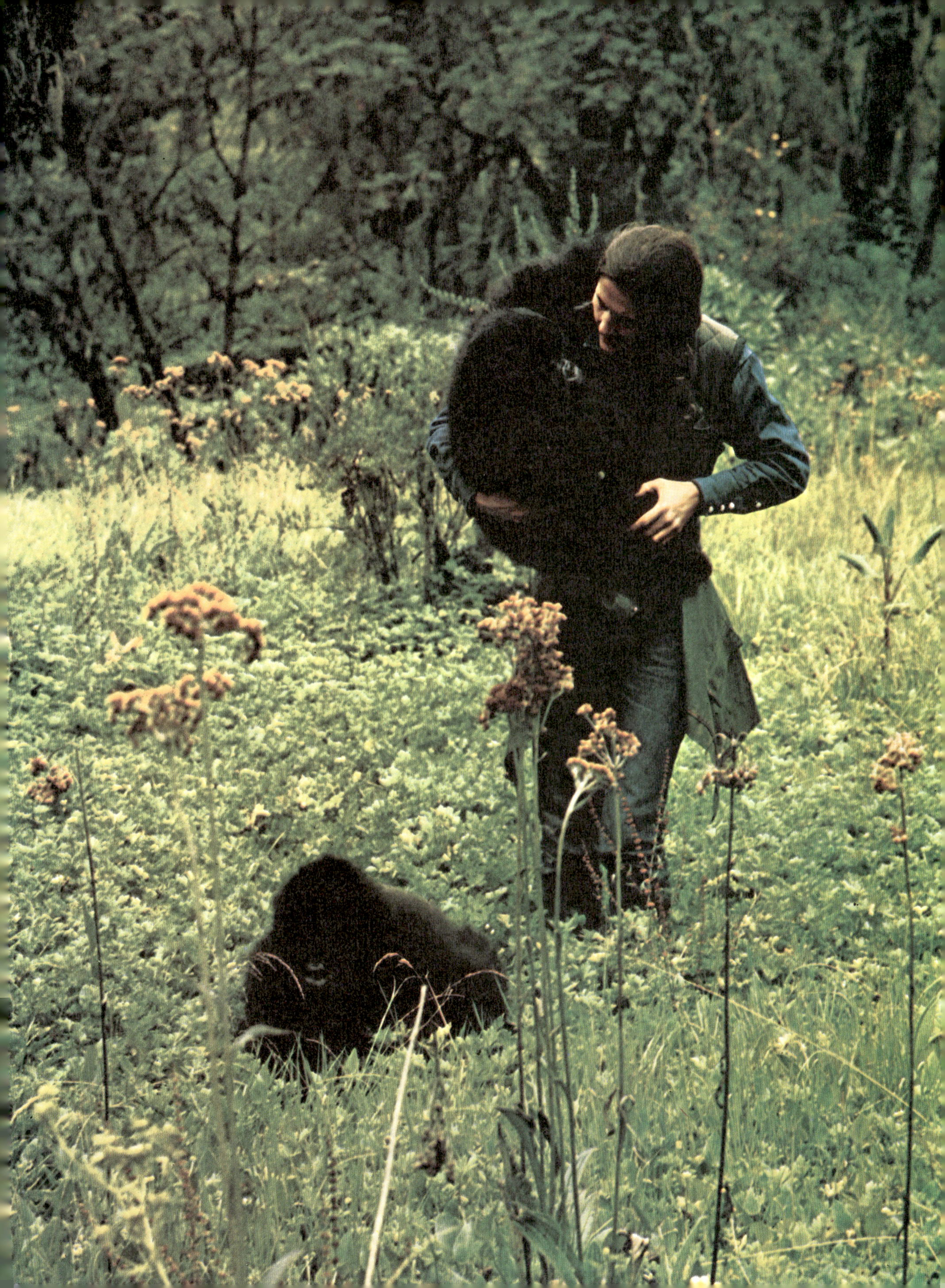

What Can Be Learned from Primate Art

In the half-century that apes and monkeys have been painting, some of their work has been seriously studied, but much of it has been used in elaborate practical jokes. For instance paintings by the chimpanzee Pierre in Sweden *(opposite)* were displayed in 1964 under the name Pierre Brassau. His works were given serious critical comment, and several were sold before the hoax was discovered.

That there is a valid purpose in studying primate art, however, is the contention of zoologist Desmond Morris, whose chimpanzee Congo painted the pictures below. According to Morris, primate art pro-

A FINGER PAINTING shows Congo's favorite design—a radiating pattern. Most of his paintings were done with a brush; with finger paints he tended to obliterate his original design.

HEAVY HORIZONTAL LINES embellish Congo's more usual fan pattern. Sometimes he stumbled upon new techniques, such as scratching the picture with his fingernails or even licking it.

A CENTRAL DOT surrounded by swaths of color suggests at least an elementary grasp of composition. Further evidence is that Congo almost always painted within the paper's borders.

vides a source of basic artistic expression that may reveal the origins of human art. Thus chimpanzees exhibit a rudimentary sense of composition, and also, apparently, they have an urge of some sort which is satisfied by painting: Congo painted avidly for three years without ever having to be enticed.

A CELEBRATED ARTIST, a chimp named Pierre sits at an easel in a Swedish zoo and chooses colors from a palette. Very highstrung, Pierre often ate a banana a minute while painting.

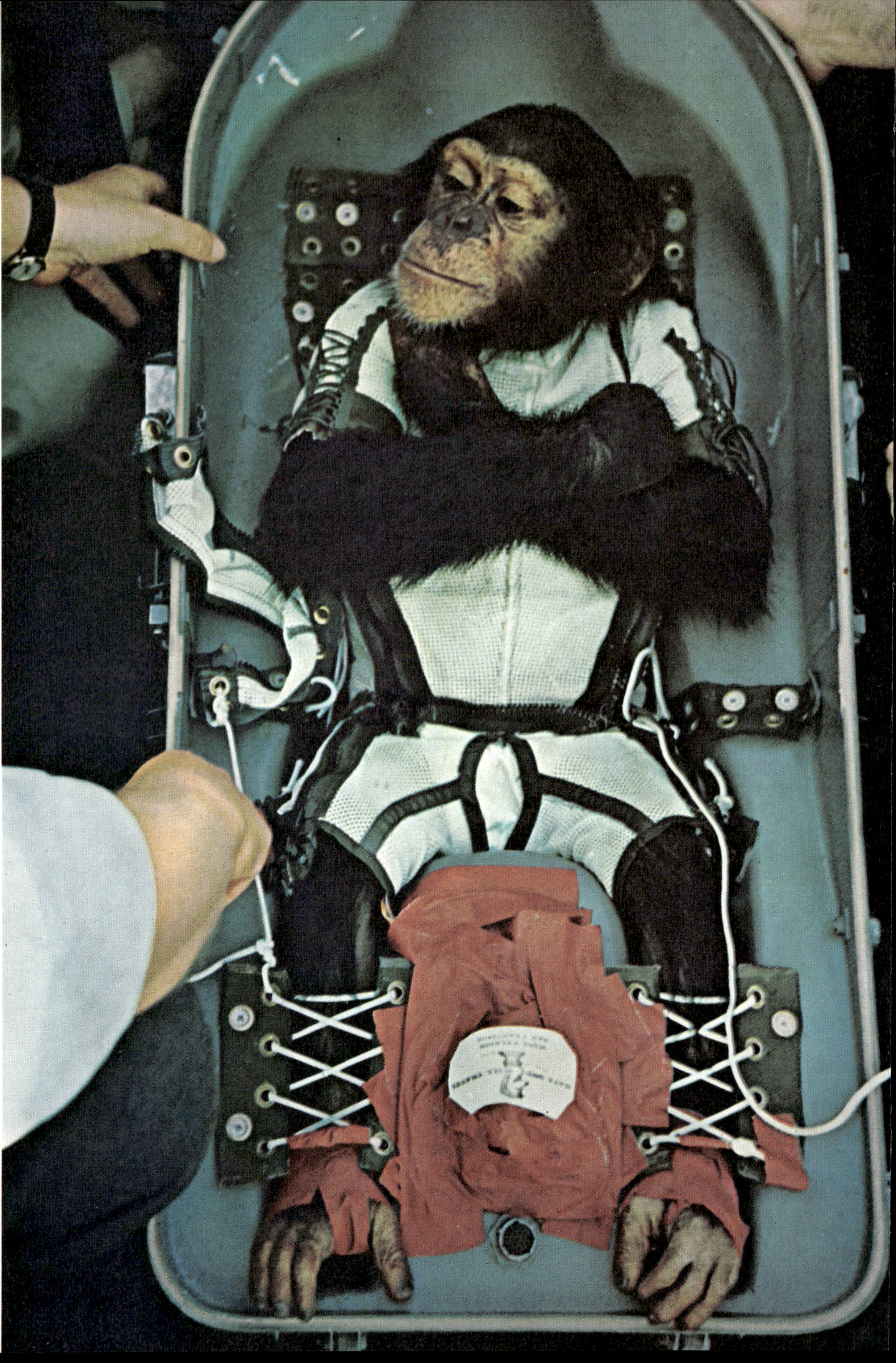

BACK FROM SPACE, chimpanzee Ham patiently waits to be released from a contour couch like those used by human astronauts. Under his pressure suit are telemetric devices to monitor his body functions.

Understudies for Man in the Conquest of Space

When the successful development of rockets in the late 1940s made the exploration of space a workable reality, animals were the first to be sent out into this unknown realm. The first "astronauts" were fungus spores and fruit flies launched from Holloman Air Force Base in New Mexico. In 1949 a rhesus monkey was rocketed 83 miles (134 km) high; subsequent tests included the 1961 suborbital flight of the chimpanzee Ham *(left)*.

One of the numerous questions that test animals helped to answer before man could embark on an extended space journey was what he should breathe. Pure oxygen at about one-third normal atmospheric pressure was settled on for moon flights after testing the effects of various gas mixtures on monkeys like the macaque named Lizzie *(right)*. Later a combination of oxygen and nitrogen was specified for extended space missions like those of the Skylab program. Reason: Pure oxygen encourages materials to burn, as was tragically proved in 1967 when three astronauts died within seconds after a fire broke out in their capsule.

BREATHING PURE OXYGEN in a test for possible toxic effects, this macaque was safely sealed for 90 days in this chamber. It exercised by having to pull a lever 80 times for a single portion of food or water.

173

QUESTION is asked by Lana of research technician Tim Gill as she punches her console keys. Symbols on the screens indicate "Lana groom Tim?" An overhead bar activates the console.

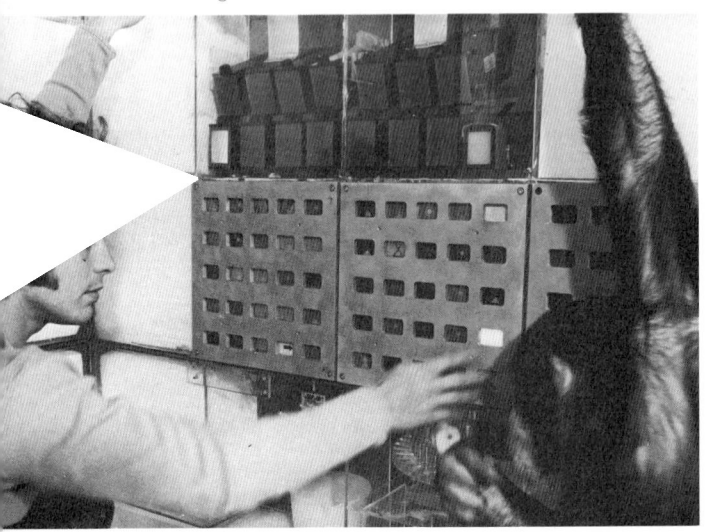

ANSWER comes as Gill punches the key calling symbol "yes" to one of Lana's screens. The symbols and positions of the keys are often changed to further test Lana's comprehension.

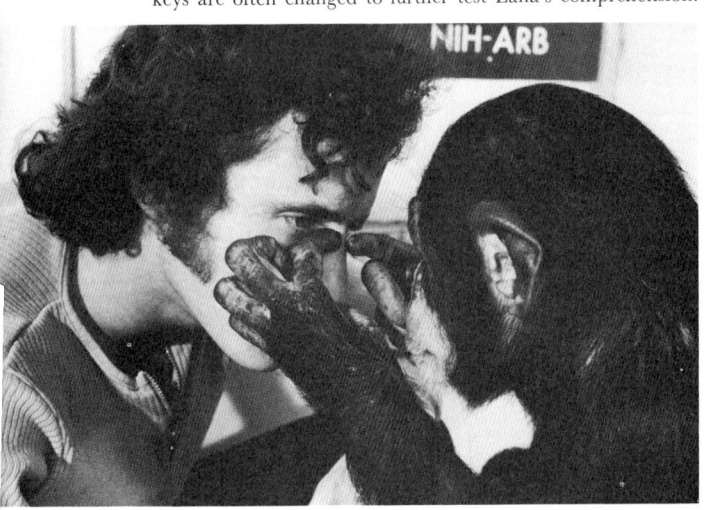

ACTION is suited to "words" as Lana proceeds with the kind of grooming she would give another chimpanzee. The action is often reversed: Lana also knows how to ask Tim to groom her.

SCREENS above the console carry the symbols, which are called lexigrams. These read, left to right: ?, and symbols for Lana, groom and Tim.

How to Talk to an Ape

Early attempts by scientists to teach primates to speak—to learn and utter human words—failed. But other ingenuous ways have been devised so man and ape can communicate. At Yerkes Regional Primate Center in Atlanta a team of scientists, headed by Dr. Duane Rumbaugh of Georgia State University, devised an electronic system not only to communicate with them but also to evaluate their intelligence.

By means of a computer-controlled training program a young chimp called Lana learned to communicate in a language of symbols fittingly called Yerkish. She is able to understand what is said to her and can give the correct reply. In addition she can initiate conversation and cause the computer to erase a communication of hers when she realizes she has made a mistake.

Lana's channel of communication consists of a keyboard console and two rows of projectors in her seven-foot (2.1-m) plastic cube. (A similar console for her trainers is outside her room.) Each key of the console carries a symbol representing a word or a punctuation mark. When a key is depressed its symbol appears on a projector above the keyboard. Thus Lana is able to view a word chain she has put together and can also read what the scientists have said in response.

In another experiment using a different technique a gorilla called Koko is being taught basic sign-language signals. She has developed a 300-word gesture vocabulary and responds to sign language as well as the spoken word, using it to indicate what she is thinking and, even more intriguing, how she feels. These experiments are proving that while an ape is unable to speak, it is capable of using words appropriately and seems to have more intelligence than it ever needs in the wild.

"WHERE IS YOUR NOSE?" Francine Patterson asks Koko, and Koko reponds in sign language by pointing to her nose. "Penny" Patterson, a graduate student in psychology at Stanford, borrowed one-year-old Koko from a zoo for her experiments in learning and communication and in 1977 purchased the gorilla. She intends to work with Koko for the rest of the animal's life.

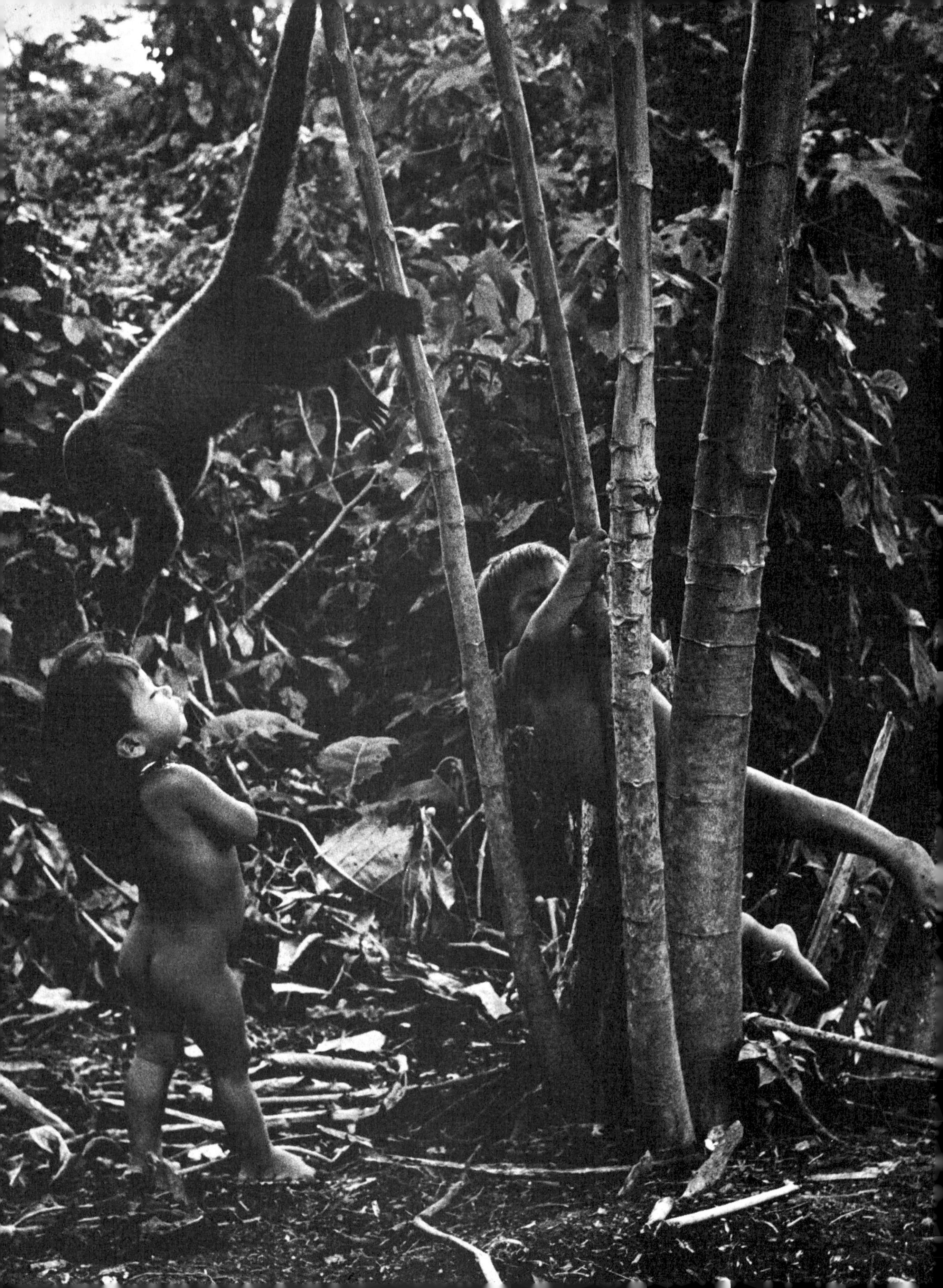

PLAYMATES STILL, a pet woolly monkey and two naked Auca children frisk in an Ecuador jungle. To these primitive Indians monkeys are an integral part of life but are kept more for the pot than as pets.

8

From Ape toward Man

Some 15 million to 20 million years ago, several different species of apes inhabited the huge forest which then stretched, unbroken by any major water barriers, from the west coast of Africa to what are now the islands of the East Indies. Then, in a slow but decisive manner, the climate changed. In many regions it became drier, and areas that had once contained dense forests were transformed into extensive grasslands. As might be expected, the altered habitat made it impossible for all of the forest apes to exist, and many of them became extinct. Of those that survived, some became adapted to spending time on the ground in more open country while the others continued to enjoy an arboreal life. Among these varied, wide-ranging populations of apes were the groups whose descendants still survive today in East Asia as the orangutan and gibbon and in Africa as the chimpanzee and the gorilla.

Unfortunately, the early stages of man's evolutionary progress along his own individual line remain a mystery. We do know that by about five million or six million years ago a manlike creature had come into existence. Between four million and two million years ago at least two varieties of early hominids were living in sub-Saharan Africa. These intermediate creatures stood about five feet (1.5 m) tall, one weighing about 80 to 100 (36 to 45 kg) and the other up to 150 pounds (68 kg). Their brains were not quite as big as that of a large male gorilla. Though they probably could not yet stride smoothly for long distances, they could run upright with their bodies balanced on their hind legs.

We owe our knowledge of the australopithecines—as these primitive, small-brained ape men were called—to the patient archeological research of five remarkable scientists. In 1924 Raymond A. Dart, a professor of anatomy at the University of Witwatersrand, perceived in a skull that had been dug up not far from Johannesburg the traces of a very early type of hominid that was part ape, part man. Some years later, Dart's perceptions were confirmed by the discovery of more australopithecine fossils. These were unearthed elsewhere in South Africa by a Scottish physician, Robert Broom, who, excited by Dart's initial find, decided to join in the search.

Meanwhile, another team of prehistorians, Louis and Mary Leakey, were also hunting for fossils of early men, at Olduvai Gorge in Tanzania. After nearly 30 years of perseverance, they unearthed the fossil remains of two early hominids—a large-boned *Australopithecus* and a slighter, more manlike creature. In 1974 the most primitive australopithecine species of all was discovered by the American anthropologist Donald C. Johanson in eastern Ethiopia. But the most astonishing find was associated with the Leakeys' manlike hominid; close to the fossils, there were tools, made out of pebbles that had been chipped to give them a sharp cutting edge. Louis Leakey thought that this species was probably the first true man and so he named it *Homo habilis*, or "handy man."

These finds provided the basis for the first coherent explanations of how man came to evolve out of his apelike ancestors. One of the most convincing interpretations of this evolutionary process has been stated in considerable detail by Professor Sherwood Washburn of the University of California, and much of what follows has been based upon his series of papers on the subject.

Washburn's explanation of how early man came into existence is not merely novel; it also contradicts a number of assumptions that had previously gone largely unquestioned. Long before Leakey unearthed his first australopithecine fossils in 1959, most anthropologists were agreed that the only animals that could properly be considered human were the ones that were able to make and to use tools. But how had man acquired the ability to use tools? The fashionable answer was that he had first developed a uniquely large, complex and efficient brain. Possessed of this extremely serviceable brain, he was able to manipulate tools. And he could do so the more easily because somehow, at some point in his evolution, man had also become a bipedal creature who could stand up and move about on two legs with his arms and hands left free.

The reader will perhaps perceive the flaw in this interpretation of man's evolutionary progress. Animals only acquire new characteristics if they provide some immediate advantage. They are never acquired merely by accident, to be stored away, as it were, like money in the bank, possibly to serve some useful purpose in the distant future. It is therefore inconceivable that man should first have acquired a large brain—and an erect posture—for no particular purpose, and then, later, should have taken advantage of these characteristics to make and to use tools. The processes of evolution simply do not allow for such lucky strokes of fortune.

Actually, as Leakey's finds demonstrated, the traditional explanation of human evolution had placed the horse with great precision right behind the

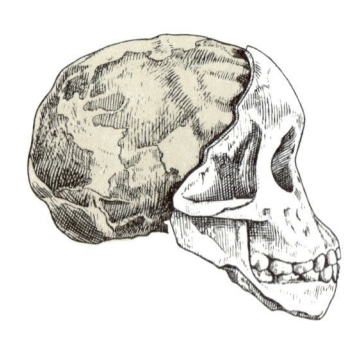

BETWEEN MAN AND APE

Australopithecus africanus—"australis" meaning "south" and "pithecus" meaning "ape"—is the name Raymond A. Dart gave to his discovery of a primate fossil over one million years old, taken from a quarry in South Africa in 1924. This fossil, the skull of a child about six years old, is in three pieces. Two parts consist of facial bones and the lower jaw. The other (shown in color) is a stone cast formed inside the skull, and denotes the shape and size of the brain, even though the brain case itself is missing. Together they give a picture of a form, no longer ape, but not yet man. It has somewhat human features and a brain capacity larger than a chimpanzee's but not as large as that of the earliest true man.

cart. Later in this chapter, we shall see how man did in fact come to acquire his unique brain. For the moment, however, we shall confine ourselves to the stages of his progress which took place much earlier, since they can be deduced from what we know about nonhuman primates and from the ever-increasing number of hominid fossils anthropologists are discovering in many locations throughout South and East Africa.

To set man's evolutionary history in the proper perspective, it is necessary to realize that the australopithecines whose remains have been discovered were not the earliest hominids. By way of illustration, let us suppose that in a few million years' time some future Dart or Leakey descends from outer space to an earth where man no longer exists, and digs up the fossil skeletons of 20th Century Americans. If he assumed that those Americans had been among the first humans, he would clearly be making a grievous error, and so would anyone who assumed that the australopithecines so far discovered were representatives of the earliest hominids.

There is, in fact, very good reason to suppose that they were comparative latecomers on the scene. Before man's apelike ancestors descended from the trees, they must have been exposed to attacks from predators and, like male baboons, macaques and gorillas, the male hominids almost certainly possessed long canines that they used to defend themselves, their females and their young. Had they not done so, the hominids would surely have been wiped out. Yet the australopithecine fossils show that these little apelike men possessed canines no longer or sharper than those of modern man. What happened to this obviously necessary defensive adaptation? Presumably they lost their long canines because at some point they learned to use weapons instead of their teeth for defense. An evolutionary change of this magnitude change must have taken a great many years to occur.

At the same time, another enormously significant change was also taking place. Judging from the habits of nonhuman primates, when they first left the trees, man's apelike predecessors must have used their hands to obtain food. But it is very likely that, by the time they began to forage on the ground, they had also discovered the value of tools: very primitive ones at first, no doubt—perhaps no more complex than the sticks that chimpanzees thrust into termite holes. The important point is that these early hominids did not stop there—they went on to develop tools that were much more elaborate and in the process of doing so they acquired fingers and thumbs that were suitable for the manipulation of comparatively complex instruments.

The australopithecines possessed such manipulable fingers and thumbs, and these very useful digits must have taken a long time to evolve. Much time, too, must have been required for the early hominids to acquire the important physical characteristics that enabled the australopithecines to move in an erect position, bipedally, with their bodies supported on their legs. How much time? Four million years, perhaps. Or six. Or eight. In the present stage of our knowledge, it is impossible to be more precise.

It was, of course, no coincidence that all these various changes—in the teeth and the fingers and thumbs, in the pelvis and the leg and the foot—should have taken place in the same animals. For the shift to bipedalism and the use of tools, as we can logically reconstruct it now, were very closely connected. With each new shift toward bipedalism, the hominids' hands were left more free to make and to use tools. As they came to rely more on tools, they had a greater incentive to depend on their legs for support. So they experienced a further shift towards bipedalism.

In other words, the hominids evolved through a continual process of feedback, with the use of tools and their bipedal posture acting as mutual cause and effect. While the idea of evolutionary progress by feedback may seem very obvious once it has been suggested, it is in fact a radical departure from traditional thinking, and has begun to win acceptance only in the past 20 years or so. Actually, all evolutionary progress, not only that of man, has taken place through a series of very tiny changes, each one at once producing some small advantage and paving the way for the next change.

But why, to pose the obvious question, was it only the hominids who benefited from the feedback interaction between bipedalism and the use of tools? Chimpanzees manipulate simple tools: They use sticks to dig out insects, crumpled leaves to soak up water. Why, then, did they not also go on to use more complex tools? The answer is that an evolutionary change will only occur if it happens to fit in with an animal's general makeup: with its anatomy, its situation and its behavior. All three depend very largely on where and how it gets its food. Being primarily fruit eaters, chimpanzees were compelled to spend much of their time in the trees. They have, in consequence, retained feet and toes suitable for climbing, and so were unable to acquire the kind of foot which is suitable for bipedal movement on the ground. This, in turn, meant that they could not go on to develop the kind of complex tools which bipedal movement made possible.

Once they were able to move efficiently on the ground, man's apelike ancestors were in a very different situation, similar in many ways to that of the present-day baboon. Like baboons, they must have eaten fruit and plants, eggs and game. No doubt they also dug for the long, tuberous roots which make up much of a baboon's diet in the dry season, and this offers one possible hint as to why the early hominids may first have taken to using tools. Digging up roots with fingernails alone is both time-consuming and tedious, so much so that a dominant baboon will sometimes wait until an inferior has almost brought a root to the surface and then will walk calmly over and take the prize away. Such digging would be much easier if a baboon used even a very simple tool, a stick perhaps or a pebble. Although they can be trained to use tools in their search for food, baboons do not do so naturally. The hominids did.

Or perhaps the hominids first began to use tools not to dig for food, but as weapons to defend themselves against predators. In any case, by the time they reached the australopithecine stage—and perhaps even earlier—the hominids had moved on to using bones, sticks and pebbles to kill small animals for food. Instead of being preyed upon, they were the predators, and very much more efficient ones than any baboon or chimpanzee.

It would be hard to exaggerate the importance of predation—or hunting—in the development of man. Together with bipedalism and the use of tools, hunting was the principal element which set him on the evolutionary path that was to lead, ultimately, to his position of dominance over all other animals. Unfortunately, the early stages of man's career as a hunter are still shrouded in mystery since the fossil remains are exceedingly scanty. Not until approximately one million years ago do we find plenty of evidence for the last stage before modern man, a period of definitely human-like creatures with much larger brains. The remains of these early men, called *Homo erectus*, have been

BABOON HARVESTERS

Ancient Egyptian paintings show that baboons were once domesticated as pets, often seen on leashes in the marketplace, sometimes doing tricks. In this 4,000-year-old tomb painting the pet baboons are depicted in a fig tree during harvest time. Although the animals seem to be eating the figs rather than dropping them in the baskets, it is thought they were really trained to aid the workers. Because they weighed less than grown men, the baboons had less chance of breaking the fragile branches of the fig trees as they gathered the fruit—work that was otherwise done by children or dwarfs.

found in Java and in Europe, in Africa and in China, where all of them had reached approximately the same stage of development.

In a whole complex of ways, *Homo erectus* was a great improvement on the australopithecines from whom he almost certainly descended. The australopithecines could run but probably could not walk as efficiently as man. *Homo erectus* had a striding walk like ourselves, and that meant he could cover, without growing too tired, the much longer distances needed to hunt large animals. He had learned to use fire, and instead of the simple tools of australopithecines, he had developed much more effective weapons: choppers and hand axes with which he was able to kill and cut open animals such as deer, and even forbidding animals like rhino and elephants.

Essentially, *Homo erectus* was much more efficient than *Australopithecus* because he possessed a larger and more complex brain. It was not, however, simply an across-the-board improved version of the australopithecine brain. It was better only in a few, highly specific ways. Judged from our knowledge of the brain of modern man, the part that controlled the fingers and thumbs seems to have been much larger; so *Homo erectus* was better able to manufacture and to handle tools. And his brain appears to have been vastly better equipped to deal with abstractions: to memorize and to plan, to talk and to speculate.

We can see most clearly why the human brain developed in these two particular directions if we think of man primarily as a hunter—a hunter especially of large animals. To kill them, *Homo erectus* needed to make and to use more elaborate tools, which accounts for his improved control over his fingers and thumbs. He had to prepare his weapons for the hunt, which required foresight. To improve his weapons, he had to recall his past experiences, which required memory. And he had also to weigh what had happened in the past against possible situations that might arise in the future, which called for considerable powers of reflection. What is more, he had to cooperate closely with his fellow hunters. For while australopithecines killed animals single-handedly or in small groups, the hunting of large animals required far greater cooperation, planning and mutual assistance.

As a hunter, then, *Homo erectus* had to be able to communicate elaborate information to his fellows. But he also needed a means of communication for other purposes which grew out of his activities as a hunter, and these activities bring us to some of the most important social differences which came to distinguish man from all other primates. So far, throughout this book, we have stressed the similarities between humans on the one hand, and apes and monkeys on the other. It is time now to stress the contrasts, especially in their social relationships.

As we have seen, monkeys and some apes lead an extremely cohesive social existence. No advocate of togetherness could wish for anything more than the togetherness usually exhibited by, say, savanna baboons or macaques. The members of a group are continually together. They move together, they eat together and they sleep together. Unless he happens to be leaving a group for good, no member of the group is ever more than a few hundred yards away from the other members.

No doubt the first terrestrial animals from which man evolved were bound to each other almost as closely. It was the shift to regular group hunting that transformed man's social behavior and launched him along the route he was to follow for hundreds of thousands of years. To begin with, large-scale hunting

A CHIMP'S EMOTIONS

The highly mobile face of the chimpanzee gives outward expression to its emotions. The following drawings depict six expressions of one chimp as analyzed by its owner over two and a half years. In the first drawing the chimp displays attention with lips pursed. In the second it is excited and its lips form a trumpet. In the third it reveals fear, its upper lip drawn back, puffy, its jaws brought forward and teeth exposed. When angry its expression is distinguished from that of fear by the jutting upper lip. Joy brings relaxation to the face, a twinkle to the eye and sometimes an "oh-oh" sound that may turn into a bark. Expressing sadness the chimp throws its head back as in joy, opens its mouth wider and shuts its eyes; it does not, however, shed tears.

ATTENTION

EXCITEMENT

radically altered the relationship between the sexes by imposing on them physical separations and a division of labor. For only the males could hunt and kill large animals. The females were not able to participate in such strenuous activity because, for much of their adult lives, they were either pregnant or were nursing their infants. Going off at dawn and returning late in the evening, perhaps even staying away for days at a time, the male hunters found themselves facing a problem that no monkey or ape ever had to contend with. They had to arrange some kind of meeting place where they could be sure to find their females and their infants. To achieve this purpose, the idea of the base camp was conceived for the first time. There the males of a group could meet with the females when the hunt was over. There they could store their weapons between hunts. And there the infants would be able to stay comparatively safe while the males were away.

The invention of the base camp was one of the decisive steps in the history of man, as one can readily see by comparing his situation with that of any nonhuman primate, such as a baboon. A wounded or sick baboon must keep up with his group as it moves around in search of food. If he falls behind, he is almost certain to be killed by predators. But once men had conceived the idea of the base camp, the individual members of the group were very much less vulnerable, for they had only to reach the camp to be safe. There, a man could rest and recover his strength or treat his injuries. A minor virus disease or a badly sprained ankle would no longer be fatal, as it must be—all too often—to a baboon. It would be merely an inconvenience. Thus men's chances of survival were vastly increased.

And so was the sense of mutual dependence that bound the members of a group together. A sick man who was helped to the camp and allowed to rest there, fed by the others while he recovered his strength, would naturally be grateful to his companions. Were the situation to be reversed, he would do the same for them—and no doubt he often did.

So gradually a growing sense of mutual trust was built up, and it was not confined only to the comparatively rare occasions when within the membership of a group someone of the group happened to find himself in danger. As a result of hunting, men and women came to rely on each other—as no monkeys or apes do—for food. Returning from the hunt, the males would bring back meat which the females were eager to share. In exchange for it, the males were given their share of the plants and roots the females had gathered, and this daily sharing of food must have further strengthened the bonds which held the members of a group together.

By the time they reached this stage, men and women had a great deal to communicate to each other. Planning base camps, sharing food, reassuring injured companions—all these activities required a system of communication that went far beyond simple expressions of alarm or threat or fear. We know how man met this need. He retained the system of communication by gestures or facial expressions used by monkeys and apes; and, in addition, he also acquired a far more elaborate language based on sounds, which enabled him to communicate ideas.

He developed, in other words, a system of quite arbitrary symbols which, by common agreement, came to represent certain facts, or situations, or thoughts. Of all the advances made by man, the invention of a spoken language probably did the most to set him apart from every other kind of animal. Pause a moment while you read, and try to imagine what your life would be like without words. Try, for example, to plan what you will do tomorrow, simply in terms of visual images without using words at all. You will not get very far. We do not use words merely to express ideas or plans or to recapture memories. We can actually think in words and without them a great mass of human thought processes simply could not exist.

While language obviously has played a vital role in the emergence of man, no one can chart the actual progress of its development. All one can say with certainty is that language must have been created very gradually. It too was dependent on a feedback system between increasingly intricate speech centers in the brain and a vocal apparatus that had to be capable of producing man's virtually limitless combinations of word sounds.

BIPEDALISM, tools, hunting, language—put them all together, and the feedback process turns out to have been one of extraordinary complexity. And so was the brain that emerged from it. As our ancestors progressed from *Australopithecus* to *Homo erectus* and from *Homo erectus* to *Homo sapiens* their brains grew steadily larger. The brain cells themselves became more elaborate and so did the myriad internal passageways that connected them. These improvements in the human brain occurred as a response to the demands made on it. Alternatively, of course, one can look at the same phenomenon from the opposite point of view and say that as the human brain improved, men and women became both more knowledgeable and more competent. The process worked both ways, and the result was that eventually man was able to acquire an increasingly elaborate culture.

At one point, a more effective hunting technique would be added to the pool of knowledge; at another, a new kind of tool; at a third, some useful refinement in language. With every additional contribution, there was a greater mass of knowledge to be passed on, and that knowledge had to be learned by each new generation of children as part of the process of growing up.

Obviously, this need made great demands on the children. In order to learn how to talk and to think, to plan and to make complicated tools, children, too, had to possess bigger brains. What is more, as the body of human knowledge grew, children needed additional time in which to absorb all the traditional information that was passed down to them. It was these twin needs that together were responsible for perhaps the most extraordinary of all the changes which have marked man's evolutionary history. A little reflection will show that, as the human brain grew larger, human females were faced with a peculiarly difficult situation. An infant's skull had to be big enough to house the enlarged human brain. At the same time, it also had to be small enough to emerge through the mother's birth canal. The obvious solution, one might suppose, would have been for the female to acquire a larger birth canal. But she could not do this and still continue to evolve by her man's side. For the characteristics needed for bipedal walking made the enlargement of the birth canal a physical impossibility beyond a certain limit.

So instead of the adaptations taking place in the mothers they took place in the infants. Gradually, over a period perhaps of several hundreds of thousands of years, human infants came to be born at a far less advanced stage of development than infant monkeys or apes. One can, in fact, almost say that they came to be born like premature babies who would acquire after birth the characteristics they had not been able to develop inside the womb. It is impossible not

FEAR

ANGER

JOY

SADNESS

183

to be astonished by the marvelously intricate pattern of complexities that combined to produce this shift. How, after all, could human infants be born at a less advanced stage and still survive?

Put very simply, the answer is that, unlike monkeys or apes, human infants did not have to cling to their mothers' hair as soon as they were born. They had mothers who walked upright; who, living in base camps, did not need to be continually on the move; mothers, in short, who were both able and willing to hold and carry them. Given such mothers, human infants did not need the sophisticated control over their nervous system that is typical of the newborn monkey or ape. They could be helpless for a very long time and still survive.

Actually the human infant's head at birth is large in relation to the trunk compared with the heads and trunks of other primate infants. But the important comparison to remember is that the human brain increases in size far more between birth and adulthood than do the other primate brains. So while the newborn human infant arrives in the world at an earlier stage of maturity, it will equal and surpass other primates in the early years of its postnatal development. In other words, a human baby is not born with a brain that enables him to speak fluently or to solve mathematical equations. What he does have is a brain with the potential to grow to an extravagant size. Today, the human brain at birth is only one quarter of the size it will eventually reach. In the time of Homo erectus, the human brain did not expand so much after birth. Nonetheless, Homo erectus' infants must have been quite helpless for several months after they were born. They must have remained dependent on their mothers for several years, and during this period they had to learn how to fit into the complicated culture that was handed down to them.

MEANWHILE yet another very important change was taking place in the human animal. Physically, as well as socially, the sexual relationship between men and women was transformed, and this transformation was in a direction that set human beings apart from all nonhuman primates. Among apes and monkeys, copulation is exceedingly periodic. The females are receptive for only a few days in every month. They conceive most or all of their young during certain months of the year, and they do not engage in sexual activity for some time—up to several years—after they have borne an infant.

Human females behave quite differently; they are, potentially, sexually receptive at almost any time. They can copulate throughout most of their monthly cycle and also at all times of the year. Why did the shift take place? What advantage did it produce? These are intriguing questions, and unfortunately we can only speculate on the answers.

Possibly human females became able to copulate at practically any time in order to meet the problem posed by their infants' long period of dependence. Or suppose that, like monkey females, human mothers had remained unable to have sexual intercourse as long as their infants were still dependent. They would have been cut off from sexual activity for years at a time, and the bonds which united the females and the males of a group would inevitably have been weakened—perhaps seriously. But if, as actually happened, a mother could start having sex again soon after her baby was born, this danger would have been neatly avoided.

Or perhaps the shift was an adaptation acquired to meet a new psychological situation that developed when men became organized hunters. While sex is a pleasurable activity, it can also be a very disruptive influence among animals

TRAINING VIKI, THE CHIMP

Although chimpanzees have been taught to say a few simple words, they have neither the vocal apparatus nor the mental development that would permit them to speak a language. The drawings show how a pet chimpanzee named Viki was taught to say "mama." First her lips were manipulated to form an "m" to supplement the "ah" sound she made naturally. Two weeks later all she needed to say "mama" was a touch of a finger (second drawing). A little later she still preferred a gentle prod to help her and would lean toward her owner's hand (third drawing). Soon she could say "mama" on her own but did so indiscriminately with no idea of its meaning.

that live together in groups. Monkeys and apes in general exhibit a marked increase in tension when females are sexually receptive. For example, observations made of a colony of rhesus monkeys showed that more males died and were wounded during seasonal mating periods than at any other time.

Sexual competition may have similarly agitated early men just as it certainly agitates us, their descendants. To hunters, fights over sex might have been exceedingly damaging, since fighting and ill will might have impaired both their ability and desire to cooperate while they were hunting. But competition would have been considerably lessened if the women of the band were receptive almost continually throughout the year.

WITH the accent in their group life on communal sharing, it is logical to assume that primitive men and women were promiscuous, satisfying their sexual needs without thought of any resulting obligations to their partner. At the same time, there must have been mutual attraction between individual males and females, as there is today. Such attractions, coupled with the complementary hunting and gathering division of labor, could have encouraged many kinds of male-female units. Although monogamy is observed in many present-day cultures, it is by no means the only popular family structure in existence. Whatever the composition, the desirability of permanent bonds between certain men and women was gradually recognized. One consequence of the more exclusive relationships may have been an altered attitude toward children. Where youngsters had once been looked after by members of the group as a whole, they increasingly became the responsibility of a family unit consisting of its parents and siblings and perhaps close relatives.

Do we thus owe the institution of family life to the fact that our ancestors were roving bands of hunters? Such a reconstruction of the past is only speculation; we do not know for certain that hunting was really the main element behind the change in human sexual behavior. But when we turn to the relationships between different groups, hunting does stand forth as the most likely cause of yet another revolutionary shift that, once again, helped to set men and women apart from nonhuman primates.

Early humans had more incentive to mingle when language began to evolve. Their groups, thought to consist of about 50 people on the average, were no larger than some nonhuman primate groups. As terrestrial meat eaters, however, they were forced to be on the move and range over large areas in their quest of game. In their wanderings bands must not only have come in contact with each other, but must also have competed for game—and for territory as well. Even when men were simple hunters possessing no weapons more lethal than a hand ax, fighting between groups must have cost them dearly. It not only endangered their lives, it also disturbed the game and dissipated the energies that could have been spent far more profitably in killing animals. So, in the interests of survival, neighboring bands of hunters gradually learned to keep the peace. And we can deduce from fossil remains in many areas that they also learned to cooperate on hunts for large game.

Coming together periodically made it possible for men and women to move from one group to another. Such interchange could have been so appealing in fact that it prompted the get-togethers almost as much as hunting itself. As long as a band was isolated, its members had to depend upon each other for sexual unions, and mutual attraction would not necessarily have excluded interbreeding. How close incestuous relationships were cannot be determined. It is quite likely that sons and mothers were inhibited, and as seems to be the case with chimpanzee behavior, brothers and sisters perhaps were too. The incest taboos of primitive man probably became more and more firmly entrenched as the concept of family developed. The taboos would also have exercised a practical value in holding down the number of young mouths needing to be fed, since productive, working members of the group would then have more food to divide among themselves.

Consequently incest taboos must have played a role in encouraging the occasional meetings of roving hunters. The meetings, in turn, established the highly acceptable practice of exogamy—marriage, or union, outside the group. While exogamy was not instituted consciously as a way to arrange alliances of a political nature—at least not at first—it did provide a basis for alliances between different groups. Brothers and sisters, cousins and nieces and nephews—all were spread by the practice of exogamy throughout neighboring bands. There, they served both as hostages and as diplomats, making members of different groups better acquainted and so reducing the chances of mutually destructive conflict.

THE practice of exogamy also had two other consequences of enormous importance to the evolution of man. As the members of different groups came to know each other, they were able to pool their knowledge and to exchange ideas: on hunting techniques, on ways to make tools, on language. This was yet another of the steps which took men far beyond the most advanced of nonhuman primates. Although groups of monkeys and apes can pass down knowledge from one generation to the next, their knowledge is inevitably confined to what the members of each group have learned. But once the members of human groups began to marry outsiders, and thus to spread beyond their own relatively narrow limits, the knowledge of one group became potentially the knowledge of all, and the possibility of human progress was vastly increased.

This was a cultural advance; it was improvement and progress through rational exchange. But biologically also, exogamy must have given a tremendous boost to the course of human evolution. So long as a group remained an isolated unit, the number of possible combinations was relatively meager. But when members of different groups intermarried, the gene pool was enlarged by a vastly greater number of combinations, and so the chances of favorable biological changes occurring were enormously improved.

We cannot be sure when these advances—biological and cultural, social and sexual—all began to exert their influence on human evolution, but they set the way for all the later evolutionary advances which man was to enjoy, notably in the size of his brain and the complexity of his thinking, until finally he became what he is today—master of the planet. As a rational, self-conscious animal, he stands far beyond any other primate. But reason, after all, is only one part of that fantastically complicated organism which constitutes man. Anatomically, he is not so very different from the great apes. In some of his social relationships, his behavior curiously resembles that of baboons and macaques. Emotionally, before he grows up and learns to behave as society dictates, he is not so far removed from the chimpanzee. Certainly man deserves to be placed in a family of his own; he has come a long way since his apelike ancestors descended from the trees. But not, perhaps, as far as we would like to think as we look with a mixture of curiosity, awe and a strange sense of uneasiness at the monkeys and the apes who stare back at us—their relatives—from their perches in the forest.

ON AN EGYPTIAN PAPYRUS A HAMADRYAS BABOON SYMBOLIZES AN ANIMAL LINK BETWEEN PROSTRATE MAN AND THE GREAT EYE OF GOD

Monkeys in Man's World

East and West, wild or captive, wherever monkeys and apes are seen, physical kinship with man has long been recognized. But only fairly recently have scientists begun to gather evidence bearing on social and psychological bonds which link these primates with man. Though we still have much to learn, the results, as this book testifies, have already been extraordinarily rewarding.

MACAQUES SWARM unmolested over a street in Ajodhya in northern India, holy capital of legendary King Rama. To protect against simian theft, merchants use bamboo screens.

ON A TEMPLE STATUE in Banaras a sacred macaque sits with the aplomb of a pigeon in St. Mark's Square. Like the sacred langurs, the macaques are tolerated in many parts of India.

In the East, a Sacred Nuisance

Any study of man's long relationship with the simians must include the East, where apes and monkeys have always lived cheek by jowl with people, becoming a part of their very culture. Effigies of Hanuman, the monkey god, who presides over the arts of magic and healing, hang in most Hindu homes. Out of doors, live monkeys have long wandered the streets, protected by the Hindu belief that all living things carry a spark of divinity and therefore must not be killed. Particularly in northern India, where the pull of religion is strong, these intelligent animals romped freely through cities and countryside alike. So tolerated were they that newspapers regularly reported pranks like raiding a train and squirting toothpaste on sleeping passengers. In recent years, however, their mischief has become more and more of a menace in the eyes of many Indians—even as their number steadily declines due to man's continuous encroachment on nature to suit his needs.

THE HINDU MONKEY DANCE, performed in Bali, honors the monkey god, Hanuman. According to Hindu legend, Hanuman and his monkey army helped Prince Rama recover his beautiful bride Sita, who had been abducted by a giant. In this Balinese interpretation, the women in the center represent Sita, while the ring of seated men mimics the monkey army.

An Endangered Existence

The worst threat to wild primates is their fellow primate, man. Fifty-four species (36 per cent of all primates) are at the brink of extinction largely because of human activities. Suburban expansion, agricultural projects and logging have left many of the habitats of primates like the orangutan and golden lion tamarin denuded of trees, while bombing and the use of military herbicides have defoliated the forests where species such as the douc langur live. Deforestation on Zanzibar may soon wipe out Kirk's red colobus monkeys, a naturally rare species found only on that island. Millions of primates have been hunted for their meat or pelts, or captured alive for use as subjects in medical research, as exhibits in zoos or as pets and entertainers.

However, today man is showing more concern for his furry relatives. Governments are establishing forest reserves for rare primate species. And the U.S. has eliminated the pet trade. But more remains to be done to ensure that the animals that figured so prominently in our past will be here in the future.

MANY DOUC LANGURS WERE CASUALTIES OF WAR IN INDOCHINA

OF THE GREAT APES, THE ORANG HABITAT IS THE MOST RESTRICTED

NEW WORLD'S GOLDEN LION TAMARIN IS SERIOUSLY ENDANGERED

THE WHITE-MANED and reddish-backed Kirk's red colobus monkeys eat only leaves and vines. Civilization has been crowding them out of their forest habitat on the island of Zanzibar.

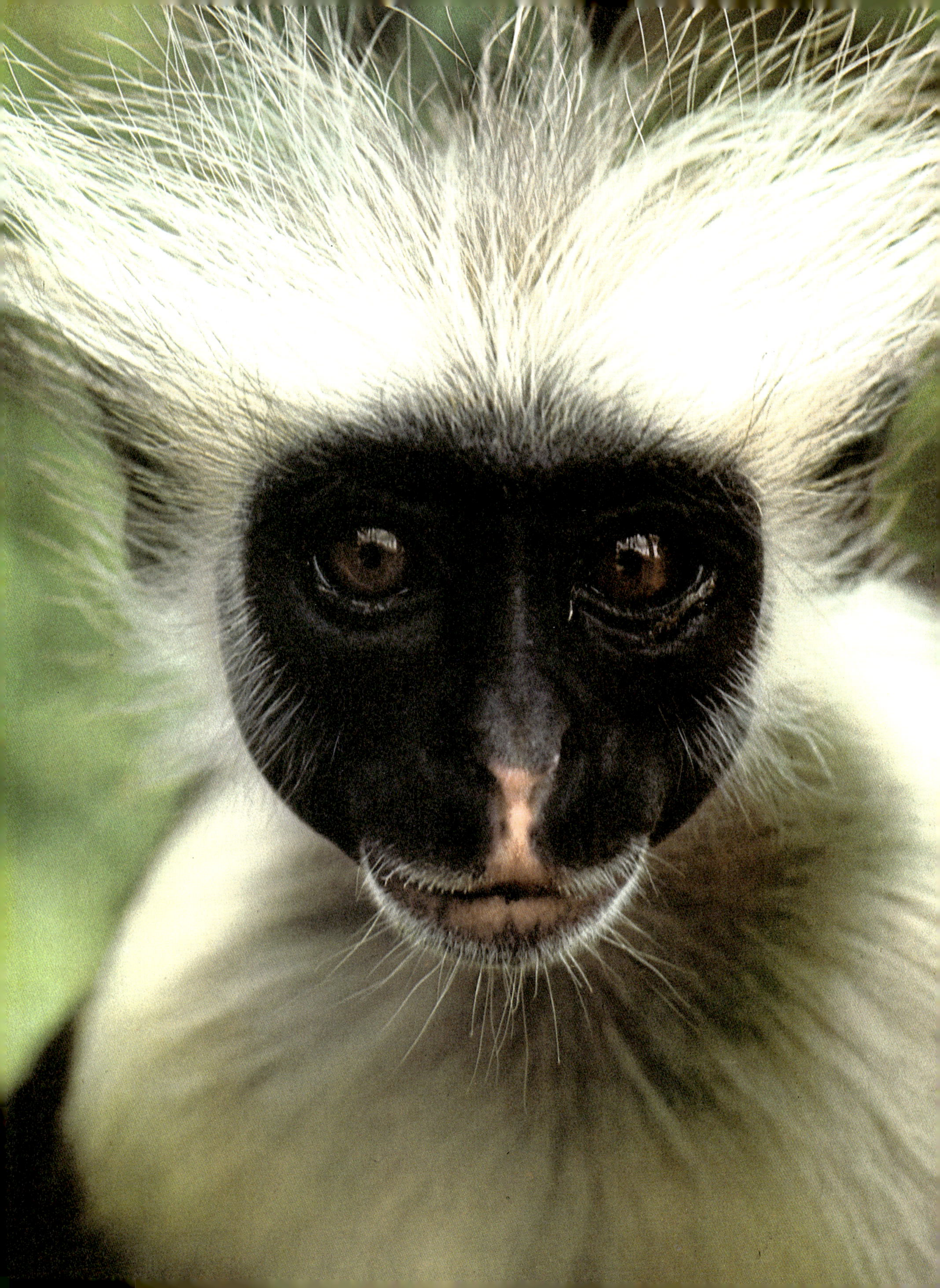

Bibliography

General

Bermant, Gordon, and Donald G. Lindburg, eds., *Primate Utilization and Conservation*. John Wiley & Sons, 1975.

Buettner-Janusch, John, *Physical Anthropology: A Perspective*. John Wiley & Sons, 1973.

Clark, W. E. LeGros, *The Antecedents of Man*. Quadrangle Books, 1960. *History of the Primates* (4th ed.). University of Chicago Press, 1963.

Goodall, Vance, *The Quest for Man*. Praeger Publisher, 1975.

Hill, W. C. Osman, *Primates: Comparative Anatomy and Taxonomy* (Vol. 1–5: 1953, 1955, 1957, 1960, 1962). Interscience Publishers.

Hooton, Earnest Albert, *Man's Poor Relations*. Doubleday, 1942. *Up from the Ape* (rev. ed.) Macmillan, 1946.

Isaac, Glynn Ll., and Elizabeth R. McCown, *Human Origins: Louis Leakey and the East African Evidence*. Staples Press, 1976.

Kurtén, Bjorn, *Not from the Apes*. Pantheon Books, 1972.

Mayr, Ernst, *Populations, Species and Evolution*. Belknap Press of Harvard University, 1970.

Napier, John and P. H., *A Handbook of Living Primates*. Academic Press, 1967.

Pfeiffer, John, *The Emergence of Man* (rev. 2nd ed.). Harper & Row, 1972.

Pilbeam, David, *The Ascent of Man*. Macmillan, 1972.

Romer, Alfred, *The Vertebrate Body* (4th ed.). Saunders, 1970.

Sanderson, Ivan T., *The Monkey Kingdom*. Doubleday, 1957.

Schultz, Adolph H., *The Life of Primates*. Universe Books, 1969.

Simons, Elwun L., *Primate Evolution*. Macmillan, 1972.

Tuttle, Russell, ed., *The Functional and Evolutionary Biology of Primates*. Aldine-Atherton, 1972.

Washburn, Sherwood L., ed., *Classification and Human Evolution*. Aldine, 1963. *Social Life of Early Man*. Aldine, 1961.

Regional Books

Attenborough, David, *Bridge to the Past*. Harper & Row, 1962.

Gee, E. P., *The Wild Life of India*. Collins, 1964.

Howell, F. Clark, and François Bourlière, eds., *African Ecology and Human Evolution*. Aldine, 1963.

Lima, Eladio da Cruz, *Mammals of Amazonia* (vol. 1). Museo Paranese Emilio Goeldi de Historia Natural e Ethnografia, 1945.

Moorehead, Alan, *No Room in the Ark*. Harper & Row, 1959.

Moss, Cynthia, *Portraits in the Wild: Behavior Studies of East African Mammals*. Houghton Mifflin Co., 1975.

Specific Primates

Baumgartel, Walter, *Up Among the Mountain Gorillas*. Hawthorne Books, 1976.

Fossey, Dian, "Making Friends with Mountain Gorillas." *National Geographic* (Vol. 137, No. 1), January 1970. "More Years with Mountain Gorillas." *National Geographic* (Vol. 140, No. 4), October 1971.

Hayes, Cathy, *The Ape in Our House*. Harper & Row, 1951.

Kummer, Hans, *Social Organization of Hamadryas Baboons*. University of Chicago Press, 1968.

MacKinnon, John, *In Search of the Red Ape*. Ballantine Books, 1974.

Reynolds, Vernon, *Budongo*. Natural History Press, 1965. *The Apes*. Dutton, 1967.

Rumbaugh, Duane M., Timothy V. Gill and E. C. von Glaserfeld, "Reading and Sentence Completion by a Chimpanzee (Pan)." *Science* (Vol. 182) November 16, 1973.

Schaller, George B., *The Mountain Gorilla*. University of Chicago Press, 1963. *The Year of the Gorilla*. University of Chicago Press, 1964.

Teleki, Geza, *The Predatory Behavior of Wild Chimpanzees*. Bucknell University Press, 1973.

Van Lawick-Goodall, Jane, *In the Shadow of Man*. Houghton Mifflin Company, 1971.

Washburn, S. L., and Irven DeVore, "The Social Life of Baboons." *Scientific American* (Vol. 204, No. 6), June 1961.

Yerkes, Robert M. and Ada W., *The Great Apes*. Yale University Press, 1929.

General Behavior

Carpenter, C. R., *Naturalistic Behavior of Nonhuman Primates*. Pennsylvania State University Press, 1964.

DeVore, Irven, ed., *Primate Behavior: Field Studies of Monkeys and Apes*. Holt, Rinehart and Winston, 1965.

Etkin, William, ed., *Social Behavior and Organization Among Vertebrates*. University of Chicago Press, 1964.

Hinde, Robert A., *Biological Bases of Human Social Behaviour*. McGraw-Hill, 1974.

Jay, Phyllis C., ed., *Primates: Studies in Adaptation and Variability*. Holt, Rinehart and Winston, 1968.

Johnson, Roger N., *Aggression in Man and Animals*. Saunders, 1972.

Jolly, Alison, *The Evolution of Primate Behavior*. Macmillan, 1972.

Kummer, Hans, *Primate Scoeties*. Aldine-Atherton, 1971.

Lancaster, Jane Beckman, *Primate Behavior and the Emergence of Human Culture*. Holt, Rinehart and Winston, 1975.

Roe, Anne, and George Gaylord Simpson, eds., *Behavior and Evolution*. Yale University Press, 1958.

Rowell, Thelma, *Social Behaviour of Monkeys*. Penguin Books, 1972.

Mother-Infant Behavior

Foss, B. M., ed., *Determinants of Infant Behaviour* (Vol. 1, 1961, Vol. 2, 1963). John Wiley & Sons.

°Harlow, Harry F., "Love in Infant Monkeys." *Scientific American* (Vol. 220, No. 6), June 1959. "Of Love in Infants." *Natural History* (Vol. 69, No. 5), May 1960.

°Harlow, Harry F. and Margaret K., "A Study of Animal Affection." *Natural History* (Vol. 70, No. 10), December 1961. "Social Deprivation in Monkeys." *Scientific American* (Vol. 207, No. 5), November 1962.

Kellogg, W. N. and L. A., *The Ape and the Child*. McGraw-Hill, 1933.

Rheingold, Harriet L., ed., *Maternal Behavior in Mammals*. John Wiley & Sons, 1963.

Miscellaneous

Darwin, Charles, *Expression of the Emotions in Man and Animals*. University of Chicago Press, 1965.

Janson, H. W., *Apes and Ape Lore in the Middle Ages and the Renaissance*. University of London Press, 1952.

Knapp, Peter H., ed., *Expression of the Emotions in Man*. International Universities Press, 1963.

Morris, Desmond, *The Biology of Art*. Alfred A. Knopf, 1962.

Polyak, Stephen, *The Vetebrate Visual System*. University of Chicago Press, 1958.

°Available only in paperback.

Films

Carpenter, C. R., *Howler Monkeys of Barro Colorado Island*. Pennsylvania State University, 1960. 27 minutes, sound, black and white. *Activity Characteristics of Gibbons (Hylobates lar)*. Part 1 – *Ecology and Maintenance*; Part 2 – *Locomotion*; Part 3 – *Social Behavior*. Pennsylvania State University, 1974. Part 1, 23 minutes; Part 2, 16 minutes; Part 3, 17 minutes, sound, color.

DeVore, I., and S. L. Washburn, *Baboon Behavior*. 1961. 31 minutes, sound, color. *Baboon Ecology*. 1963. 21 minutes, sound, color. *Baboon Social Organization*. 1963. 17 minutes, sound, color. University of California.

Gardner, Beatrice and Allen, *Teaching Sign Language to the Chimpanzee, Washoe*. Pennsylvania State University, 1974. 48 minutes, sound, black and white.

Goodall, Jane, "Jane Goodall: Studies of the Chimpanzee" series—*Feeding and Food Sharing*; *Infant Development*; *Tool Using*. National Geographic Society, 1977. 23 minutes each, sound, color.

Harlow, H. F., *Mother Love*. Carousel Films: Columbia Broadcasting System, 1960. 26 minutes, sound, black and white.

Schaller, George, *Mountain Gorilla*. New York Zoological Society, 1960. 16 minutes, sound, color.

Southwick, C. H., *The Rhesus Monkey in India*. Johns Hopkins University, 1962. 22 minutes, sound, color.

Monkeys, Apes and Man. National Geographic Society, 1972. 50 minutes, sound, color.

Credits

The sources for the illustrations in this book are shown below. Credits for pictures from left to right are separated by commas, top to bottom by dashes.

Cover—Larry Burrows
8—Jorg Klages
10, 11—Enid Kotschnig
12—drawings by Rudolf Freund
13—drawings by Margaret Estey reprinted with permission from *Introduction to Physical Anthropology* © 1965 John Wiley & Sons Inc., redrawn by Joan Hoffman
14—top drawing Rudolf Freund and Margaret Estey, bottom drawings by Margaret Estey
15—drawing by Margaret Estey
17—Nina Leen
18, 19—drawings left and background by George V. Kelvin; figures by Joseph Cellini
20 through 23—Larry Burrows courtesy of Orville Elliot
24, 25—Loomis Dean, Terence Spencer
26—Loomis Dean
27—David Attenborough
28, 29—W. Suschitzky
30—A. W. Ambler from Photo Researchers
31—H. Sprankel except bottom New York Zoological Society
32—Jean-Jacques Petter
33—Paul Popper Ltd.
34—Ylla from Rapho-Guillumette
36—drawings by Rudolf Freund; diagrams by Mark Binn
38—drawing by Rudolf Freund and Margaret Estey
39—drawing by Margaret Estey —drawing by Rudolf Freund and Margaret Estey
43—Russell A. Mittermeier
44, 45—map by Matt Greene; symbols by Otto van Eersel
46—Nina Leen
47—Shelly Grossman—Nina Leen
48—Nina Leen
49—Don Uhrbrock
50, 51—Co Rentmeester
51—Don Uhrbrock
52, 53—J. & L. Kern, Larry Burrows
54—E. S. Ross, E. P. Gee
55—Bernhard Grzimek Frankfurt
56—Eric Kirkland
57—Eric Kirkland except bottom Jorg Klages
58, 59—Jorg Klages
60—Ralph Morse courtesy of Animal Talent Scouts Inc. and L. D'Essen & V. Phifer
62—drawings by Otto van Eersel
63 through 67—drawings by Enid Kotschnig
65—quote from *No Room in the Ark* by Alan Moorehead reprinted with the permission of Harper and Row and Hamish Hamilton Ltd. publishers
71—A. Kortlandt
72, 73—Ralph Morse courtesy of Animal Talent Scouts Inc. and L. D'Essen & V. Phifer
74, 75—Nina Leen
76, 77—Terence Spencer, Paul Popper Ltd.
78—Terence Spencer
79—New York Zoological Society
80—Michael Rougier
81—Rod Brindamour © National Geographic Society
82, 83—drawings by Jack J. Kunz
84—Phyllis Jay University of California Berkeley
86—drawing by Enid Kotschnig and Joan Hoffman
89—drawings by Rudolf Freund
90, 91—The University of Chicago Press
93—adapted by Enid Kotschnig and Joan Hoffman from Phyllis Jay "The Common Langur of North India" in *Primate Behavior: Field Studies of Monkeys and Apes* edited by Irven DeVore. New York: Holt, Rinehart and Winston Inc. 1965.
95—Alfred Eisenstaedt
96, 97—George Holton from Photo Researchers, Suzanne Ripley U. of California
98, 99—Suzanne Ripley U. of California except top right Phyllis Jay U. of California
100—Phyllis Jay U. of California
101—Alfred Eisenstaedt
102, 103—Phyllis Jay U. of California—Suzanne Ripley U. of California
104, 105—Irven DeVore
108—drawings by Rudolf Freund, bar graph by Matt Greene
110, 111—drawings by Otto van Eersel
115, 116—Irven DeVore
117—Stanley Washburn
118—Irven DeVore—Stanley Washburn
119—Stanley Washburn
120, 121—drawings by Leo and Diane Dillon
122—Irven DeVore
123—Stanley Washburn except top left Irven DeVore
124, 125—Irven DeVore
126, 127—Irven DeVore except top right Stanley Washburn
128, 129—Stanley Washburn
130—Terence Spencer
132—Otto Van Eersel
133—Otto Van Eersel based on drawings in paper by J. R. Napier, Unit of Primatology and Human Evolution, Royal Free Hospital School of Medicine London
134—from Phyllis Jay "The Common Langur of North India" in *Primate Behavior: Field Studies of Monkeys and Apes* edited by Irven DeVore. New York: Holt, Rinehart and Winston Inc. 1965
136, 137—drawings by Rudolf Freund and Margaret Estey
139—George Holton from National Audubon Society Collection / PR
140 through 143—Teleki-Baldwin
144, 145—Richard Wrangham from Anthro-Photo except top Teleki-Baldwin
146—Teleki-Baldwin—Richard Wrangham from Anthro-Photo
147—Teleki-Baldwin—Richard Wrangham from Anthro-Photo
148, 119—Teleki-Baldwin
150—Novosti Press Agency Moscow USSR
152—from *Historia Naturalis* by Ulysses Aldrovandus 1642
153—drawings by Enid Kotschnig
157—drawings by Enid Kotschnig
159—Yale Joel
160 through 163—Yale Joel courtesy the Oregon Regional Primate Research Center
164, 165—Yale Joel courtesy Yerkes Regional Primate Research Center of Emory University
166, 167—Fred Sponholz University of Wisconsin
168—Phyllis Jay U. of California—Stanley Washburn—Rod Brindamour © National Geographic Society, Irven DeVore
169—Copyright National Geographic Society
170, 171—Alan Clifton courtesy Desmond Morris except top right Jack Garofalo from *Paris-Match*
172—Wide World
173—Fritz Goro
174—Frank Kiernan courtesy Yerkes Regional Primate Research Center of Emory University
175—Dr. Ronald H. Cohen Stanford University © National Geographic Society
176—Elisabeth Elliot from Magnum Photos
178—drawing by Enid Kotschnig
180—drawing by Enid Kotschnig
182, 183—drawings by Rudolf Freund and Margaret Estey
184—drawings by Enid Kotschnig
187—from *l'Homme et l'Animal* published by Editions Robert Laffont courtesy the British Museum London
188—James Burke—Alfred Eisenstaedt
189—Van Bucher from Photo Researchers
190—F. D. Schmidt, San Diego Zoo—Co Rentmeester, Nina Leen
191—Carlo Bavagnoli

Acknowledgments

The editors of the second edition are particularly indebted to John G. Fleagle, Department of Anatomical Sciences, Health Sciences Center, State University of New York, Stony Brook; Biruté Galdikas, Orangutan Project, Indonesia; F. Clark Howell, Department of Anthropology, University of California, Berkeley; Russell A. Mittermeier, Department of Anthropology and Museum of Comparative Zoology, Harvard University; Geza Teleki, Department of Anthropology, Pennsylvania State University. The editors of the first edition are indebted to S. L. Washburn, Professor of Anthropology, University of California, Berkeley, who read the book in its entirety. They also want to thank Phyllis Jay and Jane Lancaster, Department of Anthropology, University of California, Berkeley; G. E. Erikson, Professor of Medical Science, Graduate School, Brown University; and Suzanne Ripley, University of Virginia.

Others who helped in their special fields are R. J. Andrew, School of Biological Sciences, Sussex University, England; Bernard V. Bothmer, Curator of Ancient Art, Brooklyn Museum; François Bourlière, Professor, Faculté de Médecine de Paris; John Buettner-Janusch, Associate Professor of Anatomy, Graduate School of Arts and Sciences, Duke University; C. R. Carpenter, Professor of Psychology, Pennsylvania State University; Bruce Coleman; Joseph A. Davis Jr., Curator of Mammals, New York Zoological Park; the late K.R.L. Hall, Professor of Psychology, University of Bristol, England; Harry F. Harlow, Director, Primate Laboratory, University of Wisconsin; Richard Howard, Director, Arnold Arboretum, Harvard University; Caroline Jarvis, London Zoological Society; Malcolm C. McKenna, Assistant Curator, Department of Vertebrate Paleontology, The American Museum of Natural History; Desmond Morris, Curator of Mammals, London Zoological Society; John Napier, Royal Free Hospital, Medical School, London; David Pilbeam, Duckworth Laboratory of Physical Anthropology, Cambridge University, England; Edward S. Ross, Department of Entomology, California Academy of Sciences, San Francisco; Paul E. Simonds, Department of Anthropology, University of Oregon; Elwyn L. Simons, Associate Professor of Geology, Curator of Vertebrate Paleontology, Peabody Museum, Yale University; Nigel Sitwell; R. A. Stirton, Professor of Paleontology, Curator of Mammals and Director of the Museum of Paleontology, University of California, Berkeley; Richard G. Van Gelder, Chairman and Associate Curator, Department of Mammalogy, The American Museum of Natural History; and Maurice Wilson. The editors also want to thank William Montagna, Director, Flo Louise Fields, Marjorie LaSalle, C. W. de Lannoy Jr., R. M. Malinow, John G. Roth and the late William C. Young of the Oregon Regional Primate Research Center, Beaverton; Geoffrey H. Bourne, Director, Irwin S. Bernstein, Frances L. Fitz-Gerald, Charles M. Rogers, Duane M. Rumbaugh and Murray E. Townsend of the Yerkes Regional Primate Research Center of Emory University, Atlanta.

Index

Numerals in italics indicate a photograph or painting of the subject mentioned.

Adaptations: behavioral vs. biological, 64; in birth patterns, 183-184; in body structure, 16, 39, *64, 65, 82,* 179, 183; in brain structure, 10, *13,* 183; for canine teeth, 38; to captivity, 40-42, 49, 68, 70, 77, 109, 110, 136, 156, 190, 191; of digestive systems, 37, 54, 152; of finger- and toenails, 10; for grasping, *10-11,* 12-14; to ground living, 38, *136,* 138, 152, 179; in group behavior, 185; learned, 89; for locomotion, 11, 15-16, *62, 63, 64, 65, 82-83;* by man, 42; to man's residential areas, *188;* nocturnal, 23; against predators, 115, 152-153, 180-181; for protection, 37-38, 41, 94, 179; to seasons, 54; in sex differences, 38; in sex instincts, 184-185; by skin pads, *38-39;* social, 107, 113; for survival, 134, 137-138; in temperament, 41; to temperatures, *12;* to tree living, 10-11, 12, 16, 94; in use of sense organs, 10, 12

Africa: angwantibos of, 28-29; apes of, 15, 62, 63, 65, 67, 147, 177; baboons of, *map* 44-45, 107, 113, 114, 115, 136-138, 152; colobus monkeys of, 54, 132, 154; fossils in, *map* 44-45, *178,* 179, 181; galagos of, 28; gorillas of, 63; hominids of, 177-181; monkeys of, 14, 35, 36-37, 56-57, 137-138; pottos of, *13,* 28-29, *30, 31;* prosimians of, 11; vervets of, 152

African bushman, territorial ranges of, *chart* 132

Aggressiveness, 105-107, *108,* 110-*111,* 134-136

Alcoholism, experiment on chimpanzees, *164-165*

Amazon rain forest, monkeys of, *43,* 48

Amboseli Reserve, Kenya, *104-105*

Angwantibos, 28-29

Anthropoid apes, 16, *map* 44-45, 71

Anthropology: human behavior determinants, 151-158, 178; relationship to primatology, 9

Apes, 14-16, 61-71; of Africa, 15, 62, 63, 65, 67, 177; ancestors of, 15; arboreal, 15, 61, 62, 72-73, *96-97,* 132, *137;* of Asia, 15, 62; artistic ability of, *170, 171;* body structure, 15-16; daily schedules of, 131-132; disposition of, 161; eating habits of, 16; genealogy of, *chart* 18-19; genera of, 15; group behavior of, 131-134; growth patterns of, *chart* 86; habitat of, *map* 44-45, 177; maturation of, *chart* 86; modes of locomotion, 15-16, *71-73, 75, 82-83;* sense organs of, 13; similarity to man, 16, 178, 186; social groups of, 131-132; territoriality, 133-134; traditions of, 132-134. *See also* Chimpanzees; Gibbons; Gorillas; Orangutans

Arabia, baboons of, 113

Arboreal animals, 10-11

Arboreal apes, 15, 61, 62, 72-73, *96-97, 137;* home range of, *chart* 132, 134

Arboreal monkeys, 36, 38; home range of, *chart* 132, *133,* 134

Archeological research, 178-179

Arms: positions, of gibbon and macaque, *62;* structure and use in brachiation, 15, 16, 82

Art: of chimpanzees, 155-156, *170-171;* of gorillas, 155; of orangutans, 155

Asia: apes of, 15, 62; langurs of, 54; lorises of, 13, *28, 29;* monkeys of, 36-37; prosimians of, 11; tarsiers of, *22-23;* tree shrews of, 11

Auca Indians, and monkeys, *176*

Australopithecines (ape men), 178-181

Australopithecus africanus, fossils of, *178*

Avahi (lemur), *chart* 18-19

Aye-aye (lemur), *chart* 18-19, *32, 33*

Baboons, 89, 94, 107-114, *128-129, 130;* adaptations to ground living, 152; of Africa, *map* 44-45, 107, 113, 114, 115, 152, *168;* of Arabia, 113; body structure of, 37, *136;* canine teeth of, 116, *117, 136;* communication of, 116, 118, 119, 136; death reactions of, 137; discipline among, 108-109, *126-127;* eating habits of, 113, 152, 154-155, 180, 181; of Egypt, 58-59, *180, 187;* of Ethiopia, 58, 113; fear of the unknown among, 133; field studies of, 89, 111, 115, 133, 136-137, 154, *168;* geladas, 58; genealogy of, *chart* 18-19; grooming of, 107, 115, *124;* group behavior of, 40-41, *104-105,* 111, 113, 115, 118, 119, *diagram* 120-121, *124-127,* 133, 136-137, 138, 154, 180-182; growth patterns of, 89, 119; habitat of, *map* 44-45, 58, 113; Hamadryas, 40-42, 58-59, 110, 113, *187;* illness of, 182; infants of, *89,* 94, *122-127,* 137; of Kenya, *104-105,* 114; leadership among, 94, *111,* 116, 118, 119; learning ability of, 89, 137, 180; locomotion of, 37, 123; mating habits of, 113; mother-child relationships, 89, 110-111, *122-123;* as pets, 180; physical characteristics of, 38, 40, 58, *89,* 116, *117, 136;* predators of, 38, 121; protective tactics of, 37, 116, *diagram* 120-121, 133, 136-137, 138, 152-153, 182; reactions to strangers, 134-136; sex differences of, 38, 94, *136;* sex hostility of, 40; skin pads of, *130;* sleeping habits of, 113, *130,* 181; social groups of, 40, 42, 94, 110, 111, 113, *123-125,* 181-182; status among, 42, 107, *111,* 118, 119, *126;* temperament of, 40, 41, 107, 108, 111, 112, 113, 125; territorial limits of, *chart* 132, 133; and use of weapons, 152-153

Barbary "apes," 44

Barro Colorado Island, monkeys of, 39-40

Base camps, 182-184

Behavioral testing, of orangutans, 164, 165

Biochemical studies, 15

Bipedalism, 15, *71, 74-75,* 178-180; limbs for, *64-65;* structural progression toward, 82-83

Birth patterns: adaptations in, 183-184; of man, 184; of monkeys, 31, 85, 90; of mouse lemurs, 24

Body structure: adaptations in, 15-16, 39, *64, 82,* 179, 183; of *Australopithecus africanus,* 178; of baboons, 37, *136;* of chimpanzees, *11,* 15, *182-183;* of colobus monkeys, 37; differences between apes and monkeys, 62; evolution of, 16; experiments with, 162; of gibbons, 15, *62, 63, 64, 137;* of gorillas, 15, *65, 82-83,* 90; of indriidae, 152; of langurs, 37; of lorises, *10;* of macaques, *11, 62, 82-83;* of man, *14, 64, 65, 82-83,* 178, *183;* of marmosets, *11;* of orangutans, 15, 62-63; of Peking man, 181; of primates, 15, *82-83;* of spider monkeys, *39;* of tarsiers, *10, 14, 15,* 23; of tree shrews, 10

Bonnet macaques, 87

Borneo: langurs of, 53; orangutans of, 63, *81, 168;* tree shrews of, *20*

Brachiation, 15, *72-73,* 82

Brain: of hominids, 178-179, 180-181; of lemur, *13;* of macaque, *13;* of man, 178, 181, 183-184; of monkeys, 14; of tree shrew, *13*

Brain activity, experiments in, 159

Brain structure, adaptations in, 10, *13,* 183

Brassau, Pierre (chimpanzee), *170-171*

Broom, Robert, 178

Bush babies. *See* Galagos

Callithricidae (family of primates), *chart* 18-19

Callosities. *See* Skin pads

Cambrian Period, *table* 16

Canine teeth: adaptations for, 38; of baboons, 116, *117, 136;* of early man, 179; of gibbons, *137;* influence on leadership, 116

Captivity, adaptations to, 40-42, 49, 68, 70, 77, 109, 110, 136, 156, 190, 191

Capuchin monkeys, *34,* 155; genealogy of, *chart* 18-19; as predators, 154

Carboniferous Period, *table* 16

Caribbean, rhesus monkeys of, *168*

Carner, R. L., 63

Carpenter, C. R., 39, 61, 168

Cartmill, Matt, 10-11

Cayo Santiago (island), monkeys of, 42, 112-113

Cebidae (family of primates), *chart* 18-19, *map* 44-45

Celebes ape, *161*

Cenozoic Era, *table* 16

Cercopithecidae (family of primates), *chart* 18-19

Chimpanzees, 15, 66-70; adaptations to captivity, 156; and alcoholism, *164-165;* as artists, 155-156, *170, 171;* body structure of, *11,* 15, *182-183;* communication by, 67, 140, *142-143,* 150-151, *174;* Congo, 156, *170-171;* cost of, 161; discrimination of, 150, 151; eating habits of, 67, *146-147, 153,* 154-155, 180; exhibitionism of, 68; experiments with, 135-136, 150, 151, *172, 173, 174,* 184; field studies of, 67-68, 70, 154-155; genealogy of, *chart* 18-19; grasping ability of, *11;* grooming by, 107, *144-145;* group behavior of, 139, *140-149,* 154-155; growth patterns of, *chart* 86; habitat of, *map* 44-45 62; Ham (astronaut), *172;* home range of, 139; hunting by, 145, 147, 154; infant care, *148-149;* intelligence of, 70, 174; and language, 70, *174, 184;* learning ability of, 68-70, 156-158, 174, *184;* locomotion of, 15, 67, *71;* mating habits of, 68; maturation of, *chart* 86; nests of, 64; paintings by, *170-171;* physical characteristics of, *11,* 66-67, *182-183;* Pierre Brassau, *170-171;* as predators, *146,* 147, 154-155; protective tactics of, 153; "rain dance" of, 68; reaction to strangers, 134, 135-136; sex differences of, 38; sexual maturity, *chart* 86; siesta of, *144-145;* social groups of, 107, 139, *148-149;* social maturity, *chart* 86; and space experiments, *172, 173,* 184; status among, *140-141,* 143; of Tanzania, 67; temperament of, 67, 70, 156, 171, *182-183;* testing of, 164, 165; of Uganda, 67; use of tools, *146, 153,* 180; weight of, 67

China, fossils in, *map* 44-45, 181

Colobus monkeys, 37, *54-55;* body structure of, 37; eating habits of, 37, *133;* genealogy of, *chart* 18-19; habitat of, *map* 44-45, 54; Kirk's red, 190, *191;* predators of, *146,* 154-155; protective tactics of, 37; temperament of, 37; territorial limits of, 132, *133,* 134

195

Index, continued

Color vision, 14
Communication, *174;* of baboons, 116, 118, 119, 136; by chimpanzees, 67, 140, *142-143,* 150-151, *174;* by contact, 90-92; of gibbons, 62; of gorillas, 66, 69, 70, 174, *175;* by howlers (monkeys), 135; by language, 185; by langurs, *chart* 93; of lemurs, 88; of macaques, 135; of man, 182-183, 185, 186; of monkeys, 10; of orangutans, 62; of Peking man, 181; by spoken word, 185; territoriality demonstrations by, 133-134; of uakari monkeys, 51; of ungulates, 136
Congo (Belgian). *See* Zaïre
Congo (experimental chimpanzee), 156, *170-171*
Coon, Carleton, 21
Crab-eating macaques, 135-136
Cretaceous Period, *table* 16; and primate genealogy, *chart* 18-19, 21
Cynocephalus (dog-headed man), *152*

Daily schedules of primates, 131-132
Dart, Raymond A., 178
Daubentoniidae (family of primates), *chart* 18-19
Death: baboons' reactions to, 137; fear of, among primates, 135-136; gorillas' reactions to, 88
De Brazza's Monkey (guenon), *57*
Defense methods. *See* Protective tactics
Demonstrations, territorial, 133-134
Devonian Period, *table* 16
DeVore, Irven, *168*
Digestive systems, adaptations of, 37, 54, 152
Discipline among baboons and macaques, 108-109, *126-127*
Discrimination: ability of monkeys, 156-157; by chimpanzees, 150, 151
Disease research center, *160-163,* 164
Dominance. *See* Leadership; Status
Douc langur, *190*
Douroucouli (owl monkey), *chart* 18-19
Du Chaillu, Paul, 63
Dwarf lemur, *12, chart* 18-19

Ears, of primates, 10
Eating habits: of apes, compared to man's, 16; of aye-ayes, 32; of baboons, 113, 152, 154-155, 180, 181; of chimpanzees, 67, *146-147,* 153, 154-155, 180; of colobus monkeys, 37, *133;* of gazelles, 140-141; of gibbons, 74; of gorillas, 64, 67, 77, 130; of guenons, *133;* influence on evolution, 180; influence of food availability, 36-37; of langurs, 37, 54, 89, 97, *100,* 101; of lemuroids, 11; of lorises, 15, 29; of macaques, 42, 106, 181; of man, 154, 182, 185; of monkeys, 13-14, 15, 37, 86, 132, 133; of mouse lemurs, 24-25; of orangutans, 81; of Peking man, 181; of proboscis monkeys, 53; of sea otters, 154; of tarsiers, *22-23;* of tree shrews, 20; of vervets, 152; of woodpecker-finches, 154
Ecuador, woolly monkeys of, *176*
Egypt, baboons of, 58-59, *180, 187*
Elephants, *145*
Elsevier geologic time scale, *table* 16
Emlen, John, 63
Emotions. *See* Temperament
Emperor tamarin (monkey), *chart* 18-19
Environment, influence upon man, 158
Eocene Epoch, *table* 16; and primate genealogy, *chart* 18-19
Erect posture, 15, *71, 74-75,* 178, 179-180; limbs for, *64-65;* structural progression toward, *82-83*
Ethiopia, baboons of, 58, 113
Europe: apes of, 15; fossils in, *map* 44-45, 181
Evolution of primates, 10-16, 17, *chart* 18-19, 21; of body structure and size, 16; development of sex adaptations, 16; effects of isolation on, 35-36; of gorillas, *82-83;* importance of exogamy in, 185-186; influence of base camps, 182; influence of eating habits, 180; influence of hunting, 155, 181-182; influence of language, 183; in locomotion, 12-13, *82-83;* of man, *82,* 83, 151-158, 177-186; of prosimians, 11-13; relationships of man and ape, 16; of tarsoids, 13; theories of, 178, 179, 180
Exogamy, 185-186
Experience and learning among primates, 153, 156. *See also* learning ability
Experiments: on alcoholism, *164-165;* with artistic ability of monkeys, 155-156; on body disorders, *160;* with body structure, 162; in brain activity, 159; with chimpanzees, 135-136, *150,* 151, *172,* 173, *174,* 184; with gorilla, 69, 174, *175;* with isolation, 157-158; with language, 174, 184; in learning ability, *157,* 174; with macaques, 86-87, 135-136, 164-165; on monkeys' emotional make-up, 7; with mother-child relationships, 86-87, 90-91, 158; with orangutans, 165; in physical disorders, 162, *163;* with pure oxygen, *173;* with rats, 90; with sex instincts, 91-92; on social behavior, 164, 165; for space travel, 159, *172,* 173, 177; with surgery, *160, 162, 163*
Extinction, danger of, 190
Eyes, of primates, 10, 13; tarsier, sockets, *15. See also* Vision

Faces: of chimpanzees, *182-183;* of infant baboons, *89*
Fear, manifestation of, 135-136, 138
Feet, structure of, *14*
Females, status among, 110-111, 118, 119, 123, 125
Field studies: of baboons, 89, 111, 114, 133, 136-137, 154, *168;* of chimpanzees, 67-68, 70, 154-155; as clues to man's history, 151; of gibbons, 61; of gorillas, 63, 64-66, 90, 138, *169;* of group behavior, 168-169; of howlers, 39-40, 134, 168; importance of, *168;* of India, 168; of langurs, 87-89, 134-135, 138, 168; of leadership determination, 110; of macaques, 106, 111, 134-135, 168; of monkeys, 87, 90, 112-113, 137-138; of orangutans, *168,* 190; purpose of, 7; of rhesus monkeys, *168*
Fingernails, adaptations of, 10
Flying lemur, *chart* 18-19
Fossey, Dian, 64, 65, 138, *169*
Fossils, *map* 44-45: of *Australopithecus africanus, 178;* in Africa, *178,* 179, 181; in China, 181; in Europe, 181; in Java, 180-181; in Johannesburg, *178;* of man, 178-181; of monkeys, 43, 152; of primates, 18-19; of prosimians, 11; of tarsoids, 13
Fruit flies, and space travel, 173
Fungus spores, and space travel, 173

Galagos, or bush babies (lemurs), 13, *17,* genealogy of, *chart* 18-19; habitat of, *map* 44-45; locomotion of, 12, 28
Galdikas, Biruté, 168
Gelada baboons, 58
Genealogy of primates, *chart* 18-19
Genera: of apes, 15; of monkeys, 35; of lemurs, 24
Geologic time scale, *table* 16
Gestation periods of primates, *chart* 86
Gibbons, 15, 60, 61, 62, 72-73, *74, 75;* body structure of, 15, *62, 63, 64, 137;* canine teeth of, *137;* communication by, 62; eating habits of, 74; field studies of, 61; genealogy of, *chart* 18-19; habitat of, *map* 44-45, 62, 71, 132; infants of, *74;* intelligence of, 62; locomotion of, 15, *60,* 61-64, *72-73, 75,* 86; physical characteristics of, 63, *62-64,* 72-73, 74, 75, *137;* protective tactics of, 134; sex differences of, 38, *137;* sex hostility of, 62; skin pads of, 64; sleeping habits of, 74; taxonomy of, 62; territorial limits and behavior of, *chart* 132, 133, 134; weight of, 67
Golden langurs, *54*
Golden lion tamarin, *190*
Gombe Stream Chimpanzee Reserve, 67, 154
Goodall, Jane, 67, 68, 153, 154
Gorillas, 15, 63-66, 136; of Africa, 63, *169;* apparent ferocity of, 63, 66; as artists, 155; body structure of, 15, *65, 82-83,* 90; chest beating by, 64, *66-67;* communication by, 66, 69, 70, 174, *175;* death reactions of, 88; diseases of, 164; eating habits of, 64, 67, 77, 130; evolution of, *82-83;* field studies of, 63, 64-66, 90, 138, *139;* genealogy of, *chart* 18-19; grasping ability of, 82; grooming of, 107; group behavior of, 65-67, *76, 77,* 114; habitat of, *map* 44-45, 62, 63, 71; infants of, 66, *77, 78,* 86, *90-91;* intelligence of, 68, 69, 174; leadership among, 65, 66, 108, 111; locomotion of, 15, *65,* 67, 82, *90-91;* lowland, 63; mountain, 63, 65, *66-67,* 132; nests of, 64, 65, *79;* physical characteristics, 63, *65;* at play, *90-91;* protective adaptations of, 41; protective tactics of, 41, *66, 67,* 138, 152-153; reactions to strangers, 134; sex differences in, 114; silver-back, 65, 66; similarity to man, 65; sleeping habits of, 64-65; social groups of, 107, 110; temperament of, 65-67, *77;* territorial limits of, *chart* 132; testing of, 164, 165; and use of weapons, 152-153
Grasping ability of primates, 10-14; adaptations for, *10-11, 12-14;* of chimpanzees, *11;* of gorillas, 82; importance for infant monkeys, 86; of lorises, *10;* of macaques, *11;* of marmosets, *11;* of Peking man, 181; of pottos, 31; of tarsiers, *10;* of tree shrews, *10*
Grooming methods of primates, 107; by baboons, 107, 115, *124;* by chimpanzees, 107, *144-145;* by gorillas, 107; by macaques, 107, 168; by pottos, 31
Ground living, adaptations to, 38, *136,* 138, 152, 179
Group behavior: adaptations in, 185; of apes, 131-132, 134; of baboons, 40-41, *104-105,* 111, 113, 115, 118, 119, *diagram* 120-121, *124-127,* 133, 136-137, 138, 154, 180-182; of chimpanzees, 139, *140-149,* 154-155; field studies of, 168-169; of gibbons, 62; of gorillas, 65-67, *76, 77,* 114; of howlers, 134; of indri, 25; of langurs, 53, 87-90, 93, *96-97,* 134-135; of lemurs, 25; of macaques, 114, 135-136, 138, 181-182; of man, 182, 185, 186; of monkeys, 10, 102, 131-135, 188; of orangutans, 62; of rhesus monkeys, 167; of tree shrews, 21. *See also* Social groups
Growth patterns, 85-103, *chart* 86; of baboons, 89, 119; of chimpanzees, *chart* 86; of guenons, *chart* 86; of langurs, *chart* 93, 95, 102; of man, *chart* 86, 183-184, 186
Guenon monkeys, 35, 37, *56-57;* eating habits of, *133;* genealogy of, *chart* 18-19; growth patterns of, *chart* 86; habitat of, *map* 44-45; maturation of, *chart* 86; locomotion of, 57; physical characteristics of, 57; sexual maturity, *chart* 86; social maturity, *chart* 86; territorial limits of, *133*

Habitat of primates, *map* 44-45; of apes, 177; of baboons, 58, 113; of chimpanzees, 62; of colobus monkeys, 54, 132; of

gibbons, 62, 71, 132; of gorillas, 62, 63, 71; of howlers, 132; of langurs, 54; of macaques, 106-107, 132; of marmoset monkeys, 43; of squirrel monkeys, *47;* of New World monkeys, 36-42; of Old World monkeys, 36-42; of orangutans, 62; of uakari monkeys, 48
Haddow, A. J., 92
Hall, K. R. L., 133, 137-138, 153
Ham (chimpanzee astronaut), *172, 173*
Hamadryas baboons, *chart* 18-19, 40-42, *58-59*, 110, 113, *187*
Hamburg, David A., 89
Hands, *10-11, 33*, 82, 179. *See also* Grasping ability of primates; Touch, sense of
Hanuman, the monkey god, 188, 189
Harlow, Harry, 86, 87, 90, 91, 156-158, 166-167
Hindus: monkey dance of, *189;* monkey worship by, 188
Holloman Air Force Base, N.M., and space experiments, 173
Home range, 132-133, *map* 134; of arboreal primates, *chart* 132, *133;* core area of, 133, *map* 134; defense of, 133-134; defined, 132
Hominidae (family of primates), *chart* 18-19
Hominids, 177-181
Homo erectus, 181, 183-184
Homo habilis, 178
Homo sapiens, 183
Howler monkeys, 134; communication by, 134; field studies of, 39-40, 134, 168; genealogy of, *chart* 18-19; group behavior of, 134; habitat of, 132; temperament of, 39-40; territorial limits of, *chart* 132, 134
Hrdy, Sarah Blaffer, 87
Hunting: ability of *Homo erectus* 181; by chimpanzees, 145, 147; importance in human evolution, 155, 180, 181-182; influence on sex life, 185
Hylobatidae (family of primates), *chart* 18-19

Impalas, 140, *141*
India: field studies of, 168; langurs of, 97, 132, *map* 134; monkeys of, 188
Indochina, douc langur of, *190*
Indri (lemur), *25;* genealogy of, *chart* 18-19; group behavior of, 25
Indriidae (family of primates), 12, *chart* 18-19, *24-25;* physical characteristics of, *152*
Infant dependency of primates, *chart* 86
Infanticide, by male langur, 94
Infants: of baboons, *89*, 94, *122-127*, 137; causes of neuroses in, 157-158; of chimpanzees, *148-149;* of gibbons, *74;* of gorillas, 66, 77, 78, 86, *90-91;* importance of grasping ability, 86; of langurs, 89, 92, 93, *95*, 97-99, 101, *168;* of macaques, 84, 86-87; of man, 182-184; of monkeys, 10, 85-94; of Peking man, 184; of pottos, *31;* protective tactics

for, 88, 137; of rhesus monkeys, 86-87, 166-167; of sifakas, *26;* temperament in monkeys, 90
Intelligence: of chimpanzees, 70, 174; of gibbons, 62; of gorillas, 68, 69, 174; laboratory tests for, 15, 68, 69, *174;* of monkeys, 35, 69
Ischial callosities. *See* Skin pads
Isolation: effects on evolution, 35-36; effects on primates, 157-158

Japan: macaques of, *50-51*, 94, 105-114; primate research, 87, 168, 190
Jamaica, fossils from, *map* 44-45
Java, fossils from, 180-181
Jay, Phyllis, 87, 88, 110, 134, 138, 158, *168*
Johannesburg, fossils of, 178
Jurassic Period *table* 16

Kabarega National Park, patas monkeys of, 137-138
Kaufman, Charles, 87
Kenya, baboons of, *104-105*, 114
Kirk's red colobus, 190, *191*
Knuckle-walking, 15
Kohts, N., *150*, 151
Kortlandt, Adriaan, 70
Kulp geologic time scale, *table* 16
Kyushu, macaques of, 105-114

Language: chimpanzees' use of, 70, *174, 184;* experiments with, 174, 184; gorillas and, 70, 174, *175;* influence on evolution, 183; man's use of, 182-183, 185; sign, 70, 174, 175
Langurs, 87-89, *96-97*, 99; of Asia, 54; body structure of, 37; of Borneo, 53; communication by, *chart* 93; douc, *190;* eating habits of, 37, 54, 89, 97, *100*, 101; field studies of, 87-89, 132, 136, 168; genealogy of, *chart* 18-19; as gods, 54; golden, *54;* group behavior of, 53, 87-90, 93, *96-97*, 134-135; growth patterns of, *chart* 93, 95, 102; habitat of, *map* 44-45, 54; of India, 97, 132, *map* 134; infanticide by, 94; infants of, 89, 92, 93, *95*, 97-99, 101; leadership among, 88, 94, 108, *110;* learning ability of, 90, *chart* 93, 97; locomotion of, 37, *97, 102-103;* mating habits of, 93, 109-110; mother-child relationships of, 88-89, 95, *98-99, 100*, 101; number of species of, 36; physical characteristics of, 95; proboscis monkeys, *52-53;* protective tactics of, 37, *103*, 134; reactions to strangers, 134-135; sex differences in, 93, 94, 101, 102; similarity to man, 92; sleeping habits of, 108; snub-nosed, *53;* social groups of, *101*, 110; species of, 36; of Sri Lanka, 97, 98-99; status among, 110, 138; temperament of, 37, 53, 88, 93, 110; territorial limits of, *chart* 132, *map* 134; weaning of, 92-93
Leadership among primates: among baboons, 94, *111*, 116, 118, 119; basis for, 107-109; determination of, 110-112;

116-119; among gorillas, 65, 66, 108, 111; influence of canine teeth, 116; among langurs, 88, 94, 108, *110;* among macaques, 105-106, 111, 112, 135-136; in monkeys, 10; similarity to governments of man, 111
Leakey, Louis, 67, 178-179
Learning ability: of animals, 70; of baboons, 89, 137, 180; of chimpanzees, 68-70, 156, 158, *174, 184;* experiments in, *157*, 174; of gorillas, 70, *90-91*, 174, *175;* of langurs, 90, *chart* 93, 97; of man, 156-158, 183; of monkeys, 89, 90; of Peking man, 181, 184; of rhesus monkeys, *157*
Leg musculature, man and gorilla, 65
Lemuridae (family of primates), *chart* 18-19
Lemuroids, 24, 32. *See also* Daubentoniidae; Indriidae; Lemurs; Lorises
Lemurs, 11-12; brain of, *13;* communication by, 88; dwarf adaptations for temperature, *12;* genealogy of, *chart* 18-19; genera of, 24; group behavior of, 25; habitat of, *map* 44-45; hapalemur, *18;* indri, 152; lepilemur, *18;* of Madagascar, 8, 9, 24, 45, 152; mouse lemurs, 11-12, *18, 24-25*, 32; pottos, 12-13, *31;* research on, *160;* ring-tailed, 8, 9; ruffed, *chart* 18-19; sense organs of, 13; social groups of, 25; status among, 88
Limb proportions, man and gibbon, 64
Locomotion: adaptations for, 11, 15, *62, 63, 64 65*, 82; of australopithecines, 181; of baboons, 37, *123;* bipedalism, 15, *71, 74-75, 82-83*, 178-180; brachiation, 15, *72-73*, 82; of chimpanzees, 15, 67, *71;* comparisons in, 15; evolution of, 12-13, *82-83;* of galagos, 12-13, 28; of gibbons, 15, *60*, 61-64, *72-73, 75*, 86; of gorillas, 15, *65*, 67, 82, *90-91;* of guenons, 57; of indri, 25; knuckle-walking, 15; of langurs, 37, *97, 102-103;* of lemurs, 11-12, 24; of lorises, 13, 28, 29; of macaques, 62, 82; of man, 15, 42, *64, 65*, 82, 178-180, 184; of monkeys, 12, 15, 82, 86, 89; of orangutans, 15, 62, 63, *80*, 81; of Peking man, 181; of pottos, 13, *31;* of prosimians, 12-13; for protection, 92; of sifakas, 26, *27;* of sloths, 28-29; and speciation in primates, 10; of tarsiers, *14, 23;* of uakari monkeys, 48
Loeres (lorises), *28*, 29
London Zoo, baboons of, 40, 110
Lorises, 13, *28*, *29;* body structure of, *10;* eating habits of, 13, 29; genealogy of, *chart* 18-19; grasping ability of, *10;* habitat of, *map* 44-45; locomotion of, 13, 28, 29; physical characteristics of, *10*, 29
Lorisoids, 28; habitat of, *map* 44-45
Lowland gorilla, 63

Macaque monkeys, *50-51*, *84*, 94, 137; adaptations to captivity, 135-136; adaptations to ground living, 152; adaptations to man's residential areas, *188;* Barbary ape, *map* 44-45; brain of, *13;* body structure of, 11, *62, 82-83;* bonnet, 87; of Cayo Santiago, 42, 112-113; communication of, 135; crab-eating species of, 135-136; discipline among, 108-109; eating habits of, 42, 106, 181; effects of isolation upon, 157-158; experiments with, 86-87, 135-136, 164-165; field studies of, 106, 111, 134-135, 168; genealogy of, *chart* 18-19; as gods, *188;* grasping ability of, *11;* grooming by, 107, 168; group behavior of, 114, 135-136, 138, 181-182; habitat of, *map* 44-45, 106-107, 132; infants of, 84, 86-87; of Kyushu, 105-114; leadership among, 105-106, 111, 112, 135-136; locomotion of, 62, 82; mating habits of, 109; nasal structure of, *36;* number of species of, 36; physical characteristics of, *11, 36*, 106; pigtail, 87, 164-165; as predators, 154; protective tactics of, 39, *graph* 108, 134-136, 137-138, *152-153;* reactions to strangers, 134-136; on Santiago (island), Puerto Rico, 40-41; sense organs of, 13; sex differences in, 114; sleeping habits of, 181; social groups of, 42, 94, 105-111, 181-182; species of, 36; of Sri Lanka, 84; status among, 42, 106-107; of Takasakiyama (island), 105-111, 114; temperament of, 41, *graph* 108, 112, 134, 136; territorial limits of, 132; and use of weapons, 152-153. *See also* Rhesus monkeys
Madagascar, aye-ayes of, *32*, 33; lemurs of, 8, 9, 11, 24, *map* 45, 152; prosimians of, 11
Malaysia, tree shrews of, *20*
Man: adaptability of, 42; birth patterns of, 184; body structure of, *14, 64, 65, 82-83*, 178, 183; brain of, 178, 181, 183-184; canine teeth of, 179; daily schedules of, 131; eating habits of, 154, 182, 185; environment and, 158; evolution of, 82, 83, 151-158, 177-186; fossils of hominid ancestors of, 178-181; genealogy of, *chart* 18-19; group behavior of, 182, 185, 186; growth patterns of, *chart* 86, 183-184, 186; *Homo erectus* 181, 183-184; *Homo sapiens*, 183; infants of, 182-184; and language, 182-183, 185; learning ability of, 156-158, 183; locomotion of, 15, 42, *64, 65*, 82, 178-180, 184; maternal instincts of, 158; maturation of, *chart* 86; mother-child relationships of, 167, 184; physical characteristics of, *14, 64, 65*, 178, 179; as a predator, 154, 180-181, 190; protective tactics of, 167, 179, 180, 182, 185; sense organs of, 13; sex

197

Index, continued

differences of, 182, 184; sex hostility of, 185; sex instincts of, 184-185; sexual maturity, *chart* 86; similarity to apes, 16, 178, 186; similarity to monkeys, 87, 159, 187; social groups of, 182, 185, 186; social maturity, *chart* 86; speciation of, 186; temperament of, 158; territorial limits of, *chart* 132; and tools, 178, 180-181, 183; traditions of, 186; unique position of, 151, 178; and weapons, 152-153
Mangabey monkeys, *chart* 18-19, 37; habitat of, *map* 44-45
Marmoset monkeys, *chart* 18-19, 94, 154; grasping ability of, *11*; habitat of, *map* 44-45
Martin, William C., 61
Mason, William A., 133
Maternal instincts, in primates, 89, 99, 148, 158
Mating habits: of baboons, 113; of chimpanzees, 68; of langurs, 93, 109-110; of macaques, 109; of rhesus monkeys, 109, 112-113
Maturation, comparisons, *chart* 86
Merfield, Fred, 111
Mesozoic Era, *table* 16
Migration, of prosimians, 11
Miocene Epoch, *table* 16; and primate genealogy, *chart* 18-19
Mississippian Epoch, *table* 16
Mohnot, S. M., 87
Molar teeth, 10
Monkey dance, Hindu, *189*
Monkey worship, Hindu, 188
Monkeys, 13-15, 35-42, *43-59*; of Africa, 14, 35, 36-37, 56-57; ancestors of, 15; artistic ability of, 156, *170-171*; of Asia, 36-37; of Barro Colorado Island, 39-40; birth patterns of, 31, 85, 90; capuchins, 34, 154, 155; colobus, *see* Colobus monkeys; communication by, 10; daily schedules of, 131-132; differences in, 35-38; discrimination ability of, 156-157; eating habits of, 13-14, 15, 37, 86, 132, *133;* of Ecuador, *176;* effects of isolation upon, 157-158; experiments with, 7, 91-92; field studies of, 87, 90, 112-113, 134-135, 137-138; as food, 177; fossils of, 43, 152; genera of, 35; as gods, 188, *189;* grasping ability of, 14, 86; group behavior of, 10, 102, 131-135, 188; growth of species, 14; growth patterns of, *chart* 86; guenon, *see* Guenon monkeys; habitat of, 36-42, *map* 44-45, 54, 132; howler, *see* Howler monkeys; of India, 188; infants of, 10, 85-94; intelligence of, 35, 69; leadership among, 10; learning ability of, 89, 90; locomotion of, 12, 15, 82, 86, 89; macaques, *see* Macaque monkeys; mangabey, 37; marmoset, *11*, 94, 154; maternal instincts of, 89, 158; maturation of, *chart* 86; New World, *see* New World monkeys; night, 132, 154; nostrils of, *36;* number of species of, 35, 47; Old World, *see* Old World monkeys; olive colobus, 132; of Panama, 39-40, 134, 168; patas, 137-138; physical characteristics of, 14, 16, *36*, 38, *39*, 48, 53, 54; predators of, 37-38, 154-155; proboscis, *52-53;* protective adaptations of, 41; rehabilitation for, 168, 169; relationship to tarsiers, 13; rhesus, *see* Rhesus monkeys; Schmidt's white-nosed, *57;* sense organs of 13, 14; similarity to man, 87, 159, 187; skin pads of, *38*, 39, 64, *130;* sleeping habits of, 39, 131, 132, 133; social groups of, 9-10, 41, 49, 92; of South America, 14, 35, 36-37, 39, *43*, *46-49*, 132, 133, 134; space experiments with, *172*, 173; species of, 35, 43, 47; spider monkeys, *39*, *46*, 47, 131; squirrel monkeys, *47*, 94, 154; surgery for, *160*, *162-163;* tamarin, 94, 154, *190;* temperament of, 90, 158; territorial limits of, *chart* 132, 133-134; titi, 132, 133, 134, 154; traditions of, 132-134; uakaris, *48-49;* vervets, 152; weaning of, 87; woolly, *36*, *47*, 176; of Zanzibar, *55*, 190, *191*. *See also individual kinds*
Morris, Desmond, 156, 170-171
Mother-child relationships, 85-94; of baboons, *89*, 110-111, *122-123;* experiments with, 86-87, 90-91, 158; of langurs, 88-89, *95*, *98-99*, *100*, 101; of man, 167, 184; of rhesus monkeys, *166-167*
Mother substitutes, 86
Mountain gorillas, 63, 65, 132; chest beating of, *66-67;* protective tactics of, *66-67;* territorial limits of, *chart* 132
Mouse lemurs, 12, *chart* 18-19, *24-25*, *32*
Movement. *See* Locomotion
Multiple births in primates, 85

N

Nairobi Park, baboons of, 89, 136
National parks: Amboseli Reserve, *104-105;* Gombe Stream Chimpanzee Reserve, 67; Kabarega, 137; Nairobi, 89, 136; Virunga, 63
Nests: of aye-ayes, 32; of chimpanzees, 64; of gorillas, 64, 65, *79;* of mouse lemurs, 24; of orangutans, 64
Neuroses, causes of, 157
New World monkeys, *43*, *46-49*; genealogy of, *chart* 18-19; habitat of, 36-42, *map* 44-45; nostrils of, *36;* number of species of, 47; physical characteristics of, *36;* prehensile tails of, *39*, *46-47*
Night monkey, 132, 154
Nocturnal adaptations, 23
North Africa, fossils of, 181
North America, fossils of, *map* 44-45
Nose: sense of touch in, 13; shape of, 13
Nostrils, of New and Old World monkeys, *36*

O

Old World monkeys, 15, 37-43, *50-59*, 64; genealogy of *chart* 18-19; habitat of, 36-42, *map* 44-45; nostrils of, *36;* physical characteristics of, *36;* skin pads of, *38*, 39, *130*
Olduvai Gorge, fossils from, 178-179
Oligocene Epoch, *table* 16; and primate genealogy, *chart* 18-19
Olive colobus monkeys, 132
Orangutans, 15, 62-64, *80*, *81*, *190;* as artists, 155; behavioral testing of, 164, 165; body structure of, 15, *63;* of Borneo, 63, *81*, *168;* communication by, 62; cost of, 161; experiments with, *165;* field studies of, *168;* genealogy of, *chart* 18-19; group behavior of, 62; habitat of, *map* 44-45, 62, 190; locomotion of, 15, 62, 63, *80*, 81; nests of, 64; physical characteristics of, 62, 63; sex differences of, 38, 62; skin pads of, 38-39; of Sumatra, 63; temperament of, 67, 81
Ordovician Period, *table* 16
Oregon Regional Primate Research Center, *160-163*, 164
Owl monkey. *See* Douroucouli

P

Paleocene Epoch, *table* 16; and primate genealogy, *chart* 18-19
Paleozoic Era, *table* 16
Panama, monkeys of, 39-40, 134, 168
Patas monkeys, 137-138
Patterson, Francine, 174, *175*
Peking, fossils from, 181
Pelvic structure, for bipedalism, 15, *82-83*, 179
Pennsylvanian Epoch, *table* 16
Pen-tailed tree shrews, *20*
Permian Period *table* 16
Physical characteristics: of *Australopithecus africanus*, *178;* of aye-ayes, 32, *33;* of baboons, 38, 40, 58, *89*, 116, *117*, *136;* of chimpanzees, *11*, 66-67, *182-183;* of gibbons, 61, *62*, *63*, *64*, *72-73*, *74*, *75*, *137;* of gorillas, 63, *65;* of guenons, 57; of hands, *10-11;* of indrises, 24, 152; of langurs, 95; of lemuroids, 11, 32; of lorises, *10*, 29; of macaques, *11*, 36, 106; of man, *14*, 15, *64*, 65, 178, 179; of marmosets, *11;* of monkeys, 14, 16, *36*, 38, 48, 53, 54; of mouse lemurs, 11-12, 24; nostril structures, *36;* of orangutans, 62, *63;* of pottos, *30*, *31;* of prosimians, 12, 14; of sifakas, 26-27; of sloths, 29; of spider monkeys, *39;* of tarsiers, *10*, 13, 14, 15, 23; of tree shrews, *10*, 20-21; of woolly monkeys, *36*
Physiological research, *160*, 161, 165
Pigtail macaques, 87, 164-165
Placenta, 13
Pleistocene Epoch, *table* 16; and primate genealogy, *chart* 18-19
Pliocene Epoch, *table* 16; and primate genealogy, *chart* 18-19
Pongidae (family of primates), *chart* 18-19
Pope, Alexander, quote from, 151
Pottos (lemurs): 13, 28-29; genealogy of, *chart* 18-19; grasping ability of, 31; grooming by, 31; habitat of, *map* 44-45; infants of, *31;* locomotion of, 13, *31;* physical characteristics of, *30*, 31
Predators: adaptations against, 115, 152-153, 180-181; of baboons, 38, 121; capuchin monkeys as, 154; chimpanzees as, *146*, 147, 154-155; macaques as, 154; man as, 154, 180-181; of monkeys, 37-38, 49, 154-155; vervets as, 154; woolly monkeys as, 154
Prehensile tails, *39*, *46-47*
Primate Research Group, Japan, 168
Primates: genealogy of, *chart* 18-19; origin of word, 17; species of, 10. *See also individual kinds*
Primatology, 9; founding father of 69; research, 7, 135, *160-169*, 174
Proboscis monkeys, *52-53*
Prosimians, 11-14, 17, 28, 133; evolution of, 11-13; fossils of, 11; genealogy of, *chart* 18-19; habitat of, *map* 44-45; largest, 25; locomotion of, 12-13; of Madagascar, 11; migrations of, 11; physical characteristics of, 12, 14; species of, 11; traits of, 9
Protective tactics of primates, 37, 39, 41, 58, 88, 92, 94, *103*, 134-138, 179; adaptations for, 37-38, 41, 94, 179; of baboons, 37, 116, *diagram* 120-121, 123, 133, 136-137, 138, 152-153, 182; of chimpanzees, 153; of colobus monkeys, 37; and cooperation among animals, 136-137; of early man, 180; of gibbons, 134; of gorillas, 41, *66-67*, 138, 152-153; group formations for, *diagram* 121, 137; of howlers, 134; for infants, 88, 137; of langurs, 37, *103*, 134; of macaques, 39, *graph* 108, 134-136, 137-138, 152-153; of man, 167, 179, 182, 185; of rhesus monkeys, *159*, 166-167, 168
Psychological research on primates, 156-158, 187
Puerto Rico, monkey colony of, 168

Q

Quadrupedalism, 14-15
Quaternary Period, *table* 16

R

"Rain dance" of chimpanzees, 68
Ranges. *See* Territorial limits of primates
Rats, experiments with, 90
Rehabilitation, for monkeys, 168, 169
Research: archeological, 178-179; on disease, *160-163*, 164; physiological, *160*, 161, 165; psychological, 156-158, 187; on primates, 7, 135, 159, *160-169*, 174
Reynolds, Frances, 67
Reynolds, Vernon, 67
Rhesus monkeys: brain activity of, 159; of the Caribbean, *168;* of Cayo Santiago, 112-113; cost of, 161; experiments with, *157*, 161; field studies of, *168;* group behavior of, 167; infants

of, 86-87, 166-167; isolation, effects of on, 158; learning ability of, *157;* mating habits of, 109, 112-113; mother-child relationships of, *166-167;* protective tactics of, *159, 166-167, 168;* reactions to strangers, 134-135; research on, 159, 161; sex instincts of, 167; and space travel, 173; surgery for, *162-163;* temperament of, *graph* 108, 166-167. *See also* Macaque monkeys
Ring-tailed lemur, *8, 9*
Rousseau, Jean-Jacques, 131
Ruffed lemur, *chart* 18-19

Sade, Don, 112
Saki (monkey), *chart* 18-19, *43*
Santiago (island), Puerto Rico, macaques of, 40-41
Sarich, Vincent, 19
Schaller, George, 63, 64, 65, 66, 88, 90, 92, 138; drawings by, *90-91*
Schmidt's white-nosed monkeys, 57
Sea otters, 154
Seasons, adaptations for, 54
Sense organs: adaptations of, 10, 12; of apes, 13; of aye-ayes, 32; centers in the brain, *13;* of lemurs, *13;* of macaques, *13;* of man. 13; of monkeys, 13, 14; of tarsiers, *15,* 23; of tree shrews, *13,* 20
Sex differences: adaptations in, 38; of baboons, 38, 94, *136;* of chimpanzees, 38; of gibbons, *137;* of gorillas, 114; of langurs, 93, 94, 101, 102; of macaques, 114; of man, 182, 184; of orangutans, 38, 62
Sex hostility: in baboons, 40; in gibbons, 62; in man, 185
Sex instincts: adaptations in, 184-185; ecperiments with monkeys', 91-92; of man, 184-185; of rhesus monkeys, 167
Sexual maturity, *chart* 86
Shoulder, monkey vs. ape vs. man, 15, *82-83*
Shrews, trees. *See* Tree shrews
Sifakas (lemurs), *chart* 18-19, *26, 27*
Silurian Period, *table* 16
Silverback gorillas, 65, 66
Skeletal structures, *82-83*
Skin pads: of baboons, *130;* of gibbons, 64; of monkeys, *38,* 39, 64; of orangutans, 38-39
Skull shape, of primates, 10, 11; of monkeys and apes, 13
Sleeping habits: of aye-ayes, 32;

of baboons, 113, *130,* 181; of chimpanzees, *144*-145 of gibbons, 74; of gorillas, 64-65; of langurs, 108; of macaques, 181; of monkeys, 39, 132, 133; of mouse lemurs, 24, 32
Sloths, 28-29
Smell: brain center of, *13;* sense of, 13
Snow monkeys, *50-51*
Snub-nosed langur, 53
Social behavior, experiments on, 164, 165
Social groups among primates: adaptations of, 107, 113; of apes, 131-132; of baboons, 40, 42, 94, 110, *111,* 113, *123-125,* 181-182; basis for, 109; break-up of, 114; of chimpanzees, 107, 139, *148-149;* comparison of monkeys' and man's, 186; formations of, 114; of gorillas, 107; of langurs, *101, 110;* of lemurs, 25; of macaques, 42, 94, 105-111, 181-182; of man, 182, 185, 186; of monkeys, 9-10, 41, 49, 92; and territorial limits, 132-134. *See also* Group behavior
Social maturity, *chart* 86
South America: fossils from, *map* 44-45; monkeys of, 14, 35, 36-37, 39, *43, 46-49,* 132, 133, 134
Space travel, experiments for, 159, *172,* 173, 177
Speciation: by grasping ability, 10, 11, 12, 13-14; of man, 186; of tarsiers, 23
Species: definition of, 35; endangerment of, 190; growth in, 14; of langurs, 36; of living primates, 10, 190; of macaques, 36; of monkeys, 35, 43, 47; of prosimians, 11; of tarsioids, 13; territorial limits of, *133*
Spider monkeys, *chart* 18-19, *39, 46,* 47, 134
Spinal column, monkey vs. ape vs. man, *82-83*
Squirrel monkeys, *chart* 18, *47,* 94, 154
Sri Lanka: langurs of, 97, 98-99; macaques of, 84
Status: among baboons, 42, 107, *111,* 118, 119, 126; among chimpanzees, *140-141,* 143; of females, 110-111, 118, 119, 123, 125, *140;* among langurs, *110,* 138; among lemurs, 88; among macaques, 42, 106-107
Strawberry Canyon, research center of, 135
Substitute mothers: for pottos,

31; for rhesus monkeys, 86-87, *166-167*
Sumatra, orangutans of, 63, 81
Surgery, for monkeys, *160, 162-163*
Survival, adaptations for, 134, 137-138
Sweden, chimpanzees of, 170-171

Tails, prehensile, *39, 46-47*
Takasakiyama (island), macaques of, 105-111, 114
Tamarin (monkey), *chart* 18-19, 94, 154, *190;* habitat of, *map* 44-45
Tanzania: chimpanzees of, 67; fossils from, 178-179
Tarsiers, 13, *14-15, 22-23;* genealogy of, *chart* 18-19; grooming habits, 22-23; grasping ability of, *10;* habitat of, *map* 44-45; locomotion of, *14,* 23; physical characteristics of, *10,* 13, *14, 15,* 23; relationship to monkeys, 13; sense organs of, *15,* 23; skull of, *15;* speciation in, *23;* vision of, *15*
Tarsoids, 13
Taxonomy: of aye-ayes, 32; of gibbons, 62
Teeth, 11. *See also* Canine teeth; Molar teeth
Teleki, Gaza, 154-155
Temperament: adaptations in, 41; of baboons, 40, 41, 107, 108, 111, 112, 113, 125; of chimpanzees, 67, 70, 156, 171, *182-183;* of colobus monkeys, 37; of gorillas, 64-66, 77; of howlers, 39-40; of infant monkeys, 90; of langurs, 37, 53, 88, 93, 110; of macaques, 41, *graph* 108, 112, 134, 136; of man, 158; of monkeys, 90, 158; of orangutans, 81; of rhesus monkeys, 166-167; of tree shrews, 21; of uakari monkeys, 49
Temperatures, adaptations to, *12*
Territorial limits of primates, *chart* 132, *133, map* 134, 137, 181. *See also* Home range
Territoriality, 133
Tertiary Period, *table* 16
Titi monkey, 132, 133, 134, 154
Toenails, adaptations of, 10
Tools: chimpanzees and, *146, 153,* 180; hominids and, 178, 179-180; man and, 178, 180-181, 183
Touch, sense of, 13
Traditions: of man, 186; of meat eating, 154-155; of monkeys and apes, 132-134, 137
Tree living, adaptations to, 10-11,

12, 16, 94
Tree shrews, 10-11, 28; brain, *13;* body structure of, *10;* of Borneo, *20;* common, *20;* eating habits of, 20; genealogy of, *chart* 18-19; grasping ability of, *10;* group behavior of, 21; habitat, *map* 44-45; of Malaysia, *20;* pen-tailed, *20;* physical characteristics of, *10,* 20-21; sense organs of, 13, 20; temperament of, 21; vision of, 21
Triassic Period, *table* 16
Tupai (tree shrews), 20
Tupaiidae (tree shrews), *chart* 18-19

Uakari monkeys, *chart* 18-19, *48-49*
Uganda: gorillas of, 63; patas monkeys of, 137-138
Ungulates, 136
University of California: experiments with monkeys at, 135; fossil research of, 178
University of Wisconsin, primate experiments at, 86, 156-157
University of Witwatersrand, archeological researchers of, 178

Vervets (monkeys), 152; as predators, 154
Virunga National Park, 63
Vision: brain centers of, *13;* color, 13; stereoscopic, 13-14; of tarsiers, *15;* of tree shrews, 21

Washburn, Sherwood L., 89, 135-136, 178
Weaning: of langurs, 92-93; of monkeys, 87
Weapons, use by man and other primates, 152-153
Weights: of chimpanzees, 67; of gibbons, 62, 74
White-faced saki, *chart* 18-19, *43*
White-nosed monkey, Schmidt's, *57*
Wisconsin Regional Primate Center, 166-167
Woodpecker-finch (bird) 154
Woolly monkeys, *chart* 18-19, *36, 47, 176*
Wrist, of apes, 16

Yerkes, Robert M., 69
Yerkes Regional Primate Center, Georgia, 164-165, 174

Zaïre, gorillas of, 63
Zambia, baboons of, 114
Zanzibar, monkeys of, *55,* 190, *191*

199

PRINTED IN THE UNITED STATES OF AMERICA